Creutzfeldt-Jakob Disease

Bovine Spongiform Encephalopathy

Scrapie

From Sheep to Cow to Man

The Link

D0275134

Harash Narang
Newcastle upon Tyne
1997

Published by

Jodhpur Academic Publisher,
G-139, Shastri Nagar,
Jodhpur - 342003, India.
(Tel. 0291-32139)
&
H. H. Publisher,
40, Brentwood Avenue
New Castle-upon-Tyne NE2 3DH
England

Foreword

Knowing of my interest in the Meat Industry and my opposition to the use of Nuclear Irradiation to conceal contamination in food, Dr. David Clarke, P.C., M.P., the then Shadow Minister of Agriculture, Food and Fisheries in the British Parliament suggested in 1990 that I meet Dr. Harash Narang. That I did and listened with interest to what he had to tell me of his struggles with the British Medico-Scientific Establishment. I heard how, although the only experienced researcher into Spongiform Encephalopathy working for The Public Health Laboratory Service, he had been refused funding for the development of a Urine Test for the early detection of BSE and CJD with the potential that might offer towards the subsequent development of a vaccine against these diseases. I had no alternative but to fund his research abroad for the last seven years, because he was not allowed to do this work in the UK.

As a businessman, I am well aware of the damage the BSE epidemic has done to our agriculture, our Economy and the reputation for safety enjoyed by the food we eat. For over a decade it has become a subject of public debate. To find the truth it became very difficult not to be involved in controversies - turned into a political football. The present fascinating saga started in middle of secrecy and one-sided economic consideration. Policies changed - modified - billions lost - the views on economic consideration never changed.

In this book, Harash Narang not only explains the origin of the epidemic and the problems it holds for the future but also provides the scientific facts and evidence behind it together with the links between BSE and other neurological diseases. It will prove of interest to both the professional whose daily work brings him into contact with human patients, animals or food and also to the man in the street whose prime interest is the food on his plate.

He merits your support and encouragement.

Ken Bell   MBE
Chief Executive
Ken Bell International
Brentwood Avenue
Newcastle upon Tyne

1997

Contents

Bovine Spongiform Encephalopathy of Cattle 128

x

Abbreviations

Alzheimer's disease	= AD
Bovine spongiform encephalopathy	= BSE
Central nervous system	= CNS
Cerebrospinal fluid	= CSF
Creutzfeldt-Jakob disease	= CJD
Electroencephalograph	= EEG
Electron microscope	= EM
Human growth hormone	= hGH
intracerebral inoculation	= i.c.
Mechanically Recovered Meat	= MRM
Ministry of Agriculture, Food and Fisheries	= MAFF
Multiple sclerosis	= MS
Narang Disease	= ND
Nemavirus particles	= NVP
Proteinase K	= PK
Protease-resistant protein	= PrP or PrP-sc
Scrapie associated fibrils	= SAF
Sodium dodecyl sulphate	= SDS
Specified bovine material	= SBM
Speciified bovine offal	= SBO
Spongiform Encephalophathies	= Ses
Spongiform Encephalopathy Advisory Committee	= SEAC
State Veterinary Service	= SVS

Spongiform Encephalopathies

Introduction

Ten years ago, one new word and two new acronyms entered our everyday language: Scrapie, BSE (Bovine Spongiform Encephalopathy) and CJD (Creutzfeldt-Jakob Dementia). Similarities and differences linked them. Each described a different but similar disease. Each disease attacked the central nervous system (CNS). All were terminal diseases for which medical science could offer no effective treatments and very little to mitigate the anguish of the sufferer. Common to each of them is the striking neurological change brought about to a greater or lesser extent: spongy degeneration of the brain and spinal cord.

The differences, however, are fundamental. So far as we know, scrapie affects only sheep, BSE is found only in cattle, and CJD is peculiar to man. Although the public was barely aware of it until recently, scrapie has been widespread and endemic in British sheep for at least 250 years. CJD, known to science for only 75 years, had remained extremely rare - roughly one case per million worldwide. BSE, previously unknown to anyone, burst in on public awareness as "Mad Cow Disease" following its outbreak in 1986, and has since generated considerable concern. It has claimed over 160,000 cattle in the UK to date.

Responsibility for all BSE research, and for issuing, through its minister, the necessary policy rulings and regulations, fell to the Ministry of Agriculture, Food and Fisheries (MAFF). Essentially it's a trade ministry; "We have no brief for human health - and thank God for it," as the then Chief Veterinary Officer, Mr. Keith Meldrum, told the Mail on Sunday. The alarming novelty of the disease, and the speed of its rampage through the British herd, made two matters urgent: the development of early diagnostic procedures, of which there were none, and the formulation of an effective official policy to deal with the outbreak. Then as now, such urgency is still lacking. From the outset, for example, there was the problem of disposing of the vast numbers of contaminated cattle, and ensuring the elimination of their infectivity. Given the violently infectious nature of the virus - buried in earth, it can survive three years or more - the only safe way to destroy carcasses was to burn them whole at high temperature - a minimum of 800° C. Initially, Britain simply did not have sufficient suitable incinerators. Hence, despite the known risks, as many as 30% of carcasses were either burned in the open at ordinary bonfire temperatures, or simply buried.

Further steps were taken to prevent the spread of infection, but they were usually delayed. Only in 1996, for example, was the use of Bone Meal Fertilisers on agricultural land finally banned. MAFF, throughout, not wishing to upset its natural constituency - cattle farmers, the beef and milk trade, and the disposal industries - was less than rigorous in policing its own regulations. A nod being as good as a wink, sections of the disposal industry are now known to have widely ignored the regulations. Now in 1997, for example, some Kentish landowners are still allowing raw waste products from abattoirs - blood, and li-

1

quid waste etc - to be spread on their land with no consideration for human, animal or environmental risks.

Almost immediately following the BSE outbreak in 1987, MAFF came by two pieces of knowledge. First, BSE was akin to the scrapie agent in sheep. Secondly, BSE was caused by a different strain of the agent. Had MAFF chosen, to follow the science of these findings, step by step, BSE could have been eradicated from the national herd within five years. As it was, both the science and the scientists were immediately waylaid by a political agenda - specifically, to refuse to acknowledge the BSE danger at the ministerial level, and to do nothing of an active nature that would arouse public suspicion to the possibility of danger. The chief priority was to assure domestic consumers and the world at large that British beef was safe to eat. The BSE outbreak was thereby prolonged and its threat to man increased.

British experience with scrapie could have provided reliable guidance for BSE's control and further spread. Although the number of experienced scientists involved were few, Britain then led the world in the ready lessons available from epidemiology of scrapie. At ground level, too, generations of sheep farmers had long been aware of the only sure way to eradicate the disease from their flocks: namely, the speedy removal of affected sheep and the prevention of their any breeding further. Electing to ignore this wealth of knowledge, MAFF adapted a machiavellian course, putting its suspect faith instead in committees comprising various medical and veterinary scientists who, although eminent in their own specialities, were complete beginners in the complex area of spongiform diseases. Perforce, these committees were too often obliged to rely for scientific advice on MAFF which, with self-given agenda of insisting BSE posed no danger, was hardly impartial. Outside offers of genuine expert help were rejected. Thus the policies produced by MAFF were flawed from the outset, and required repeated revision at horrendous cost both to our agricultural industry and national reputation. Any individuals who questioned MAFFs' purportedly scientific suppositions were ridiculed and sometimes slandered.

In the UK in the 1970s, there were three units dedicated to the study of SEs. I had joined one in 1970, the Medical Research Council, and later transferred to Public Health (PHLS) in Newcastle upon Tyne, where I began what has become my life's work and greatest challenge. As one of the few researchers in the country with specialist knowledge of SE, I recognised that the BSE outbreak, if unchecked, would become one of horrific proportion. My early warnings were ignored. My actual findings - which included identifying the first four cases of BSE-like, new-strain CJD in man, and the means of developing a simple diagnostic tests for both CJD and BSE - prompted me to offer whatever help I could to MAFF and to the Ministry of Health. These several offers were declined. The PHLS offer was declined because, inside word was that it would create panic if Public Health was seen to be involved in the investigation. For continuing to press my arguments, and embarrassing the say-nothing, hear-nothing, see-nothing status quo, I was made redundant by PHLS following a long period of suspension based on unsubstantiated allegations against me. PHLS admit that I was a thorn in their flesh. Fortunately, through the help of a private individual, Mr. Ken Bell, of Ken Bell International, whose brother had died of a neurological disease, I was able to continue my research, mostly working in America with the encouragement and help of SE experts there. In that way, working closely with fellow-researchers, with farmers whose herds have been affected by BSE, and with courageous families whose sons and daughters have died of new-strain CJD, I have been intimately involved with all aspects of the problem before and since the first appearance of BSE in 1986. If we seriously wish to eradicate BSE from the national herd and to end the threat to man, it is my contention that we have to start - even at this disastrously late date - with the historical lessons of the disease. Thus, in this book, by bringing together the accumulated knowledge of these related diseases, and linking it with my own findings and observations, over 25 years of study, I hope to provide a better understanding of these diseases and the basis for their eventual restoration.

Scrapie, as devastating as it was for sheep, only came to public attention when scrapie-like BSE suddenly began afflicting cattle in the 1980s, and worry and fear grew that eating beef from affected beasts might infect humans - as indeed it was soon to do. Until then the widespread incidence of scrapie had been concealed, largely by the natural reluctance of breeders to disclose that their flocks were infected. In this, they were aided both by the long-established custom of the regular culling of flocks, as practised by farmers, and by the nature of the disease and the manner of its incubation and development. Fortunately, scrapie was either not transmitted to man through the food chain or else man had developed a natural immunity against all SEs other than those transmitted via an intermediate host. Belief in that hypothesis explained the low incidence of CJD - long understood to be a human variant of scrapie - transmitted to the occasional man through an intermediary, which, in the opinion of some researchers, may be cats.

Once established in cattle, BSE was transmitted through food into cats, zoo animals and ostriches and recently in the UK into hens. Before the BSE epidemic appeared, based on clinical characteristics and lesion distribution in the brain, at least 20 stable strains of the scrapie agent had been identified. The BSE agent, however, represents a major new strain which is more virulent than scrapie and is naturally transmitted in food from one species to another. In sheep, based on clinical signs, two main types of scrapie have been identified: "Type One Scrapie" causes sheep to lose their wool and is the more common. Cattle experimentally inoculated with 'Type One' do develop the clinical symptoms but there are no equivalent BSE-typical lesions found in the brain. The second, 'Type Two', although the rarer form of scrapie, clinically shows up in sheep as trembling ataxia - the major clinical symptom of both BSE and the "new strain" CJD.

3

The precise nature of the infectious agent responsible for these diseases has so far not been identified, and its properties are very different from those of all other known viruses affecting animals and plants. It does not initiate an antibody immune or inflammatory response that will diagnose subclinical illness. Further, its biological resistant properties, the degree of its physiochemical stability and the fact that a remarkable quantity of the agent can often survive a heat of 132° C for half an hour and still be capable of producing the disease, put this agent into a class of its own in medical science.

Because of the similar, naturally occurring human diseases, CJD and kuru, the sudden appearance of BSE generated considerable public interest and worry. The agent causing the disease has established its reputation as uncontrollable, incomprehensible, indestructible and incurable. The new disease has produced a major challenge to the resources of research.

In 1988 the Government appointed a working party under the chairmanship of Sir Richard Southwood, later reconvened as the Spongiform Encephalopathy Advisory Committee (SEAC). Even as it introduced new measures along the way, the unchanging attitude of SEAC throughout the BSE crisis has been that all the measures necessary to protect public health were now in place and beef produced in the UK is safe to eat. They wanted to avoid the public becoming unduly panicked by what they initially regarded as a passing "problem". The protection and safeguarding of the long-term interests of the agricultural industry and the economy appeared their first consideration. With the best of intentions, they regarded the link between BSE and CJD as only tenuous and the likelihood of the one causing the other as "remote". Their initial BSE control measures in the UK were intended primarily to protect animal health. The committee convinced itself that scrapie was not associated epidemiologically with CJD and, even without preventative measures being taken, that the risk of BSE affecting humans was 'minuscule'. The 'fail safe' policy, adopted and advocated by SEAC was quickly shown to be fundamentally defective and, however well intended and based on independent advice it was, it failed to safeguard either human or animal health and necessitated continued revision. All along, SEAC's public message was identical to MAFF's: that beef was safe for human consumption.

Essentially a manufactured disease, born out of modern feed processes, BSE has created major problems for the Government and for veterinary and medical science throughout the world. The epidemic has also been the largest and most expensive modern-day food-born epidemic ever. It is to be hoped that such an event will never again happen and that the lessons learned from this tragedy will help prevent any such recurrence. These lessons are many. Official public relations throughout the continuing crisis left much to be desired both at home and abroad. Much of what it knew, the public learned from the media and, too often, the official policy was to blame the media for overreacting. Government nonetheless failed to convince the people both here and abroad that their policy was working and that beef was safe. Too often the official, relying on their own in-

4

terpretations of studies of other researchers, have got it wrong.

The research into the epidemic, orchestrated by MAFF (and paid for at a cost of millions to the public purse), led to surprising and unwelcome results so far the Authorities were concerned. Until August 1988, it was permissible to move restricted clinically diagnosed animals under license, and for restricted clinically diagnosed animals to be sent to slaughterhouses, and thereafter for their meat to be sold by the butchers for human consumption. In the fundamental field of diagnosis, no progress has been made to test the safety of beef going into the human food chain. As long as nine years ago, the author developed a simple means for testing. MAFF, however, showed no interest and to SEAC it seemed not to be an important issue. MAFF were granted additional funds by the Government to ensure the thorough and effective investigation of the disease and its spread, but continued in the same blinkered way as before, considering no outside points of view. Once it had been postulated that contaminated meat and bone meal (MBM) prepared from sheep remains was the cause of BSE, a ban was introduced for cattle feed in July 1988. However, as of May 1996, there have been over 29,000 confirmed cases in cattle born after that MBM ban, and the number continues to increase. That raised the question of whether the infection could possibly be transmitted from cow to calf as vertical transmission - a question that MAFF, their own preconceptions excluding vertical transmission, refused to consider. In sheep scrapie, the epidemiological evidence indicates a predominantly maternal pattern for its transmission prenatally, or post-natally when ewes and lambs run together either by direct contact between unrelated adults, or as a consequence of contamination of the environment. The pattern of the incidence in the kudu (detailed elsewhere in this book) added weight to the concept of maternal transmission, since the mother died of diagnosed SE. Her calf, which was born a few months after the feed ban had been introduced, also developed SE but without the calf having been fed contaminated feed. Several cases of maternal transmission in cows have also been recorded and confirmed but MAFF refused to recognise the existence of vertical transmission until forced doing so when the results of their own study were made public in 1996.

Originally, because of the long incubation periods, it was considered necessary for animals to be inoculated during weaning if the disease was to be established experimentally. Subsequent experiments have demonstrated the opposite to be the case, that the incubation period is reduced by increasing the host's age at inoculation; and that the older the animal when infected, the shorter the incubation period.

Questions were also asked whether the infection could possibly be transmitted from cattle to humans in the form of CJD. Eighteen CJD cases have been found to have symptoms and changes not normally associated with the traditional sporadic CJD. These 18 people were young, between 18 and 41. None of these cases fit established typical diagnostic criteria for CJD. The number of these "new strain" CJD cases also continues to increase. The main differences between

5

the "old" and "new" strain CJD are that the old starts with "dementia" while the new starts with "ataxia"; however, we must be sure that the laboratory criteria used to differentiate them are sufficient, adequate and effective. It does appear that humans are susceptible to the BSE agent, but further research is required.

The term "slow" is applied where the course of infection follows an initial long asymptomatic incubation period of months or even years, with the animals appearing completely healthy. The incubation period in slow viruses appears to be related to the dose, the route of infection, the strain of the scrapie agent and the age of the host at the time of inoculation. Within a short time of the disease reaching a recognisable clinical stage, and symptoms becoming visible, it follows a set predicted and pre-determined pattern till death, and there appears to be no means whereby the host can defend itself.

From all the known practical experience, these SEs - human or animal, by whatever name they are called - can be transmitted by the experimental inoculation of diseased tissue into many other animal species, resulting in similar predicted clinical disease. All SEs result from the same pathological processes, involving a transmissible slow virus that eventually destroys the CNS. Therefore, it would appear that the separation of transmissible SEs into veterinary and human categories is fundamentally artificial.

In laboratory experiments, animals inoculated with a single dose develop the clinical disease. It therefore is obvious that one infective dose alone is sufficient to start the disease process. Once the animals are infected, death is inevitable. It has generally been accepted that the long incubation period of the disease may mean that humans, even if infected, may not clinically develop the disease in their life-time. This implies that the humans infected with a low dose of the agent and disease may remain subclinical. However, it would be wrong to presume at this early stage that this would be true of all individuals, and to take it for granted that humans face little or no risk from consuming infected tissues. The average life of humans is at least 10 to 20 times longer than the incubation period in sheep and other animal species. Since knowledge in the field is limited, it would be potentially dangerous to conjecture and predict categorically that there is no danger of infection from handling or eating contaminated food.

To safeguard the health of animals and humans, a Consultative Committee was quickly set up by the British Government and a major research programme started to find answers to the many questions raised by the epidemic. The epidemic and the disease causing it, however, were completely unprecedented with very little existing knowledge or experience to act as guideposts. The need to gain that knowledge was of paramount importance. The government made an excuse that scientists in the specialised field of SEs were thin on the ground and, too often, the policy seemed to rely on the "general expert" to tackle the specialised field. Demonstrably this led to mistakes and misunderstandings.

Probably one of the most important questions to be answered is the nature of the agent and how the infection spreads; can it be stopped? The central argument

6

has focussed on the virus vs protein hypotheses. All transmission studies reveal the existence of different strains, with the agent behaving in the manner of a replicating infectious virus, which would imply the disease being caused by a virus. The agent has some unique properties, and, to account for them, various assumptions were therefore required and made. One of the original arguments used frequently against the virus theory is that treatments that destroy nucleic acid do not reduce infectivity, and that some human cases are inherited while others are not. It is important to stress that there is no other comparable virus which could be used with which to match the SE agent and provide a comparison of their respective properties. Other extraordinary features have hindered progress in many ways. Researchers have often followed wrong clues, and taken the wrong path in their research. Rather than treating research discoveries as tentative findings, they are accepted as established facts about the disease, and have become part of the scrapie dogma. The arguments presented are based on indirect evidence and are therefore open to misinterpretations and one-sided assumptions. They are not based on facts.

There appears to be a common infectious agent, but the true nature of the agent responsible for these diseases remains controversial. Many hypotheses have been proposed. Morphologically, two structures have consistently been seen by electron microscope (EM) in all SEs, in both experimental and natural diseases: 1) Scrapie-associated fibril (SAF) and 2) Nemavirus. Both are considered specific ultrastructural markers. Opinions differ as to whether the whole Nemavirus or merely its central core protein is the actual agent. This remains to be resolved. The appearance of Nemavirus and SAF in experimental scrapie and CJD precede the onset of clinical disease, and can be demonstrated by simple methods a quarter of the way through the incubation period.

The definitive diagnosis of SEs is based on a time consuming histological examination which takes up to six weeks, while the transmission of the disease to selected animal hosts to provide further confirmation can take a year or more. Further MAFF know that cattle which have been injected with the BSE agent will develop the clinical disease with incubation period of about 70 to 90 weeks. Obviously with this kind of knowledge they must tell the public at what stage these animals incubating the disease should be killed so that a Neuropathologist by examining the brains has no difficulty in confirming the presence of the disease. MAFF would like to see development of a reliable accurate test for BSE while they simply do not have a suitable test to confirm the state of the disease during its long incubation period until clinical symptoms appear. They simply put   hurdles in my way of developing a proper test by refusing even to supply with urine specimen. Diagnosis, however, can be made within an hour by a recently developed "touch" impression technique. This test is based on demonstrating NVP and SAF in brain and urine specimens from suspected cases. It could, and should have been used as a matter of routine.

7

It was the assumption that BSE does not and will not transmit that has caused much of the problem for the British Government. The assumption proved false and led to many policies based on it proving ill-founded. The history of viral infections leads us to believe that the acquired disease can be prevented by understanding the mode of infection and pre-immunising potential hosts. In the case of BSE the spread of the disease can be avoided by not breeding from infected progeny and not eating contaminated food.

This disease has cost the public purse more than any other disease in modern history, including AIDs. The House of Commons Agricultural and Health Select Committees have made enquiries but no one has been held responsible for this. The disease has had such disastrous effect on public confidence, that to gain trust back, it is essential for the British Government to have an independent enquiry.

The question uppermost in the public mind is: Who is at risk? I do not personally believe that all those who have eaten BSE-contaminated food will become infected. I say this on the evidence of science. We know from animal experiments, for example, that if a creature has already been infected with one strain of the disease, it cannot be infected with another. The first strain effectively immunises the creature against any other strain. Hence, it seems very likely that those people who have inadvertently eaten scrapie-infected lamb in the past could then eat BSE infected beef without succumbing to BSE.

But we also know from laboratory experiments that if a creature is infected with a mix of strains - Scrapie and BSE together - that BSE, being the more virulent, will be the strain that takes hold. Similarly, if BSE is ingested first, no subsequent intake of Scrapie will have any immunising effect. BSE will persist onto death.

All of which may explain why younger people appear to be at the greatest risk from BSE. Thirty years ago, lamb was eaten more often then beef. More recently, however, younger people have developed a greater predilection for beef. Hence, not only are they less likely than older people to have developed an immunity through eating scrapie-infected lamb; because they favour beef over lamb, they are more at risk from BSE. It surely goes without saying that research priority should be given for the development of an anti-BSE vaccine both for humans and animals.

As it is fairly well known, CJD developed in those recipients of human growth hormone who were treated with CJD-contaminated product. The question has naturally arisen: What are the chances of a patient developing CJD from a blood transfusion when the blood was taken from a donor who subsequently died of CJD? We know that mice inoculated with human blood from CJD cases develop the disease. By way of attempting to refute the risk to humans, however, Sue Cunningham of the National Blood Authority told the Daily Telegraph (25th March, 1997): "The experiment (with mice) was not a procedure that would be carried out on humans." But of course the procedure - blood transfusion

- is carried out all the time, routinely. And if the blood donor turns out to have had CJD, the risk would be equal to that demonstrated in mouse experiments: a lethal one. Cunningham's refutation, in other words, refutes nothing at all.

Not the least problem is that MAFF and its co-opted scientists are at pains to maintain a monopoly on BSE material research, and total control on where and how the research is done. Just recently, when a suspected instance of a BSE-like disease in a chicken was brought to my attention, and the near-to-death creature given over to me to observe and to test for spongiform disease after its death, I was threatened with court action and arrest by MAFF officials if I didn't immediately hand over the corpse and all tissue samples.

How much longer can MAFF and SEAC be allowed to continue ignoring the basic science of the matter? In order to eradicate BSE, for export, MAFF has agreed to a culling policy of animals over 30 month old, those most likely to exhibit obvious symptoms if they had BSE. Under such a policy, year after year, thousands of BSE-free animals are condemned to die. To make an unpleasant but fitting analogy, the culling policy makes as much sense as claiming that if all humans over the age of 50 were killed, Alzheimer's disease would be eradicated. The last mass cull did not win concessions from Europe or build public confidence. The final cost of the culling policy will be enormous. Even after such huge expense, however, the national herd will still not have been cleaned of BSE.

In 1988, I observed, and was the first scientist to report, a series of CJD cases with pathology that closely resembles that seen in BSE. That it took SEAC's scientists another eight years to identify the BSE-like "new variant" or atypical" strain of CJD remains a cause for grave concern. Out of historical precedence, and for ease of classification, I suggest that this atypical" and "new variant" strain be termed hereafter Narang Disease (ND).

In 1988, to protect human health and for eradication of BSE, I proposed the following:
1 It is important to determine the nature of the agent.
2 To test all cattle before meat is sold.
3 To develop a simple live diagnostic test.
4 Trace affected animals to their farms and selectively cull their progeny.
5 Restrict the movement of cattle from affected herds to clean herds.
6 Public Health is paramount.

Ten years later my views remain unchanged.

Abbreviation

Alzheimer's disease = AD

Bovine spongiform encephalopathy = BSE

Central nervous system = CNS

Cerebrospinal fluid = CSF

Creutzfeldt-Jakob disease = CJD

Electroencephalograph = EEG

Electron microscope = EM

Human growth hormone = hGH

intracerebral inoculation = i.c.

Mechanically Recovered Meat = MRM

Ministry of Agriculture, Food and Fisheries = MAFF

Multiple sclerosis = MS

Narang Disease = ND.

Nemavirus particles = NVP

Proteinase K = PK

Protease-resistant protein = PrP or PrP-sc

Scrapie associated fibrils = SAF

Sodium dodecyl sulphate = SDS

Specified bovine material = SBM

Specified bovine offal = SBO

Spongiform Encephalopathies = SEs

Spongiform Encephalopathy Advisory Committee = SEAC

State Veterinary Service = SVS

Scrapie

History of Scrapie

The disease scrapie has been recognised among sheep *(Ovis aries)* in the UK for over 250 years. This ovine (sheep) disease, however, in spite of its devastating effect, was unknown to the general public in England until 1986. Its importance was only realised when a scrapie-like disease - bovine spongiform encephalopathy (BSE) - the so called "Mad cow" disease - appeared in cattle. There were a number of reasons why the public was not aware of the existence of scrapie.

First, the slaughter of sheep for food is carried out well before the symptoms of scrapie develop, which is when sheep reach the age of about two years. Clinical scrapie cases are observed principally between three and seven years of age, while clinical scrapie in sheep of 18-24 months of age would be seen in only a few early cases noticeable only by shepherds and flockmasters. Lambs are sold-off their native farms at about six or seven months old, for fattening, and later pass into the hands of butchers before reaching the age of 18 months. As the disease seldom or never shows itself before this age, these animals are presumed scrapie-free. The age at which sheep are slaughtered, therefore, appears to determine the apparent incidence and prevalence of the disease in the flocks.

Secondly, flock-owners unfortunate enough to have the disease amongst their stock,concealed it. As M'Fadyean (1918) wrote: "There is no doubt that the disease has hitherto received little or no professional notice simply because it has been the almost invariable habit of flock-owners to conceal its existence. Now that the folly of this policy has been recognised by many of the breeders in those parts of the country in which the disease prevails, it is reasonable to hope the properly planned investigation will before long clear up many points which are at present very obscure, especially with regard to the manner in which it is spread." He continued: "Ovine disease termed scrapie should until recently have been almost entirely unknown to the veterinary profession in this country." The economic viability of a sheep flock depends on the chief purpose for which the sheep are reared. For mutton production, losses would probably be small, but where production was for breeding stock and for wool, the loss from the disease could be greater.

Since farmers could recognise the very earliest symptoms, they took steps to minimise their losses. They did not consider the disease worthy of widespread concern. Affected sheep were sent off at once for slaughter, the farmer was satisfied and as far as the public was concerned, the meat of such sheep was not considered harmful to human health and, in fact, there are no apparent reported cases of the transmission of this disease to man.

Scrapie in the Goat *(Capra hircus)*

A clinical case of scrapie in a goat under natural conditions was first observed

11

by Chellé (1942). He reported two further cases in goats which had been kept in association with scrapie sheep. MacKay et al (1961) reported a case of scrapie in an uninoculated three year old goat bought from a dealer and kept as a control animal for their experimental, inoculated group of goats. In this experiment, inoculated goats developed the clinical disease seven months post-inoculation. The uninoculated goat, which was brought to their Moredun Institute, Edinburgh seven months before the experiment, also developed the disease in the same manner as the inoculated animals. They tried to trace the previous history of the goat and its former owner and could not rule out the possibility that the goat had, in fact, had contact with scrapie-affected sheep in the past.

In 1961 Stamp reported scrapie in five uninoculated goats which were housed, since they were day-old animals, with numerous scrapie-affected sheep for 40 months. Gordon et al (1957) drew attention to the high degree of susceptibility of goats compared with sheep; 100% of goats were readily infected experimentally when inoculated intracerebrally. In sheep, however, the percentage "take" varies with the type of sheep inoculated, and it is rarely anywhere near 100%. They also demonstrated that scrapie can be passed serially from goats to goats, and the scrapie goat material can be passed-back to sheep, again producing the symptoms of scrapie. They also showed that cerebro-spinal fluid, pituitary gland, adrenal gland, spleen, pancreas and liver from scrapie-affected goat induced scrapie when inoculated intracerebrally into healthy goats. However, the thyroid gland tissues failed to produce the disease.

The outstanding clinical features of the clinical disease in goats can vary (MacKay et al, 1961). The sick animals show a slowly developing incoordination and tend to stand with their hind legs drawn forward and withers low. These animals are less active and often stand with their heads cocked sideways as if staring at a fixed object. The sick animals become progressively duller and the incoordination becomes more obvious. Some animals show evidence of intense itching and these animals scratch vigorously with their hind legs or horns or both so that the affected areas become denuded of hair. The experimentally transmitted clinical disease in goats is insidious in onset and accompanied by restlessness, as well as tremor, especially of the head. Scratching and rubbing of the skin - 'scratchy' scrapie - where the most obvious features were incoordination of gait and difficulty in maintaining normal posture with periods of somnolence and drowsiness, are the characteristic clinical symptoms. Progression usually leads to terminal prostration in 3 to 4 months.

In view of the fact that natural scrapie in goats is rare, or is hardly known to occur in goats in Great Britain, and that the goats came from a farm where the disease had not been seen, Stamp (1961) concluded that the disease in the goats arose as a result of intimate contact in the open with affected sheep. This added considerable weight to the hypothesis that contact transmission in grazing was a real possibility.

12

Local names used in the past for scrapie

The disease has been known for over 250 years under one or another descriptive name, mostly referring to the major clinical features of the disease which were variable in type and duration e.g. "Euky Pine", "Rickets", "Scratchie," "Rubbers," "Shakings," "Cuddie Trot" (this refers to the gait), "Goggles" a disease having "Itchiness" as symptoms (Complete Farmer, 1807) Shrew Croft, (Palmer, 1959) and many others (M'Gowan, 1914). Some of these names were discussed in a school prize essay in 1840 entitled "Practical Essay on the Diseases of Sheep". As early as 1759, Leopold described the disease under the name of "Traps". French of Paulet in "Contributions to the History of Diseases of Cattle,' etc., published by Rumpet in 1776 described the disease pretty accurately under the name of "Staggers." The modern name "Scrapie" was well known in Roxburghshire about 1850 (Gaiger, 1924). In France, the disease was likewise called "la Tremblante", "Prurigo lobbaire" (lumbar itch), "La maladie folle" (the mad disease), "Maladie tremblante," "Maladie chancelante," Brandeleuse," "Nevraxite enzootique du Mouton". In Germany, it was commonly referred to as "Zitternkrankheit" (trembling disease), "Traberkrankheit," (trotting disease); "Grubberkrankheit," (nibbling disease); "Reiberkrankheit" (rubbing disease), "Wetzkrankheit" (whetting disease) and "Schruckigsein" (shrugging disease). Although the disease had many colloquial names throughout literature, earlier accounts given of the syndrome are remarkable for clarity of clinical description and observations of the behaviour and development of the disease.

Accounts and description of symptoms

One of the earliest accounts of the occurrence of the disease in Britain is given by Thomas Davis who described the disease as "Goggles" (Davis, 1811). He did not find any written record of when the disorder appeared in county. Many of the accounts given by shepherds were accurate. On the other hand, the disease in some parts of the country was being described under different local names - or even two different diseases - were considered to be the same. An experienced shepherd mentions: " they rub through in all attitudes-skin clean, some jump stagger as drunk and are taken as mad and eventually are wasted away to die in three to four months. The flesh is quite green and not stinking." In 1772, Comber wrote to Dr. Hunter, a physician in York, describing the disease under three principal stages, as given by Mr. Thomas Beal, a farmer of Morboune parish: "The principal symptom of the first stage of this distemper is a kind of high headedness. The affected sheep appear much wilder than usual. He bounces up suddenly from his laire and runs to a distance as though he were pursued by dogs. In the second stage the principal symptom of the sheep is his rubbing himself against trees, posts, etc., with such fury as to pull off his wool and tear away his flesh. The distressed animal has now a violent itching....appearing stupid, separates from the flock,.........These symptoms increase in degree till death follows..... not one sex attacked more than the other, nor lean rather than fat, nor gelt sheep rather than breeding ones."

In 1914 M'Gowan, during his investigation into the disease, described the symptoms in great detail. In his accounts he stated that, frequently, from four to six weeks - or longer -before the actual unmistakable disease becomes apparent, the affected animals get 'a peculiar fixed look'. "The ears often limp and the affected sheep start trembling whenever the sun shines on them with any strength. In some descriptions, it has been observed that at the actual commencement of the disease, the sheep appear shy, timid, and very easily frightened. They lose the vigour as seen in healthy sheep, and while standing, let the head and ears drop. They tremble and frequently run for no obvious reason. The affected rams butt less often than the normal animals, and frequently sink to the ground with weakness. Their walk becomes stiff and uncertain, and they totter with their hind-legs far apart. Sick animals cannot gallop or run, or if they do move quickly, they fall and rise up with great difficulty. These animals also find it difficult to step over high door-sills without sinking down or falling. The wool turns pale in colour and becomes uneven. The animals stop and often look at their bodies especially the sacral region. This is followed in most cases by a feeling of itching in the lumbo-sacral region and the legs. The animal starts rubbing and gnawing, and, in some individual cases, knotty swellings appear. Later, with time, the skin becomes dry and either scaly or scabby. At the start of the clinical symptoms, the animals feed normally, but later the desire for food decreases and rumination appears to slow down." "As the disease progresses, the ears hang more limp than ever, and their gaze becomes more exhausted and vacant. The voice changes, bleating becomes less frequent and gradually changes from a hoarse voice to a growl. For sick animals, rising from the ground becomes difficult. Sick animals fall down easily and spend a great deal of time lying down. They often crawl along the abdomen without using their legs. Weakness grows while shaking intensifies and the animals are rendered to skeletons. They grind their teeth, gnaw at themselves until ultimately they die, or are killed." Stockman also described the symptoms of the disease developing in three stages.

M'Fadyean (1918) wrote: "In spite of the fact that the actual cause of the disease still remains unknown, and that its diagnosis, therefore, lacks the precision and certainty which are possible in diseases caused by demonstratable parasites, there is little danger of mistaking scrapie for any other affection, except during its earliest stages." On the other hand, another writer, Youatt (1837) described two diseases: "Among the diseases of the skin in British sheep the scab stands foremost in frequency of occurrence and mischief to the wool, the flesh, and the general constitution of the animal. The same disease, or one much resembling it has been known in some parts of the world from time immemorial. It assumes different forms in different seasons and on different animals; and there are several varieties of it. A sheep is occasionally observed to scratch himself in the most furious manner....He rubs himself against every projecting part of the hedge,

14

against every post and wool comes off...... there is no appearance whatever of cutaneous disease."

Dickinson et al (1965), after many years of experience with scrapie flocks, described the clinical features of the disease which vary both in type and duration with both pruritus and incoordination. However, in some cases, either pruritus or incoordination can be virtually absent from the clinical syndrome. They suggested "because of the nonspecific nature of all except the terminal clinical signs it is possible, despite considerable experience with cases of scrapie, to make incorrect clinical diagnoses." In Icelandic sheep, for instance the form of scrapie present, known locally as Rida, exhibits primarily an incoordination of gait but without prominent pruritus (Palsson et al, 1959). On the other hand, in the hill sheep from Northern India, scrapie usually shows as severe pruritus without a protracted period of locomotor incoordination (Zlotnik et al, 1961).

Thomas Davis, in "General Views on Agriculture, Wiltshire, for the Board of Agriculture" (1813) referred to the disease as "Goggles", which brought discredit to Wiltshire sheep. He wrote "The disorder with symptoms above-mentioned called the "rickets" is now prevalent in some parts of Cambridgeshire. I am informed that all sorts of sheep are subject to this disorder, though known by various names; and that continuing the breed, without introducing rams from other flocks (provincially, breeding in and in), will produce it." In the past, statements with regard to the knowledge of the existence of the disease originated from the farmers and shepherds in the affected areas. Around 1755, in the county of Lincoln, the disease had been observed for the past ten years. During this period the disease must have been very prevalent as it is recorded in the Journal of the House of Commons (1755), that a memorial was presented to the English House of Commons by farmers, breeders and feeders of sheep from Boston (Lincoln, England) drawing attention to the seriousness of the disease and the economic losses it was causing (Davis, 1813). Apparently, "jobbers" had a monopoly of the sheep trade, and the Boston farmers asked that they be restrained from mixing "distempered" animals with healthy ones for resale. A special committee was appointed which, in its report, gave an accurate account of the clinical signs of the disease. According to the petition, for the past ten years, a disorder which they called the rickets or shaking had prevailed among their sheep, and was transmitted in the blood (meaning hereditary) by rams. The disease would frequently be in the blood 12 months or 24 months before becoming apparent, and once a sheep had this disorder it never recovered. Although on 28th February 1755, permission was recorded to introduce a Bill to prevent the spread of the disease, no further record is available and it appears no further action was taken.

That the disease was indeed a serious menace to many flocks was well publicised, for one can read many statements made at the time. Claridge (1795) wrote, "This disorder has been known to be fatal to the greatest part of a flock and is considered as the most calamitous circumstance the sheep-owners have to

15

dread." Willich (1802) added, "Trot malady is one of the most fatal that can happen in a flock."

Origin of Scrapie in England

The current name "scrapie" was first used in 1853. At this time, the disease was well-known in Roxburghshire, Scotland, although an extensive historical review by Dr. M'Gowan puts the first recognition of the disease known by one or other name in England as far back as 1732. There is much evidence that scrapie occurred in waves of infection, probably due to the dispersal of badly tainted flocks, disposed of for the very reason that they were seriously tainted. Gaiger (1924) believed that dispersal was one of the main reasons behind the waves of infection spreading scrapie throughout England. There seems little reason to doubt that the disease has been known in Britain for much longer than has been documented - possibly for several centuries.

According to some authors, the disease was probably first introduced into England with imported sheep, the so-called Spaniards, commonly known as "Merinos" either from Spain or Saxony between 1780-1790. Stockman (1913) quoting an historical account given by G. A. Brown (Bruni) stated that 3,000 Merinos were first introduced into England in the time of Edward IV, in the fifteenth century, by permission of the King of Spain. These Merinos were known to thrive in England up to the time of Queen Elizabeth, when the breed was lost without any explanation being available for the loss. George III, in 1787, imported fresh Merinos, but without the permission of the Spanish sovereign. It was said that these sheep were of very poor quality. Subsequently, in 1791, George III, this time with the permission of the Spanish King, imported some very fine "Negretti" breed of sheep, 4 rams and 36 ewes. It is reported that the entire old stock of Merinos was disposed of on the arrival of this last batch. From the Royal flock in 1804, 45 sheep were sold, 8 of these being exported to Australia. It is in the records that Mr. Tollet of Swinnertonhall, Staffordshire, raised fine true Merino from His Majesty's sheep. Again in 1808, King George III was presented with over 2,000 Merinos by Spain. In 1811, the Spanish Merino sheep were bred by Lord Aylesford at Packington, and Mr Thomas Jackson at Alveston Pastures, near Stratford-on-Avon, whose flock was about 600 (Murray, 1811). A Merino Society was formed in England in 1811, and one of its prominent members was Lord Western, who is stated to have owned a flock of Saxon Merinos.

The earlier literature (Young, 1799) suggested that sheep of this breed were particularly susceptible to attack by the incurable disease, "staggering." According to Stockman (1913), accounts of the disease in Great Britain were given in connection with a flock in which there is direct evidence of Merinos having been introduced into England. A shepherd recorded that, after a very severe unpleasant winter, he noticed that the Spaniards did worst, next the new Leicesters, whereas the Southdowns sheep did much better. The spread of the disease appeared to be

16

as a result of the various methods of transportation, and could be related to animal husbandry practices of the Merino breed, and, since these sheep were crossed with the Leicester and other breeds, this might account for the dispersal of the disease. Certainly in the mid 18th century, scrapie was widespread over the southern part of England particularly in Lincolnshire, Norfolk, Cambridgeshire, Wiltshire, Hampshire, Dorset and Yorkshire. It appears to have gradually penetrated north to the Border counties of Scotland by about 1800.

The view expressed by Stockman, that scrapie appeared in England about 1799, and that it was introduced by Merinos, was strongly contested by M'Gowan (1918). M'Gowan believed that historical outbreaks of the disease in Britain, Germany and France all synchronised with determined efforts on the part of private individuals or governments to develop improved races of the sheep by consanguine breeding. Further, the history of the "Electoral" and "Negretti" breeds of Merinos in Germany is revealing itself in this connection. The Electoral sheep consanguinely bred for "points" were riddled with the disease. However, he suggested that the Negrettis, a commercial sheep, among which inbreeding was not practised, had practically none of the disease.

Scrapie as it occurred in other countries

It had been suggested that the introduction of scrapie into Germany also followed an importation of the Merino breed of sheep from Spain in 1765 (Greig, 1940). However, there is a great deal of evidence that the disease was known in Germany before 1750 (Hurtrel D'Arboval, 1828). Many authors considered that the subsequent distribution of the disease followed from the import of the Saxon Merinos breed of fine-wooled sheep which were being interbred with the aim of improving the wool. The farmers and other workers in Germany also gave good accounts of the disease. In an article (1868) entitled "Die innern und äusseren Krankheiten des Schafes", Dr. Georg May described the "trotting disease" as a chronic disease which attacks Merino sheep and their cross-breeds when they are one to three years old. It was also mentioned that the disease becomes rooted as hereditary, and caused devastation in some flocks which was very difficult to eradicate. The preliminary symptoms described are no different from those seen in English sheep by shepherds and flockmasters, but, in their accounts, they tried to subdivide the condition into two diseases; the "Trotter" and "Nibbler." In the "trotter", the gnawing phenomenon was absent and the disease was considered less dangerous. There was an awareness of the progress of the disease. Once it appears, the symptoms increase and last from 6 to 12 weeks or even longer. In a flock, the disease rarely eliminates by itself, leaving farmers no alternative but to start afresh with new healthy stock.

The transmission of the disease to healthy sheep by contagion was accepted without question by many at the time. The theory advocated, and generally accepted, was that the transmission took place either by copulation or was effected by means of nasal mucus secretions towards the end of the disease. In 1827, the

17

Royal Bavarian State Property Administration of Schleissheim established a stock of Negretti, Electoral and varied crossings of these sheep. In 1827, a fresh stock of 100 sheep was brought in from Silesia. The new flock of sheep became the victim of the trotting disease, and, thereafter, the disease raged in the rest of the old-established Schleissheim stock. The recommendation given for the prophylaxis treatment was: "do not rear sheep with fine wool with exceedingly delicate bodies, ...In buying rams and ewes, be careful not to get them from flocks affected with the trotting disease. If the disease breaks out in a flock, under no circumstances, employ the suspected animals for breeding, on the contrary, kill at once and spare none of the progeny so that suspicious animals are prevented from breeding." It was also considered that rams sicken most readily, especially the young, compared to ewes, and should not be used till after their second year. The disease was described as exceedingly contagious, not solely by breeders but also by veterinarians, and it was suggested in their study that the disease was not hereditary, the evidence being that the progeny of certain rams became ill in one district and not in the other. A few instances were noticed where the rams were healthy, but their offspring were trotter, and therefore it was considered that the disease could be bred through to the offspring, although the disease did not display itself in parents. The predisposition was that the disease was inherited by animals begotten by fathers or born of mothers suffering from the "trotting disease".

The disease in these high-rated wooled animals was explained by the practice of mating the same rams and their male progeny for up to 12 years, and also prolonged and premature breeding. For extensive breeding, ewes were lambed three times in two years, and family relatives were continuously coupled, thus producing a closely related family. Some writers stressed nutritional variations, over-nutritious food in winter, rich pastures where normal ingredients were missing, and extraordinary variation between summer and winter food. Articles on 'Sheep Diseases and Sheep Breeding', mentioned that the years of famine and insufficient nourishment of rams and lambs, on the whole, produced the "trotting disease". However, M'Gowan (1918) compared the environmental conditions in the South of Germany, Bavaria, Wurtemberg, Baden and Austria, where German and Merino cross-breed, Negretti and Electoral sheep were bred and kept in similar conditions to those in North Germany. In countries which are at an altitude of 1600 feet above sea level, with rough climate, the majority of the breeders had not known or heard of the scrapie-like disease.

Scrapie in France

According to French shepherds and veterinary surgeons, France experienced the first scrapie cases soon after the Merinos were introduced into France about 1767-1776, (Stockman, 1913). Stockman tried to trace reliable records on the subject of the disease, but failed to discover any information bearing directly upon the introduction of the disease into France. A flock imported to France in

1786 was greatly reduced by disease on its way, without any explanation being available to account for their deaths. In 1797, a flock of 1,000, and then in 1802, another 3,000 sheep were imported to France from Spain. Importation of sheep stopped in 1811. However, Girard (1829) believed "La tremblante" occurred in France before the introduction of Merino sheep, when farmers were becoming more interested in breeding for improved stock and became more disease conscious.

In France, scrapie was particularly prevalent amongst the improved flock and milk sheep of the Larzac breed, but there is very little written on this disease by farmers. According to M'Gowan, Tessier called the disease "Maladie folle" staggering disease, and then in 1819 gave it the name "Vertigo". Girard, Director of Alfort in 1821, studied the disease under the name of "La tremblante" and divided it into two forms. A fairly good description of the disease in France appeared in 1848 (Roche-Lubin). Although the disease was described under many other names including "Maladie convulsive", mad disease, the story was similar. In French bibliography, the description of the disease and clinical symptoms also recognised two varieties of the scrapie disease. In one, the convulsive phenomena predominate; in the other, prurigo (itchy skin conditions) is the principal feature.

The convulsive type begins with dropping of the ears and conjunctiva accompanied by some stiffness of the lumbar region. Soon, these symptoms are followed by restricted movement and staggering with intermittent trembling. Later, convulsions occur in the sick animals with noticeable stiffness of some regions, especially the neck and lips. They hold their heads high and tails down. On being approached they struggle to get away, tumble and agitate with convulsive shakings. Towards the end, the animals get dizzy and feeble, and can no longer stand on their legs. They are killed, or die.

The pruriginous variety of scrapie shows itself by intermittent biting at the tail-end, and the affected animal rubbing against posts and walls. Pruritus gradually spreads to the rump and lumbar region, and the tail shakes violently during an attack. The animal bites, scratches and pulls-off its wool and bares itself. At this stage of the disease, the animals have a wandering, frightened look on their faces with heads high and ears down. They stumble, remain lying for long periods on the ground, biting, using the negligible power they have left. When standing-up becomes impossible, eyes become rolling and haggard, conjunctiva become livid red, but they still have appetite and thirst. After the clinical symptoms appear, the sheep can live from three weeks up to several months. Eventually they will die, probably of starvation and dehydration.

Scrapie in Iceland

In the early 1930s, the Icelandic sheep farmers were hard-hit by the great world-wide economic depression. In an attempt to help the farmers improve their sheep, the Icelandic Government, in 1933, imported 20 sheep from Germa-

ny, of the Karakul breed, for wool production. Although these sheep were certified free of known diseases by standard tests, and were kept in quarantine for two
months on arrival before distribution to 16 farms around Iceland, they apparently
introduced three or four sheep diseases to Iceland. In S.W. Iceland, one of these
disorders was a disease syndrome characterised by neurological symptoms, especially hind-leg paralysis, which was found to be associated with maedi, a pulmonary condition. At first, it was confused with another central nervous disease of
sheep, rida. It was sporadic, but sometimes its clinical manifestations resembled
chronic sheep pneumonia which was prevalent in Iceland from 1939 to 1952
(Sigurdsson 1954). In Iceland, the disease was referred to by the name "maedi"
meaning dyspnoea or breathlessness, and Johne's disease, a mycobacterial infection. Further investigation revealed that maedi was slowly progressing to pneu-
monitis in which the lungs became ineffective and rubbery. In this way, maedi
primarily appeared as a pulmonary disease. Outbreaks of the disease were correlated to the distribution of the imported sheep. Sigurdsson and his co-workers
soon suspected that the southern rida (scrapie of sheep) was quite different from
the classical northern rida.

He estimated that during the years 1939 to 1952, at least 150,000 animals
were lost from maedi. Losses from maedi on individual farms were reported with
a mortality of 10% to 20%. There were no methods of control available, and the
Icelandic government tried to combat this serious disease by launching a programme of organised slaughter in the infected districts. By the end of 1952, all
the sheep in infected areas had been destroyed, and lambs from uninfected areas
had been introduced to replace them. During this process, approximately
300,000 adult sheep were destroyed. The potentially destructive diseases were
introduced into the sheep population in Iceland, where contact with other sheep
populations had not occurred for many centuries.

Sigurdsson, during the same period, observed a chronic encephalopathy of
sheep in several districts in Iceland. The Icelandic name for this trembling disease is "Rida", and it was prevalent for many years. The clinical disease begins
very gradually, with uncertain gait, and slight tremor of the lips. The symptoms
consist of spastic movements, uncoordinated gait, and tremors, without prominent itching. He observed similarities between this disease and that of scrapie in
Great Britain. This disorder was also recognised as a slow developing process
with a long clinically silent period and it was recognised as delayed developing
visna. Sigurdsson introduced the modern concept in a study of "slow virus infections". He gave an account of several slowly developing diseases in sheep in
Iceland which had made their appearance in that country immediately following
the importation of Karakul breed of sheep from Halle, Germany in 1933.

Sigurdarson et al (1990), suggested that the "rida" was brought to the north of
the country, in 1878, by importation of an English ram of the Oxford-Down
breed from Denmark. The sons of the imported ram had been sold to many
farms within the area. All the disease cases, which had occurred in the middle-

north of the country, were traced back through several generations to this Oxford-Down ram. During the following 70 years, the disease became endemic and prevalent in a limited area of Iceland causing heavy losses on a few farms. However, in 1953, scrapie was found for the first time outside the original area. In Iceland, in the early years, a few people suspected this disease to be infectious. Several outbreaks in increasing numbers were reported during the next 20 years. The mortality rate varied from 0.5% to an extraordinary rate of 50%. However, a considerable variation from year to year was noted. Mortality rates of 10 to 20% were not uncommon.

They reported that during the period 1968-1978, scrapie was found in all major sheep districts in Iceland. The disease appeared to have changed and spread rapidly with contact to the neighbouring farms. They reported that, in most of the new scrapie areas, itching was observed, and in other areas pruritus was the first and most prominent symptom. Scrapie was becoming a great economic problem for sheep production, and there was real danger that disease would spread throughout the whole country leaving no scrapie-free sheep for restocking.

The Icelandic farmers believed that the disease was contagious and transmitted, in some way, from diseased to healthy individuals. It was also considered that some unknown environmental factor of fundamental importance played a part in epidemics. Sigurdsson (1954) recorded that a single diseased animal apparently transmitted the disease to a small flock of 30 sheep, almost all of which died within two years. Since there were no known methods of control, the Icelandic government tried to combat serious maedi disease by slaughtering the diseased sheep in an attempt to eradicate it from infected districts. This also included areas where Rida had been prevalent. When the healthy sheep were brought into the same areas again, the farmers were surprised to find that the disease reappeared the following year on the same farms in the newly introduced flock. Rida had not been known to occur in the areas from where the imported sheep were completely removed, and it did not appear in the sheep from the same areas introduced on to farms which had previously been free of rida. Sigurdsson concluded from this that the rida virus had survived outside the known host on the farms where it had been prevalent, and that it was ready to infect an intermediate host or vector which might play a part in the spread of the disease.

Although previous preventive control measures had failed, culling of scrapie-affected flocks had some effect in reducing the recurrence of the disease. To stop the spreading of the disease to new areas, a determined campaign to eliminate the disease started in 1978 (Sigurdarson et al, 1990). During the eradication programme, the country was divided into quarantine zones. Then, the culling of all sheep on infected farms, and in some cases uninfected but heavily exposed farms or groups of farms in one quarantine zone to another, was undertaken. All these procedures were supervised and approved step by step by a government inspector. Farmers were offered a free veterinary inspection of all scrapie-suspect sheep. They also received reasonable financial assistance for cleaning, and compensation

21

while out of business due to scrapie culling. The farms were left without sheep for two years. A year before restocking the sheep, houses, barns, equipment etc. were thoroughly cleaned and disinfected with hypochlorite, then also sprayed with iodophor or burned with gas flame. All surfaces in barns up to 1.50 m high were sealed and painted with oil-base paint. All sheep-houses that could not be properly disinfected, were burned or buried. The surfaces in front of the sheep-houses and other heavily exposed areas were covered with a minimum of four inches of gravel. The first harvest of hay from the infected fields was not allowed to be used for feeding the new stock. The sheep from new stock was in-spected at the autumn gathering and also in houses on the farms. Every year since 1978, random sheep brain samples have been histopathologically examined systematically from abattoirs as well as for sheep possibly exposed to the infection on farms where scrapie had never been confirmed. Histological examination of brains by this method identified some 15 infected farms (Sigurdarson et al, 1990). Some of the new stock has been running on 76 farms for over five years, and on 102 other farms for over 4 years without reappearance of the disease. So far the results of this eradication programme appear promising.

Scrapie in North America and Canada

The first reported scrapie cases both in Canada and the USA were blamed on imported British sheep (Schofield, 1938; Hourrigan, 1965). Since the initial diagnosis of scrapie in 1947, scrapie in the USA has spread to 39 states. In these studies, out of 478 infected-flocks in the USA, the Suffolk breed provided 75% of the scrapie diagnosed cases (Marsh, 1990). Further studies found 46 additional scrapie-infected flocks in 1991 compared to 47 in 1989, with most flocks located in the States having small numbers of sheep per flock (USDA, 1993). Flocks with 30 or less animals had a higher ratio of newly-detected sheep with scrapie.

A Voluntary Flock Certification Programme was started in the USA on 1 October, 1992 and has relied heavily on an economic incentive, whereby a flock can be "certified" if it has been scrapie-free for a minimum period of five years, thus enhancing the animals' marketability and value.

In the USA, until four or five years ago, very little animal protein was fed to the cattle (Marsh, 1990). In the last two to five years, only lactating dairy cows were being fed more MBM, hydrolysed feather meal, fish meal, poultry meal and blood meal in their rations than previously. The risk of BSE in the USA is considered low, because of a lower prevalence of scrapie, a smaller population of sheep, and the practice of feeding MBM, mainly, to only lactating animals. This is in contrast to the UK practice where calves were exposed to starter rations which contained the BSE agent in the MBM (Marsh, 1990). Some scientists consider that the feeding of animal MBM to young calves in Britain was the major contributory factor for the transmission of BSE. If the trend of feeding animal MBM to cattle in the USA has changed to younger stock, there still remains a threat of exposure as a result of feeding MBM to younger cattle.

Each outbreak of scrapie in the USA was carefully studied in order to establish the epidemiology of the disease. These studies, in the majority of cases, suggested that the dispersal was from a limited common reservoir. Once these foci were identified and eliminated, the disease ceased to disseminate further (Hourrigan, 1965). However, it is impossible to determine the losses which may have occurred in the USA. From 1947 to June, 1964, scrapie had been diagnosed in 26 States in 138 flocks, and around 80,000 sheep had been slaughtered at a cost of $3 million paid to flock owners in Federal and State indemnities. Regulatory officials in the USA and Canada worked closely together in the Scrapie Eradication Programme the objective of which was the prevention, control and eradication of the disease. Preventing exposure to the affected sheep was the only known procedure of avoiding additional outbreaks (Hourrigan, 1965). Since the agent of scrapie has been demonstrated to be present in all body tissues, affected sheep had to be destroyed. This linked with the long incubation period, necessitating the slaughter of exposed animals. Since it was also known that the scrapie agent passed from parent to offspring by direct or indirect contact, the immediate progeny of the exposed animals were in danger, and also had to be destroyed.

The programme adopted in 1952 in California included laboratory confirmation of the disease in animals showing clinical disease, and the quarantine and slaughter of all sheep and goats in the infected flock. Even the animals which had been moved away from the infected flock, and their immediate progeny, were traced and destroyed. In this eradication process, 55 premises were cleansed and disinfected. After this, no new outbreaks were reported over a 12 -year period (Hourrigan, 1965). From the results of the census, it appears that the Scrapie Eradication Programme has held the scrapie disease well in check.

Scrapie in Australia, and New Zealand

The disease has not been observed in Merino in Australia, although Seddon in 1962 reported an outbreak, which was traced to Suffolks imported at the end of 1950. All these animals along with their progeny were slaughtered in February 1952, and there has been no further record, or any suspicion of scrapie in Australia.

Scrapie in India

It is important to note that scrapie in its classical form is unknown in India, and so far no cases of the disease in lowland sheep have been reported. Zlotnik et al (1961) investigated scrapie in India, which according to the local authorities was unknown amongst native sheep in the Himalayan foothills, and appeared only after the introduction of rams for breeding around 1940. They reported the presence of scrapie in sheep with severe pruritus in hills in Northern India. Protracted periods of locomotor incoordination were not observed. According to the

23

account given, about 20 years ago a hitherto unknown fatal disease, associated with persistent rubbing, appeared amongst the mountain sheep of the Tons and Gangotri valleys in the Kumaon hills on the Indo-Tibetan borders - part of the Himalayan mountains and situated between 1,000 and 13,000 feet above sea level. The affected districts are not easily accessible as they are 30 to 80 miles from the nearest rail station. The sheep population consisted of about 700,000 animals of a nondescript mountain breed. They investigated this disease, which local farmers called "Khujali", meaning scratching, and distinguished from other local disease conditions of sheep. The farmers knew how to treat other diseases of sheep, but were not aware of any cure for the scratching conditions. According to the local consensus of opinion, the disease had been completely unknown in the Himalayan foothills in 1940. The occurrence of scrapie in mountain sheep, in a remote and isolated part of Northern India, was unexpected in view of the assurance that scrapie was unknown in other parts of the subcontinent. Before this time, a number of Rambouillet rams were introduced into the valley of Tons and Gangotri. These rams were imported by the late Raja Saheb of Tehri and distributed amongst the farmers to improve their stock. However, the true origin and breeding record of these rams is unknown. If this report is true, scrapie may not have been present in the Himalayan sheep until it was introduced in some way by these Rambouillet rams imported about 20 years previously. The disease spread to 33 villages and the incidence varied in different flocks from 1 to 10%. Most of the affected animals were between 1 and 3 years old, both sexes being equally susceptible to the disease. Clinical symptoms were identical with those observed in British scrapie-infected sheep.

Incidence of the disease in the past

In over two-and a-half centuries, the virulence of the condition seems to have abated, although occasionally farmers faced a new outbreak in sheep which caused havoc. As already explained, it may be quite natural for farmers to conceal it for commercial reasons; therefore it is difficult to formulate any true estimate of the number of cases, or the proportion of farms, on which it has occurred. Information about scrapie-infected sheep has often leaked-out, in casual gossip from one shepherd to another. Arthur Young, writing in the Annals of Agriculture, said in the year 1799; "I lost from 40 to 50 ewes by a complaint which has been for some years fatal to this neighbourhood and called by the shepherds the "rub" or the "rubbers", from their seeming to rub themselves to death by which, some very capital flocks of Norfolk in the vicinity of Bury have lost several hundreds". Another flock-owner was reported to have lost 240 sheep out of 500 in one year. In 1797, another farmer mentions, that because of 'rotten sheep' a great number of his very valuable breeding ewes had to be sent to Smithfield Market. The butchers disliked sheep of this type saying that, 'though the sheep appear light, when killed and cut up, they were even lighter; there being such a small portion of lean meat on those prime parts, and less fat within them than could possibly be imagined, compared to other sort of sheep'. Butchers often regarded such sheep as a great waste of their time and effort.

M'Gowan described in great detail, the history of the disease in Britain and quoted a passage from 'General View of the Agriculture of Wiltshire,' published in 1813 and written by Thomas Davis. The author described the disorder as "Goggles", and stated that, "This disorder, we must observe, has tended, more than all other reasons combined, to bring the Wiltshire sheep into discredit. It is not clearly known, when this disorder first made its appearance in Wiltshire, nor is it certain that it is peculiar to this kind of sheep. It was very little noticed in Wiltshire till about twenty-five years ago, and yet it is certain that a disease which was undoubtedly the same disorder was known in Lincolnshire about sixty years ago."

It would appear that the disease in those early years must have been of great economic significance since, in a Bath newspaper in 1778, a "gentleman in Wiltshire" wrote; "Within these few years we have had a disease among the sheep now generally known by the name of goggles, a disease which has destroyed some in every flock round this County and made great havoc in many. The sheep most subject to it are "two teeth". It is not infectious, but hereditary, and undoubtedly runs in the blood...". Another writer, Claridge, in 1795, in the same paper, wrote "This disorder has been known to be fatal to the greatest part of a flock, and is considered as the most calamitous circumstance the sheep owners have to dread. It is very difficult to assign the cause of this disorder, but some of the old-fashioned farmers think that as no such disease existed prior to the introduction of the breed from other counties, consequently its origin may be imputed to this cause".

In a footnote the editor of the Bath paper added: "The subject is important in proportion to the destruction made in flocks by this disease, even were it peculiar to the county of Dorset; but the idea of its being introduced [from other counties] by mixture implies the existence of the disease elsewhere: and indeed it is a fact too generally known by experience. That it has been so little treated on in our best publication on the agriculture is a matter of surprise". From this editor's note, it would appear that the disease was widespread. During those years many writers on the subject arrived at one common conclusion on the spread of the disease. A note in 1810 in "Agriculture of Hampshire" reads "The goggles is a disease sometimes but by no means generally complained of: it is so well known as not to require a particular description in this place. The means of its prevention is, in the opinion of many flockmasters and shepherds, to change the rams as frequently as possible". Mr. Bridges of Winford writes in 1815: "Goggles is a hereditary disorder, but it is not very prevalent at this time".

Records examined suggest that around 1813, the disorder commonly known as rickets was prevalent in some parts of Cambridgeshire. All sorts of sheep were subject to the disorder, and it was believed that continuing the same breed without introducing rams from other flocks, and "high keep", would bring-about the disease. Although various names were given, the disorder became known as "Wiltshire disorder". The reason being that the majority of the Wiltshire wethers were sold off as lambs, and fattened before they were two years old with the view that "high keep" will bring out scrapie if it was present in the blood of the flock. It is considered that many thousands of wethers sold from Hants and Dorset were also affected by the disorder. The sellers were obliged to make good the loss, and this breed of sheep has been, in consequence, brought into discredit.

Because of the economic importance of sheep husbandry to wool production, the need for improvement was recognised. Incidentally, with the introduction of the Merino, the disease became more clearly recognised, as well as the subject of record and subsequent discussions. William Pitt, in "General Views of Agriculture, County of Stafford" (1813), wrote: "By an act of 13 Geo. III. Chap. 81, sect. 21, after taking notice, that the improvement of the breed of sheep is a matter of great national importance, and the turning of rams upon wastes, and upon common fields at certain times of year has been found very prejudicial, it is enacted. That no ram shall be turned upon, or be suffered to remain upon any waste or common field, between the 25th of August and 25th of November every year."

Palmer (1959), in a review of past literature of scrapie, reported that, in various countries, investigations into scrapie were frequently instituted by official Agricultural Departments, possibly to look into the complaints due to the severity of the disease during an outbreak.

Before BSE materialised in England, scrapie in sheep seemed to have been a disease of the past. It had been believed that scrapie usually occurred in the extreme north of England and south of Scotland. Scrapie cases have been recorded in Haddington (Lothian), Peeblesshire, Selkirkshire, Fife, Aberdeenshire, Caithness, Kirkcudbrightshire, Sutherlandshire and the island of Tiree. North Country ewes were generally recognised in border counties as being exceptionally clear of scrapie taint, since they had an insignificant number of sick animals.

In the South of England considerable sheep farming was carried out for two purposes; namely the production of wool and mutton, the latter being the main objective. For this reason, the sheep were genetically inbred for meat market purposes and, since slaughter was carried out before the clinical disease appeared in the animals, they were presumed to be free of scrapie. M'Fadyean 1918, stated: "So far as it is known, the disease has now ceased to exist in this country except in Northumberland and adjacent Border counties of Scotland. That the disease, without any concerted method of dealing with it, should have disappeared from the other counties in which it was once was common is remarkable, but explanation is probably to be found in the fact that the disease finds the conditions most favourable for the spread in the large hill flocks ...". Probably the true explanation for the clinical cases of scrapie, is that, in these districts, sheep were kept over a certain age for the chief object of breeding and wool growing. This was principally because of the age difference between southern and northern flocks. Scrapie was noticed largely in the Cheviot, the Border Leicester and its crosses, the half-Breeds, and the Cross Suffolks, which were kept for the purposes of breeding and wool. Scottish Blackfaces, Greyfaces and Mules have also suffered from the disease. In the eighteenth century, scrapie occurred in almost all English breeds. There is no evidence to suggest that any breed of sheep has a natural immunity against scrapie.

However, there is a marked variation in the susceptibility of different breeds which was recognised early; Merinos being especially affected. Gordon (1966) found that Herdwick sheep were 78% susceptible to experimental infections, while Swaledale had an incidence of 54%. At the other end of the spectrum, of the 24 breeds examined, Gordon found that not one of 48 Dorset Down sheep breed inoculated developed the disease. Statements made regarding the incidence of the disease have been open to dispute for many years. Attempts to assess the incidence of the disease by voluntary reports or its distribution have, all too often, lent support to supposed arguments based on mere probabilities. On seeing a diseased animal, flockmasters have endeavoured to slaughter any near relative of affected sheep as soon as the condition is observed. The striking features are wide fluctuations in the attack-rate in different flocks over a period of years and even from year to year. Often, it appears that the disease seems absent and then reappears suddenly in epidemic form under similar management and similar environmental conditions. Sporadic cases occur, but Stockman gave the annual loss as from "4% to 19%" of all sheep. There is evidence to suggest that scrapie occurred in waves of infection.

It has been documented that the prevalence of scrapie was particularly high at intervals of 50 years from 1750 until the 1930s. The traditional practices of sheep-raising changed when the disease erupted and then the disease would disappear by introducing clean selected stock. The usual history is that the disease begins with a case or two on a farm, and, once the disease is established there, a larger number of affected cases appear in the flock. From what one knows of the slow-onset of the disease, and from the grip that it took of a flock over a number of years, farmers gradually learned by bitter experience how to deal with the disease. It appears strange that, from time-to-time, the disease, without any concerted method of dealing with it, should disappear and, as mentioned previously, this may be due to the purpose for which the sheep were kept - mutton or wool - and the age of the sheep when killed. Very occasionally, without obvious reasons, the number of cases in a scrapie flock may rise rapidly and may even reach over 50%. On some farms, once the disease appeared, and, if efforts were not made to control it, there was a progressive increase in affected animals year after year. It was considered important to avoid breeding from tainted stock, otherwise the disease would, in all probability, in the course of time, exterminate the whole flock.

A report in an East Yorkshire newspaper of 1812 stated that the disease had been prevalent for the last few years and caused great devastation. Stockman

27

(1913) reiterated that, prior to this outbreak, the disease was unknown before crosses were introduced. Particularly, crossing with the long-wool Lincolnshire was blamed for the introduction of the disease to sheep in the East Riding of Yorkshire. Some farmers eradicated the disease by changing the whole flock; a measure strongly recommended and practised by a large number of flockmasters.

Recently, results were published of the prevalence of scrapie in sheep in Britain (Morgan et al, 1990). The authors carried out two independent surveys. In one, they handed the farmers an anonymous, self-administered questionnaire form at a major National Sheep Exhibition. In the other, they sent out questionnaires to members of the British Dairy Sheep Association. At the National Sheep Exhibition stall, which was attended by 12,000 people, of whom 9,600 were sheep farmers, they were able to distribute 300 questionnaires of which 295 were returned. They rejected 16 because the respondents were not residents of the UK or did not keep sheep. In their report, the authors pointed out that the selection bias was self-evident from the very start, at the exhibition show, as some people saw the survey poster and avoided the exhibit. A further 10% of the farmers refused to answer the questionnaires. This might have influenced the results, as, of those who responded, 34.5% reported scrapie on their farms. It also became apparent that, out of 37 counties represented in the exhibition, scrapie was identified in 29.

In the instance, where the questionnaires were sent to 300 members of the British Dairy Sheep Association, only 89 were returned, out of which one farmer kept no sheep. Of the 88 results analysed, 17% had scrapie on their farms, and 5.7% did not know whether scrapie was present. The important point, which emerges from this study, was that the a large number of owners were unwilling to participate in the study. This may be because of the stigma which is associated with acknowledging the presence of scrapie in their flocks. It would therefore appear that the true number of infected flocks of sheep will never be known by voluntary techniques.

Hourrigan (1965) reported estimated figures from different workers in France, and revealed that 10 to 30% of flocks were infected, with 4 to 25% sheep developing the clinical disease. Iceland showed 3 to 16% per year in infected flocks, and India 1 to 10%.

Seasonal variation of scrapie

The usual observations indicate that there are a greater number of cases in the first six months of a year. The majority of cases develop in spring and early summer months, but new cases occur at all times of the year. M'Fadyean (1918) believed: "there is reason to think that the greater frequency with which sheep are attacked during the period stated is determined by the fact that gimmers (two-year-old ewes) furnish the majority of the victims, and that there is less regularity in the season at which the symptoms are first exhibited by older sheep." This coincides with the late pregnancy and lactation in the ewe and follows the

28

period of reproductive activity in the ram. Many shepherds considered that, if females become pregnant when eight months old, instead of the usual twenty months of age, the younger group develop the disease earlier; probably due to nutritional stress, or pregnancy, or an early infection by an asymptomatic ram.

Features of the Disease as Described by Shepherds

The clinical features of the disease vary both in type and duration, hence the different names used. Nearly all cases show early fatigue with moderate exercise, and general weakness. There are two readily recognisable varieties of scrapie: one 'itchy' variety, and the second 'trotting' variety.

'Itchy' variety: In Britain, by far the commonest type is that of intense itchiness, which increases with loss of wool followed by weakness and ultimate death. One of the early symptoms is lighter colour of the wool, which is not easily noticed by the casual observer, but readily observed by experienced flockmasters and shepherds. At this primary stage of the disease, it is reported that the sheep manifested signs of pleasure when the skin was scratched. The animals would lie down and get up frequently changing their position with general restlessness. The sick animal would stand apart from others moving in a rather aimless and stupid fashion. In between grazing, the animal would look up anxiously, and without reason walk away to another place to graze. In some cases, a suddenly frightened or chased animal would fall down in an epileptiform fit, with loss of consciousness. The fit may last a few minutes, and if repeated, death could follow.

In the secondary stage, the disease progresses rapidly. Itchiness increases and the sheep have a peculiar fixed stare as though listening. Ears may be seen to move and restlessness becomes clearly evident. When an affected sheep is watched quietly in the field, nervous twitching, muscular tremors and trembling may be seen. Itchiness is such that the animal looks for trees and fences, and rubs against them causing the wool to come off in tufts. The itch sometimes commences at the head, and sometimes at the tail, eventually becoming equally intense all over the body. To rub its tail, the sheep may sit on the ground like a dog on hind quarters. The animal gnaws and bites, when scratching, and eventually becomes denuded of fleece. Injuries and scabs from rubbing appear in due course, creating abscesses which are always secondary to itchiness. There is a steady decrease in vitality. The sheep becomes weaker and more emaciated until reduced almost to skin and bone. There may be as much as a 30 lbs loss of weight in a few weeks. Affected sheep in a normal flock show nervous symptoms, peculiar gait, abnormal carriage of the head, and may pass faeces and urine from nervous excitement.

Symptoms of paralysis appear in the tertiary stage, in particular, the inability to use the hind limbs. Mental disorders lead to behavioural and personality changes, and quite frequently, dementia occurs. Many animals become uncooperative, fearless and refuse to be driven; whereas others are very excitable and extremely distressed. Blindness has been reported occurring in about 5% of cases. Such cases might last a few weeks. Death occurs more quickly in winter months, but in summer, an affected suckling ewe also succumbs more quickly than one without suckling lambs. There has been no evidence to support one sex being more susceptible than the other. Naturally, the extraordinary majority of the cases occur in ewes, because rams make up only a very small proportion of the entire sheep stock. Rams are said to go down with the disease more quickly than ewes.

In the 'trotting' variety of the disease the animals exhibit a peculiar action of the forelegs while running, the so-called "cuddie trot", and is almost comical to watch with a flopping action of both ears and head. It is totally unlike the normal gallop of a healthy sheep (Gaiger, 1924). When a sheep so affected is unduly chased, or excited, it collapses to the ground in a faint and exhausted condition and is unable to rise. Such fainting attacks have also been reported while the sheep is quietly grazing and undisturbed. The sheep may lie down on the ground as if dead, or continue to show movements of the limbs in an effort to rise. Undue excitement of such sheep may cause sudden death. In the trotting variety, the disease is more quickly fatal and itchiness may also be apparent, on the skin. In this form of the disease, though itchiness may be apparent there is seldom any loss of wool.

Wilson et al (1950), in their studies of scrapie in sheep, observed that, of 14 animals admitted to their institute as established clinical cases of the natural acquired scrapie during the previous four years, seven survived more than five months; whereas, of 42 experimental cases recorded during that period, not one survived as long as five months.

Age of individual sheep when clinical disease develops

Farmers, shepherds and flock masters witnessed early cases of scrapie in 18 to 24 month old sheep. Since the farmers believed that the disease was either hereditary or that it was passed during the sexual act, its eradication was a paramount objective in their minds. Therefore, the majority of full and half brothers and sisters, daughters, sons, mothers and fathers of all affected animals were killed for commercial reasons, in order to exterminate the whole of the affected progeny from the flock. Around the 1950s, extensive field studies were conducted where half brothers and sisters, mothers and fathers of affected animals and their progeny were allowed to live a natural existence. It soon became apparent that the majority of cases manifested clinical disease between three and seven years of age. A review of the USA scrapie programme revealed that only 7% of all scrapie diagnosed was present in ewes younger than 24 months of age (USDA, 1991). The majority of scrapie cases (89%), however, occurred between 25 to 72 months. As noticed by shepherds and flockmasters, scrapie cases had been observed principally in 18 to 24 month old sheep. However, this only represented a few early cases, as the majority of sheep manifested the disease when they were

30

over three years old.

Dickinson et al (1965) conducted breeding experiments using sheep not less than one year old collected from both affected and scrapie-free flocks. They examined, histologically, brains of sheep which died or were killed. Their results from this extensive study, using hundreds of sheep, disclosed a number of incipient cases of scrapie. About 10% of their cases were identified by histopathological examination of brains. These would otherwise have escaped detection. Since histopathological changes would start many months before onset of the clinical symptoms, it is difficult from this study to demonstrate how soon after the infection the lesions appear, and at what stage of the incubation period the clinical symptoms would become apparent. Males have a different culling rate, but the actual age and incidence pattern, based on male and female adult population observation, has revealed no difference between sexes.

Early investigations of the cause of scrapie

A special breed of investigators, with endless patience, are required to study and assess the progress of a disease incubating and developing over a period of 7 years, or even longer. About fifty years ago, it was said, that he who would embark on an investigation into the field of scrapie must be possessed of a stout heart and long life. Features of extreme wasting leading to death, with no significant post-mortem changes to account for the symptoms, baffled investigators working with the disease. Gaiger (1924) pointed out that the investigations were further hampered by those who had a vested interest because of the movement of the stock, and the secrecy maintained by those who had the disease on the farm. He wrote, "It is only the fortunate few who have escaped, and with these few it is more by good luck than otherwise, and it is only a matter of time till they do get what is popularly termed a dose of it". Even after 150 years, there still appears to be a widespread general tendency towards concealment. This general tendency towards concealment is no different where BSE is concerned. Knowledge of the existence of the disease on a farm often does leak out by information passed out in a casual way from one shepherd to another. Often, existence of the disease has been disclosed by the sale of sheep from an infected flock, as some sheep may develop the disease in the possession of their new owner.

Flocks in which the disease had been present for many years were obviously useless for the purpose of inquiry. In those in which the disease was of recent origin, inquiries were difficult because of the long incubation period and, at the onset, almost all owners were inclined to conceal the fact that their flocks were infected.

In one instance, where some information was made available, it was revealed that a farmer with no scrapie on his own farm bought 140 Cheviot ewe lambs at a public auction from a neighbouring town in autumn of 1907. They were mated with rams in November 1908, along with thirty other young ewes of the same age but born on the farm. In total he had a stock of 560 sheep with no

31

strict separation between any of them. They had a wide run of hill pasture. In February and March of 1909, pregnant ewes were takeoff hill pasture and folded together to feed on turnips. In the next six months during lambing and suckling, thirty ewes succumbed to scrapie. All of them were from the new lot of 140 Cheviot bought from the neighbouring town. In the autumn of 1909, the farmer was determined to eradicate the disease and he fattened and sold all the surviving ewes of this lot, and at the same time, he sold all their lambs. No more cases appeared until April 1911, when two ewes went down with the disease. Subsequently, two more died during the summer months. Several more were also noticed to be affected in November of the same year. In the autumn of 1909 and 1910, the farmer bought some more stock from another farm, where he later heard that scrapie had also occurred in the past. From this time on, a number of other cases appeared over the years; some in his original flock, and some in the stock he bred and sold to other farms. The disease did not appear to be contagious, although the farmer thought that the disease might have been spread in his flock via the rams. It is possible, though not confirmed, that the farmer might have used his old rams which he used originally to tup the Cheviot sheep bought in the autumn of 1907. He kept 11 rams to service his flock, which they did over three or four successive seasons without a single ram developing any symptoms of scrapie.

There are almost identical stories of the origin of scrapie on other farms which were also free of the disease up to the spring of 1909. All the cases which occurred on these farms, were in sheep which had also been bought as lambs in the autumn of 1907. These accounts were very common and were recorded by many farmers, flockmasters and shepherds with excellent understanding and experience. They excluded heredity, because the imported, affected stock and their progeny were completely slaughtered out, and the disease also appeared in animals which had no ancestral connection but had contacts with affected animals. On some farms, disease appeared only in ewes which were tupped by new, suspected rams. It is also known that some of these suspected rams developed scrapie in due course. They suggested that the scrapie was caused by the multiplication of "some parasite" in the sheep's body, and that it spread by direct or indirect transference of this parasite from the diseased to the healthy animals. Explanations were given such as: the lambs acquired congenital infection from mother, father or both. It was not essential that either of them should show any clinical symptoms of the disease at the time of lambing. Based on the evidence from these observations, it was considered that the disease might be transmitted to a ewe or ram by the sexual act, that it might be transmitted to the lambs in utero owing to infection on the part of the sire (male) or dam (female), and that it may be transmitted from animal to animal by direct or indirect association at pasture.

The Origin of Scrapie on Clean farms and Its Spread

The method by which natural scrapie of sheep spreads from flock to flock or within a flock remains unknown even after 250 years of research. It has been considered that the frequently favoured route of spread is through breeding, either hereditary or by congenital transmission or by contact, either directly or through physical mingling of the affected with non-affected animals, or indirectly through the medium of contaminated pasture. M'Gowan (1918) stated: "I have no desire to enter into academic and barren disquisition, as has been attempted, relative to the exact distinction between the term 'hereditary' and 'congenitally infectious.' To the simple minded the first term is more inclusive and could include the second as a special case. For the purpose, I will designate as hereditary in connection with disease, any disease obtained by offspring through the functioning of paternity or maternity as such. This obviously makes the term hereditary include other diseases than those due to infectious agents, as also it makes the term include diseases contracted by offspring subsequent to birth, consequent on the act of its feeding on its mother's milk. The term 'congenitally infectious or contagious' would therefore stand in contradistinction to 'contagious' as ordinarily used in connection with diseases contracted through other less intimate, ordinary, everyday association." However, M'Fadyean disagreed with the definition of hereditary given by M'Gowan. In truth, the definition of hereditary encompasses the disease of genes, inherited by the offspring from the parents, and the initiated disease should not be infectious to other animals. From the numerous previous records, there is a general agreement that scrapie is not highly infectious, but frequently appears in a clean flock some months or years following the introduction of one or more fresh animals into the stock. In this way, it has always been difficult in field studies to eliminate the spread of the disease due to mating.

Stockman (1913) gave an account of the disease while tracing scrapie in the UK. He reported that, in 1853, there was a flock of half-bred Cheviot and Leicester sheep on a farm near Yetholm. The Yetholm farmer held an annual sale of his stock, and a neighbouring farmer, about 1853, bought two tups at the sale, and let them run with his ewes. The native ewes originally, at the neighbouring farm, did not contract the disease themselves, but it appeared in 1856, in the stock sired by the tups brought in from the other farm and in their progeny when they reached two years old. The tups were believed to have brought the disease which caused the appearance of scrapie on the farm and, from that time, for several years, fifty sheep a year from out of a stock of 1200, (4.2%) died of the disease. The disease continued to rage in the flock. Several diseased sheep were slaughtered and buried. The farmer decided to cut his losses and sold-off the remaining sheep not showing the symptoms and vacated his farm. Some time after this dispersal sale, buyers of the sheep complained that scabby sheep had been sold, as they were rubbing themselves. This suggests that many buyers were still unaware of the existence of such a disease as scrapie.

Pattison (1964) stated: "it has long been known by shepherds that the disease can be controlled within a flock, if not entirely eliminated, by slaughter of affected animals and their progeny." Spread of the disease through ingestion of foetal membranes from scrapie-affected animals, or of material contaminated by such membranes, would appear to offer an explanation for the perpetuation of scrapie within a flock.

Sigurdsson, in 1954, organised a programme to eradicate scrapie by a policy of slaughtering all sheep over a large part of northern Iceland in which the Icelandic scrapie disease was prevalent. As already stated, the healthy sheep were brought from areas free from the disease, but after about a year the disease reappeared on farms where the disease had previously existed. Sigurdsson (1954), concluded, that, since the rida virus had survived outside the known host on the farms where it had been prevalent, it suggested that an intermediate host or vector must be present, which might play a part in the spread of the disease.

Spread of Disease By Ram-Letting

Marshall, in his 'Rural Economy of the Midland Counties', stated the price of ram-letting prior to 1780, to have been from one to ten guineas for the season; while Parkinson (1813) in 'General Views Of Agriculture', stated that this price, for Mr. Bakewell's stock by year 1786, rose rapidly from 10 guineas to 100 guineas; and that he let two thirds of his rams in that year. From then on, the prices of letting rams kept rising. Letting rams was quite a profitable business.

Parkinson (1813) continued "numbers of rams are now sent from Dishley and by Mr Stubbins, Astley and others, annually into Ireland. Two instances recorded in history illustrate how the "movement of flock" might have an important bearing on the spread of infection from the south to the Northumberland and Border areas (Stockman, 1913). The Messrs. Culley settled at Fenton near Wooler, Northumberland, in 1767 bringing with them some of Mr. Bakewell's Dishley sheep (Mr. Bakewell was a successful sheep breeder and jobber in Leicestershire) and then established a very successful business of letting rams. These rams were sold or let for 50 to 200 guineas a season. At about the same time, Messrs. Cleaver and Kenal in the Morpeth market also established a regular profitable business hiring out Yorkshire Wold sheep tups, a cross with Lincolnshire blood. It has been mentioned that, by crossing with Lincolns, the Wold sheep were badly infected with scrapie. The disease was very prevalent in Lincolnshire from 1799 (Stockman, 1913). This was considered by Stockman (1913) to be one of the important contributory explanations for the introduction and spread of disease towards the north of the country, and from there into Scotland.

In an answer to a question put to Fink by the Board of Agriculture of England in 1804 concerning the breeding of Saxony sheep, he reported "There is another distemper to which our sheep are liable and which is also propagated from one generation to another. It consists in this that the sheep afflicted with it has got a

34

stiff hinder leg, and reels in moving forward as if its back was broken. In this state it usually bites its own hinder legs, and tears off from them the hair, together with the skin. it's strength abates,..... till at last it cannot any longer keep up with the rest of the flock... and perishes. The cause of this disease seems to be a gouty matter."

He continued: "I had once bought some rams which belonged to a breed where this disease had gained great influence. Knowing nothing about this circumstance, I put those rams to my ewes without any apprehension of danger; but ere long I got acquainted not only with the name but also with the nature of this dangerous distemper. Soon after this accident it happened, I know not how, that some rams of my flock got admittance into the flocks of a farmer, and it was observable in a little time that they had introduced into these flocks the same disease, with all its fatal consequences, though it was before that time never known on that farm. To rescue my sheep from so destructive an enemy, I tried after some years to incorporate with my flocks sound and strong rams taken from a herd perfectly free from the disease, and I am happy to say that by this means the evil gradually diminished so as to leave no trace behind it. The same remedy was also applied by other farmers, and their flocks were likewise restored to health."

This statement was substantiated by a very detailed study of enquiries made personally by Gaiger on farms used for breeding and purchases of stock. The importance of such examples is that they show direct infection of ewes through the agency of an infected ram, and that a ram may develop scrapie at about two years of age. It was also believed that an uninfected ram could get infected by an affected ewe, and that a ram himself may not get infected, but may cause infection from infected to uninfected females and never himself show clinical symptoms.

Gaiger gave two actual illustrations of the introduction of scrapie into a flock by a tup: "Mr. Z., who has always bred half-breed with half-breed, had bought in no new ewe stock for twelve years, but had purchased half-breed tups. He managed to keep clear of scrapie. In September 1920 at a ram sale he purchased a tup which he used in October 1920 and 1921. This tup developed scrapie in July 1923, and died later, having shown typical symptoms. This tup's first progeny were gimmers in lamb in 1923, and out of sixty, eight became affected at or near lambing. His second crop of lambs were gimmers in lamb in 1924, and out of forty-eight nine died of, or were disposed of as having, scrapie at or near lambing." He also mentioned another exactly parallel instance, that other tups from the same seller had developed scrapie on other farms in the identical manner, and had transmitted the disease to their progeny. He concluded that this tup infected his offspring in October or November, 1920, a period of two years and eight months before the ram himself showed symptoms.

In the second incident, a ram, which never exhibited symptoms himself, transmitted scrapie to his progeny. Mr. Y. purchased a tup and brought it to his own scrapie-free farm, but, despite his endeavours, the tup failed to live up to expectations. It showed skin eruptions first on one fore-leg and then on the other, but the owner kept him for four years and he never showed the clinical signs of scrapie, though he might have developed the disease had he been kept alive longer. Every batch of lambs sired by this ram showed scrapie at or near lambing as gimmers, and, out of one lot of forty-five lambs by him, every one eventually went down with scrapie. Such latency of the disease in the tup may account for some farms having incurred heavy losses without knowing where the disease originated from, particularly on the farms where more than one ram was in use for mating.

Stockman (1913) stated that he had found plenty of evidence to show that the disease was introduced into formerly clean farms by the purchase of breeding ewes from farms where the disease existed, or by the hire or purchase of rams from such places. One well experienced farmer told him "that the disease broke out in a flock of his sheep from which he was in the habit of breeding rams for ewes on other farms in his occupation. He did not quite realise the serious nature of the disease, and he used the rams, born from apparently healthy ewes, for his clean flocks on other farms a year after the disease had broken out. As a result of this, the progeny of these rams developed the disease, and the clean flock became infected. I have also many observations collected in this country, and in other countries where the disease exists, which show a similar result following upon the introduction of rams apparently healthy but bred in an infected flock."

It seemed that the sire infected the progeny while mating, without all mothers necessarily developing the clinical disease. In this instance, all left over animals were fattened for slaughter and not used for further breeding. According to the account given by Stockman: "this farmer thought that the disease might be also contagious directly or indirectly from pasture, so in another year took all lambs off their mothers, under the impression that they would remain healthy if removed to a different district. About eighteen months later, some new cases of scrapie occurred in the lambs moved to the other district which were now gimmers. The same farmer observed that a gimmer had two lambs and remained perfectly healthy to all appearances while being suckled, and for some months afterwards, but the following spring the mother developed the disease. Subsequently both the lambs, one as a gimmer and the other as young ewe also, developed scrapie." Since these observations were made in a diseased flock, it is difficult to differentiate whether congenital (vertical) or pasture (horizontal) infection occurred. The chances of developing the disease in the affected flocks were considered high, particularly if the mother showed the disease in early life. The disease developed even when the progenies of these animals were moved to different clean farms.

There are also records in which ewes, tupped by a suspected ram, did not become infected with the disease, although it has been said that they were kept under observation for a considerably long time. It must be stated that scrapie

36

cannot be diagnosed for certain until it is more or less at the advanced clinical stage. It is possible that many early clinically suspected sheep, which recovered, might never have had the disease. It appears, from most of the observations made by farmers, flockmasters, shepherds and scientists, that the origin of the disease among the healthy sheep, *de nova*, depended on a certain system of breeding sheep. Dickinson et al (1965) examined histopathologically brains of several sheep suspected of recovery, and not one showed the specific brain lesions, thus demonstrating clinical misdiagnosis of the disease in some sheep.

In particular, in-breeding and the breeding of high-class stock have been alleged as the major cause of the disease. For mating the rams were selected mostly when about 6 to 8 months old for good growth, wool and muscular development and, after satisfactory breed confirmation. They were first used as sires when they were about eight months old, and kept for two to three years, and, occasionally, until seven years old, mating ten to forty ewes each year. To maintain the purity of the breed, these stud rams tended to have a number of common ancestors, or in particular, an outstandingly successful sire. In their ancestry, many rams might have a common grandparent which produces a concentration of a certain line in each breed and formed virtually a closed breeding population of extreme polygamy.

Records of scrapie in Britain over the past 200 years are of great interest. They show some of the views held by farmers and shepherds regarding the nature of the disease which has been handed down from generation to generation. Traditional views held by farmers and shepherds have not changed much over the last 100 years. There was some evidence which appeared to indicate that scrapie was an infective disease. However, many of the features of the disease also seemed to suggest that it did not represent a simple infective process, but resulted from hereditary diathesis. There is an instance on record where the entire progeny of a tainted ram, forty-five in number, developed the disease, in a previously clean flock. Some farmers believed that good high-feeding helped to bring out the disease which might otherwise have remained latent. Farmers had only one radical method of getting rid of the disease, namely, by culling the whole flock.

Preventive measures

M'Gowan was of the opinion that an infected flock can be freed from the disease by the less drastic method of gradually selling-off old ewes and buying in a corresponding number of fresh young ewes from clean flocks. M'Gowan stressed, however, that the process can be hampered by the difficulty, intrinsic and unavoidable, of the flockmasters being sure that fresh animals are from an absolutely clean flock and, to substantiate this, he quoted a prominent Border farmer: "It is every year becoming more difficult to secure clean stock." Failures arising from this method of dealing with the disease, therefore, should not be attributed to the fresh stock being infected from the old and diseased which it replaces, until unimpeachable evidence has been adduced that the incoming animals were absolutely free from all taint.

M'Fadyean considered that these measures could, to a large extent control and hold a check on the disease, but he thought that the only certain method of eradicating the disease, from the large flock, was to dispose of all of the sheep, young and old, and to restock with ewes and rams obtained from sound flocks, despite the heavy cost involved.

There has been great debate in this area as to how an affected flock can be freed from the disease - by gradually selling-off the old stock and not breeding affected animals. Stamp (1961) suggested that, since scrapie has strong familial association, control of scrapie, on a rational basis, can be achieved by the elimination of all family contacts, which would go far in keeping scrapie in check. Unfortunately, owing to the lack of evidence bearing on the point, and even now after another 50, 100 and even 150 years further experience, it is not yet possible to give a definite answer as to how the disease is transmitted from the diseased to the healthy. Even the emergence of BSE, and consequent pressures for research, has been unable to obtain a definitive answer as to the mode of natural transmission. Since the disease is much more frequent among the progeny of diseased ewes than among the progeny of healthy ones, it is an unshakable belief held by flockmasters and many investigators, that in many cases healthy lambs, born of infected ewes, will develop the disease over the following two years.

The question then being asked was whether, in those cases in which the lambs born of diseased ewes themselves developed the disease when about two years old, the infection had been passed on before or after birth. In many observations, it has been reported that, even when the healthy lambs were immediately separated from the mother and fed on cow's milk, they developed disease with typical symptoms of scrapie when they were about eighteen months old. M'Gowan in his studies described that six lambs born from healthy Cheviot mothers, remote from the scrapie area and in which scrapie was unknown, were 'twinned-on' for milk to mothers who had clinical scrapie and were dying from the disease. The mothers' own lambs had been killed off in order to accomplish this experiment. The lambs were suckled on these foster-mothers from a week or so to six weeks depending on the length scrapie-infected mothers survived. All of the lambs 'twinned-on' scrapie-infected mothers, died when between two and two and a half years old from typical scrapie. However, amongst the mothers themselves of all ages, and healthy lambs, born from and suckled on these healthy mothers, which lived in intimate association with the diseased animals during the course of the experiment, not a single case was noticed. It showed that the incubation period of scrapie had increased from eighteen months to about thirty months.

These are retrospect studies carried out by various workers, and most of the accounts collected were given by sheep farmers who had the disease in their flocks. Many of these observations and views held by farmers years later, were tested by the experimental investigations of Stockman (1926). He held the view

38

that scrapie was more likely to be transmitted within infected progeny. It was recognised by all farmers experienced with scrapie that an affected ewe was more likely to produce healthy lambs at birth which would later, after an incubation period of eighteen to twenty months, develop the symptoms of the disease. Since the disease developed in eighteen to twenty four months, this was termed the scrapie age. Even if the lambs were removed from their mothers soon after birth to completely new surroundings or to a new district, the disease showed itself at the scrapie age.

The problem of prevention was compounded, since the flockmasters were aware of the fact that the progeny of affected sheep were considered not suitable for breeding and such sheep would be fattened and sold for meat. With these facts in mind, it was considered that either the disease was hereditary from one or both parents, or that it arises from infection transmitted by either parent to the ovum, embryo, or foetus.

For treatment and prevention, Stockman (1926) considered that the old flock should be eradicated while gradually starting anew. Rams were considered the probable disseminator of infection. Since one tup could infect a large number of ewes, it was considered important to destroy the tup, after the season, if it appeared to have run with affected or suspected ewes. Affected sheep should be slaughtered; this would remove the infected progeny and also would fetch a good meat price. The progeny were considered to be unsuitable for breeding purposes. Stockman stated: "but I must take no responsibility for a legal opinion, that a man sells potentially infective sheep to another the latter has a remedy in common law. Even if that is so, however, I do not see how any sheep farmer could be adequately compensated for the misfortune of having scrapie introduced into his flock.... It has been suggested that with all sheep sold by auction for breeding purposes there should be a guarantee that they have not come from a farm where scrapie exists. He considered that the adoption of this procedure to keep the disease under control may be a method of eradication. It is difficult to say whether any of these rules were applied in practice.

Stockman (1913), however, gave an example of one farmer, who had never had a case of scrapie on his farm until some sheep, he bought some years previously, began to show signs of scrapie. The farmer, after finding the disease amongst his infected stock them together with their progeny for slaughter. He had no cases of scrapie for the following eighteen months, but, about this time, his other stock, which had no ancestral connection with the lot purchased, began to show symptoms of the disease. The second lot was also sent for slaughter, but about another 18 months later, the disease reappeared in another of his stock. He recorded such happenings frequently, and therefore believed that scrapie was directly or indirectly contagious and that it may be transmitted from animal to animal by association at pasture.

Scrapie is frequently associated with the period for sexual activity in the ram and with lambing-time in ewes, but it is also known through field experiments that rams not used for service and untupped ewes may also develop scrapie.

The literature of the eighteenth and nineteenth centuries showed that the cause of scrapie has long been a matter of dispute. The method by which scrapie spreads from flock to flock or within a flock even at the present day still remains unresolved. It was widely believed by breeders that the incidence of scrapie followed a familial pattern. However, many of the earlier writers considered that either the disease was, in the true sense, hereditary or that the transmission occurred during sexual activity. Several hypotheses have been put forward of which two are most favoured. First: by breeding and inheritance from ancestors. Second: by contact, either direct physical mingling of affected with unaffected animals or from contaminated pasture surroundings.

Evidence for the spread of scrapie by contact

During 1913 and 1918, M'Fadyean presented circumstantial evidence that scrapie could spread among sheep at pasture without mating between affected and non-affected sheep. Greig (1940) reported that Dryerre and Bogue had shown that the metabolic rate remained relatively unaffected throughout the disease. Later, Greig (1940) wondered whether contamination of pasture would infect the animals. Using 26 sheep obtained from a "clean" farm for this experiment, he allowed them to graze twice a week on pastures where affected sheep grazed for the rest of the week. He took care that there was no immediate contact between the experimental and affected animals.

After three years, the experimental animals were removed to another clean farm. During the following two years, he recorded the occurrence of scrapie in seven of them and confirmed his results by demonstrating the presence of vacuolated neurons in histopathological examination of the brains. He concluded that scrapie had occurred following intermittent exposure to contaminated pasture over a period of three years, and therefore, contamination of pasture can spread the disease. However, Greig pointed out the difficulties of working with the disease, since there were no tests to detect scrapie in animals before clinical signs are evident, and it is very difficult to be certain that the animals used in the experiment were indeed free from the disease. Gordon (1957) also considered that scrapie can spread by co-habitation at the pasture from affected to healthy sheep. He gave evidence that, during a large scale inoculation experiment on a scrapie-free farm, scrapie did not appear in the two year period following sheep being inoculated with tissues from scrapie sheep. However, in the next two year period, the disease occurred in sheep inoculated with both broth and normal sheep tissues, and in non-inoculated controls. He recorded nine affected out of 150 sheep. According to some observations, even the closest contact between the diseased and healthy animals confined in a house does not appear to spread the disease. However, this was disputed by some experiments carried out in the field, in which the disease did develop with an incubation period extending over three years in 10 out of 26 ewes.

Stamp (1961) suggested that the evidence that a flock has been free from scrapie for a number of years must, in fact, be treated with the utmost caution. Further, he made the point: "It must be emphasised that scrapie appears only in a fairly low incidence in the sheep population of Britain, so the difficulty is not in obtaining animals which are likely to remain free, but in obtaining ones which are certain to remain free if kept in a clean environment. Further, the sheep must be of diverse breeding so as to include some animals which are susceptible if, of course, susceptibility to infection with reference to scrapie is meaningful. It is useless to establish that resistant animals remain free from the disease both in contact and isolation! Nothing more is claimed, but that contact transmission does occur in sheep for there have been considerably more cases of scrapie in the sheep kept in a heavily contaminated environment than in the comparable group in animal contact.

Dickinson et al (1965) examined the incidence of scrapie exposure in various degrees of contact with clinically affected stock, and also in attempted isolation. Of the proportion of affected animals, 57% was the highest in maximum contact, with 25% to 38% in moderate exposure, decreasing to 18% in partial on and off early isolation with moderate exposure. They also recorded 0 to 13% cases in attempted isolation. In a very different type of experiment, 30 month old ewes from scrapie-free stock were placed in day-to-day lifelong contact at pasture with many advanced cases of natural Suffolk scrapie. The contact ewes were mated with scrapie-free rams year after year, and scrapie occurred in 40% of the immediate progeny of those ewes which had maximum contact with the scrapie cases.

Sigurdsson, in 1954, thought there was conclusive evidence that the virus of rida (Icelandic scrapie) survived outside the host on farms where it had been prevalent, and suggested that an intermediate host or vector might play some role in its spread. He recorded that, during the eradication of rida by the slaughter of all sheep over a large part of northern Iceland, an area in which the Icelandic form of scrapie was prevalent, all sheep and goats were cleared from the area for up to three years. Healthy sheep were re-stocked from scrapie-free flocks. Unfortunately after several years of grazing on these fields, the disease reappeared in a number of sheep. However, the source of the flocks remained scrapie-free. Sigurdsson considered that an intermediate non-ovine host reservoir or vector of another animal species, insect or even vegetation might be hosting the scrapie agent. An alternative explanation is that the remarkable capacity of the scrapie agent to survive leads to persistent infectivity in earth and on grass of the contaminated area. Recently, Brown et al (1991) buried scrapie-infected hamster brains in soil in the garden. After three years of continuous exposure to weather in the Bethesda Maryland USA area, where summer is very hot and winter is very cold, it was demonstrated that the scrapie still remained active in the soil.

Stamp (1962) reported that scrapie developed in five out of six goats, which were housed together for 40 months, since they were one day old, with numerous scrapie-affected sheep. Many other authors have tried to establish the transmis-

41

sion of scrapie by direct contact with affected and non-affected animals. Chelle (1942) also referred to a similar incidence in two further goats born in contact with infected flocks of sheep. He considered that scrapie was a contagious disease, but with a long incubation period. MacKay et al (1961) knew of no other reports than these of the natural occurrence of scrapie among goats until they observed the disease in a goat which was being used as an uninoculated control in a biological transmission experiment. They could not be sure, however, whether scrapie in this goat was of natural occurrence and contracted before the animal came to the Institute or whether it had arisen from a contact at the Institute with scrapie-inoculated goats in the same pen.

On the other hand, however, in another study Fitzsimmons et al (1968) did not observe the contact spread of the disease among 17 South Scotland Cheviot sheep held indoors for 55 months in direct physical contact with a succession of sheep and goats affected with experimental scrapie. At the same time, in a separate associated experiment, 192 healthy goats were maintained in a scrapie environment for a period of 60 months. None of these developed the disease. They, however, found scrapie in 15 of 49 mice held in direct physical contact with successive batches of scrapie-inoculated mice. The disease appeared between 34 weeks to 65 weeks after the first contact was established. Since fighting took place between such animals, Pattison thought that the disease might have resulted from ingestion of tissue fragments containing the scrapie agent, and he concluded that; (a) contact transfer of the agent from affected animals involved ingestion of the agent and; (b) hereditary or congenital transmission is important in the sheep and much less so in the goat. However, Brotherston et al (1968) found that scrapie developed in 10 out of 17 goats kept over a prolonged period in contact with sheep with experimental scrapie, which were used as the source of the infection. These experiments on contact transmission were carried out in different institutions, however, and the possibility of a vector operating at one site and not the other has not been ruled out. The possibility that mice might provide a reservoir of scrapie infection has been raised by Field et al (1968) who found lactate dehydrogenase elevating virus (Riley agent) present in wild mice. Dickinson et al (1964), Morris et al (1965), have also reported the spread of scrapie in mice, from affected mice to healthy animals by contact.

There was obvious evidence, from a vaccine accident in the 1930s, which suggested that an infective agent was present in the brains, spinal cord and spleen of sheep which apparently appeared healthy. Three batches of Louping-ill vaccine were prepared in November and December of 1934. Brains, spinal cord and spleen, derived from sheep five days after their infection with Louping-ill virus, were used for vaccine preparation. In the preparation, homogenates of the tissues were treated with formalin. The vaccine was given to 18,000 sheep by subcutaneous injection in March, 1935. Although a few cases of scrapie were being reported as early as November, 1936, after about eighteen months incubation period, most scrapie cases were reported during the month of June, 1937 in sheep vaccinated with vaccine from one particular batch. Many of the affected sheep were black-face, a breed in which scrapie seldom occurred. Total figures are not available since many of the eighteen thousand sheep were over four years old when vaccinated and were disposed of by the autumn of 1937. The incidence in the remaining sheep was of the order of 1 to 35%. From this tragic blunder, in which several thousand sheep were accidentally inoculated with scrapie-infective material, evidence was produced that an infective agent played a role and that the agent remained infective even after treatment with formalin, but with a prolonged incubation period.

Scrapie A Hereditary Disease?

The evidence for both a hereditary and congenital mechanism in the spread of scrapie among sheep, is very strong in scientific literature. Hereditary disease is controlled by host genes and defective genes can be passed from one generation to next. However, genetic material of a virus can link with host DNA in the egg or sperm and be passed down via vertical transmission. An important distinguishing point is whether a replicating organism is involved in the disease process or not. Dickinson et al (1965) have been experimenting with this since 1955, and they concluded that a major gene might control susceptibility of the host to a infective agent.

The known hereditary condition of man has never been known to have transmitted disease to any other species of animal. He also considered kuru, a trembling, fatal neurological disease, to probably be due to a dominant gene causing death in childhood in both sexes when homozygous, but, in the heterozygous form, only lethal in adult females when over the reproductive age. It has since been proven that kuru is caused by ritual cannibalism, and is spread by the handling of fresh brains, and subsequent inoculation through mucous membranes and wounds or skin abrasion.

Bosanquet et al (1956), described scrapie as "a widespread muscle-wasting disease." They dismissed the idea that scrapie was due to a transmissible agent which affected the CNS. Instead, they considered that the lesions in muscles were primary intrinsic degeneration of the muscle-fibres, and the disease in the CNS had no relationship to the disease. They compared the scrapie muscle-wasting disease to human disease, where the principal lesion is muscle degeneration as in muscular dystrophies and polymyositis. These authors did not accept that the vacuoles described in the CNS were produced by the scrapie agent. They suspected that the sheep used in experimental inoculation studies were not originally completely scrapie free.

Parry (1962), a great believer in hereditary scrapie, considered scrapie to be primarily a muscular disease, and that the scrapie gene was linked with a certain phenotype character which gave selective advantages to the scrapie gene. He further investigated and collected data that suggested that scrapie could be explained in terms of a single autosomal recessive gene being the sole cause of the disease.

Parry considered that the scrapie gene is linked, unfortunately, with certain phenotype characteristics of sheep which are highly preferred by several breeders, so giving a high gene frequency in certain breeds of sheep. He collected data from 1,200 cases, of which over 1,000 had individual records, and divided individual sheep into groups depending on the genetic make up. Most of the data was collected between 1952 to 1960 from a group of some 50 recorded pedigree sheep flocks of 10 breeds dispersed in 17 counties of England and Scotland. He cited an example of a flock where a shepherd kept a notebook for each lambing season in which tupping and other details were noted. As each ewe lambed, information on the date, her health, milk flow, sex and number of lambs, and their sire, was recorded from 1939. After analysis of the record of these affected cases, Parry (1960) suggested that the prime cause of scrapie was heredity. He divided the sheep into homozygous, recessive, presumptive, genotypes "ss" and "SS". He considered that only individuals of the homozygous recessive presumptive genotypes, "ss" as opposed to "sS" and "SS", manifested the disease. He also concluded that affected animals harboured a transmissible agent, which is infectious artificially, but not naturally.

There is a weakness in his main argument, either 1); because the number of sheep in the study is either not given or is very small or 2); the allocation of presumed genotypes to rams is based on the presence or absence of scrapie in the progeny. Parry deduces, from his observations, that 90% of potentially affected animals would have developed scrapie by four and half years of age. In a population subject to commercial culling, at least 10% of affected animals would be misclassified as unaffected. Dickinson et al (1965) suggested that the error rate at four and half years would be one in four instead of one in ten, and that the corrected figure was presumably an underestimate if the disease was contagious.

In further studies, Parry (1962)   agreed that the disease can be passed from the affected to clinically normal sheep by inoculation. However, he did not believe that scrapie being a genetic disease is naturally contagious. To convince himself that the disease arises under controlled breeding conditions, and that the disease was transmissible, and the fact that the experimental disease was the same as natural disease, he carried out his own inoculation studies. He inoculated five lambs from each of two breeds of sheep and left a similar number of lambs of the same age and sex which had not been inoculated as controls. All inoculated lambs developed clinical signs of scrapie and showed histopathological lesions similar to those seen in scrapie sheep where scrapie had occurred naturally. Parry wrote: "Thus the tissue of a sheep suffering from a typical form of hereditary scrapie will, when inoculated into young lambs, cause a scrapie-like syndrome to develop in the recipient animals at an age when the natural disease, is not known to occur. An affected "ss"(homozygous recessive genotype) animal thus contains a transmissible agent which is artificially infectious." In effect, from this study, the authors could conclude that a lethal recessive gene is, in fact, not solely responsible for causing the disease recognised as familial. Fur-

44

ther, when it is known that the disease is transmissible by inoculation from one species to another, and there is sufficient evidence to suggest strongly that it is contagious, then the evidence supporting the hypothesis of scrapie being due to an intrinsic single gene effect, must be very clear-cut indeed, and must depend upon the proof of Mendelian segregation.

In order to determine whether a recessive gene without involvement of a virus was solely responsible, Dickinson et al (1965) tested this hypothesis on selected Suffolk sheep. One group, coming from 19 flocks, comprised 700 animals directly related to cases of scrapie. The second group, consisting of 600 animals whose forebears had not been affected by scrapie for at least a few generations, came from four different flocks. It was reported by the researchers that they had great difficulty, having had to search hard to collect scrapie-free stock. Their conditions were very stringent, involving an assessment of the reliability of flock records, the trustworthiness of owners, and their abil ty to have recognised whether scrapie had occurred in their flocks. After purcha e, these animals were observed for an initial period of four years loosely isolated in separate fields from each other. These formed the foundation stock for the researchers' planned experiments.

During the observation of the foundation stock over a period of four and half years, an overall average incidence of 29% occurred where the male was the affected parent. Incidence among stock born where the dam was affected reached 66%, which was more than twice as much, compared with males. Among the scrapie-free foundation stock ,three cases of scrapie developed during the same period. The authors considered two cases to be due to contamination from one or other source.

In the second part of their main experiment, the ewes from the scrapie-free group were mated with scrapie-affected stock rams. The following combinations were used: 1; scrapie-affected rams were mated with scrapie-free ewes and 2); Scrapie-affected ewes stock were mated with rams from scrapie-free stock. In these cross mating experiments more than half of the ewes had four or more offspring. Unaffected animals mated with affected ones developed scrapie at a rate of about 66%. In another mating experiment, where five "unaffected" rams were mated with females from affected foundation stock, the incidence of scrapie in offspring was 81%. Where both male and female sheep were from the affected foundation stock (F. scrapie-affected X M. scrapie-affected), the incidence was around 95%.

The results obtained by these researchers, published in 1965, showed a very high incidence of scrapie in the offspring of affected sheep mated with unaffected sheep. They systematically analysed all the possible reasons including unlikely assumptions, misclassification, and presented their results in great detail. The conclusion seems to be that offspring of affected ewes, mated with unaffected sheep, have a high chance of developing scrapie, while the offspring of affected rams have much lower chance. Thus an important role was assigned to maternal transmission, by experimentally infected mothers to their uninoculated offspring, as had been recognised by other studies (Gordon, 1959). However, maternal transmission does not alone explain the origin of all cases of scrapie which occur in the field. Stamp (1961) stated: "Numerous breeding experiments, which are being carried out at Moredum Institute in Scotland, have so far failed to determine under what circumstances this happens." From his own data, however, Stamp strongly believed that scrapie was an infectious disease.

Dickinson et al (1965) did not find any support in their experimental data for the solely genetic origin of scrapie. In summary, they concluded: "The total evidence on the scrapie is shown to be consistent with the interpretation that a biologically independent pathogenic organism causes the disease and that in some types of sheep at least there is vertical transmission of this organism from mother to offspring which contributes to correlation incidence of the disease in some classes of relatives, and hence the superficial appearance of a genetically determined origin of the disease."

Further, the recessive gene hypothesis proposed by Parry (1962), could not be explained from Dickinson et al (1965) experiments, since the incidence of the affected sheep exceeded the highest Mendelian Law expectation by the order of 50% and suggested that Parry (1962) deduced the presence of a recessive gene from the phenotype mating fitting Mendelian theory. There is a natural selection against the affected genotype animals. This is because the affected females die young, and obviously leave few offspring compared with the unaffected animals. It is a very different story for males. The best males are selected based on their show quality, and the rest of the male population is killed young, almost all being disposed of when four years old.

So, Dickinson et al (1965) were greatly in favour of a pathogen being involved in the disease process. The mechanism, they said: "must be present in non-genetic transmission of the infective agent from the parent to the progeny." This might be helped by a long connection between mother and offspring which would offer the most obvious route. Since the disease always appears in the progeny of affected mated with affected sheep, and the incidence of scrapie is also high where only one parent is affected, it is obvious that the agent must be ubiquitous and highly infectious.

Evidence that the agent causing the disease is infectious

This discussion, whether scrapie was caused by a transmissible agent, should have ended when, in 1959, Chandler successfully transmitted scrapie to mice and then into rats. The agent was also passed into hamsters (Zlotnik, 1963). Subsequently, the disease has been experimentally transmitted to over 20 different species of animals. Once the fact was established that the disease could be transmitted by inoculation, although the incubation periods might be long, the incidence rate of disease proved to be nearly 100%. The fact is that different stable strains of the agent exist, and that infectivity can be abolished or reduced by heating, treatment with sodium hydroxide and sodium hypochlorite. All these points support the belief in the involvement of an infective agent.

Similarly, mice born of pregnant females, inoculated during the gestation period but separated from their own dames at birth, become infected prenatally or perinatally (Narang, 1990). All mice, except the foster mother (not inoculated), developed the clinically recognisable disease and died following an incubation period which was nearly identical with that of their inoculated mothers. These studies demonstrated beyond doubt that the congenital route plays an important role in the transfer of the scrapie agent.

Vertical transmission

Although dissemination of the disease from parent to offspring, namely vertical transmission, has been talked about most, this, in the broad sense, includes exposure in utero. Maternal transmission has been used in many studies to mean vertical transmission, including both prenatal and neonatal infection (Dickinson et al, 1974). Attempts to detect the virus in foetuses of affected sheep have failed, although the virus has been detected several times in the placenta from infected sheep. Also the scrapie agent has been often detected in various parts of the ewe's reproductive tract (Hourrigan, 1990). However, the virus has not been detected in foetuses or lambs under 10 months. In experimental infection of foetuses in-utero, and of new-born Suffolk sheep with the scrapie virus, the virus was not detected in their lymphoreticular tissues until the lambs were 6 to 9 months old (Hadlow et al, 1984).

The overall role of the placenta and reproductive parts of infected females during gestation is not known but provides an added complication. The dichotomy between vertical and horizontal transmission cannot be absolute. The role of the placenta in the transmission process is not completely known and since, after the birth has been completed, it, together with other infected organs, may subsequently be ingested by the mother or other sheep it may provide a possible vehicle for the continuing horizontal transmission of the disease. Equally, the role played by the mammary glands, colostrum and milk, in maternal transmission, needs further evaluation.

It has also been shown, using various combinations of different breeds of sheep, that maternal transmission of scrapie can take place experimentally, where ewes have been inoculated with the scrapie agent at mating time (Gordon, 1960; Dickinson et al, 1964), and it is therefore possible for natural transmission to occur through the maternal route.

It should be emphasised here that the scrapie disease can be established by inoculating all pure breeds, homozygous type "SS" or any other sheep of unknown genetic makeup. These findings would suggest that, once the animals have been infected, the makeup of the host sheep does not influence the final outcome of the disease, although one cannot rule out the possibility that the host genetic makeup might influence the incubation periods of the disease. This point will

47

be discussed later in some detail. There are over 20 known strains of the transmissible agent which require for their spread a special combination of a susceptible genotype host and unusual environmental factors.

Based on susceptibility to the scrapie agent, sheep have been classified into two major divisions, *Sip* pApA and *Sip* sAsA. Since it was realised that natural scrapie has never been recorded in the *Sip* pApA genotype of NPU Cheviot sheep, they were used in the embryo-transfer technique to investigate maternal transmission of scrapie in sheep and of BSE in goats (Foster et al, 1994). In these experiments, ewes with *Sip* sAsA genotype, which readily develop scrapie, were used as donors. They were experimentally infected with the scrapie agent, and artificially inseminated six months later with semen from an uninfected, but scrapie- susceptible, ram. Embryos from donor sheep were harvested five to six days post-insemination, and transferred unwashed by laparoscopy into *Sip* pApA genotype recipient ewes genetically selected for low susceptibility to scrapie. Ten of 26 lambs born of these recipient ewes developed scrapie. All donor sheep eventually developed the clinical disease, while the recipient ewes remained healthy. In the goat experiments, kids were derived from BSE injected donor nannies, and 10 of 11 died of scrapie-like disease. These studies conclusively reveal that eggs in the affected ewes carried the infective agent. These studies suggest that it is more than likely that BSE-affected cattle will also be maternally affected. Based on these results, it is very hard to predict what proportion of calves born of affected cattle would develop clinical BSE.

A Review of transmission studies

Conditions and circumstances have so changed that in the very early 1900's one hypothesis forwarded was that sarcocysts parasites were involved (M'Gowan, 1914). M'Fadyean (1918) disputed the sarcocyst theory, arguing instead that the disease was infectious, although his own transmission experiments had failed. Bigoteau (1919) suggested that scrapie was due to infection with *Corynebacterium ovis*. Gaiger (1924) tried to produce active immunity to scrapie in sheep by using carbolized heavy emulsion of brain and spinal cord from infected animals, but without success.

For many years, as is evident from its history, it was widely believed by breeders that the incidence of scrapie followed a familial pattern. Palmer (1959), in a review of the scrapie literature, cited May's work (1859), where he summarised the earlier works of Thaer, Kanert, Ernst, Störig, Spinola and Funke. All these researchers had failed in their attempts to transmit the disease experimentally. In a series of papers, Cuillé et al (1936; 1938; 1939) claimed to have artificially transmitted the disease by intraocular inoculation of brain and spinal cord emulsion from an affected sheep into healthy animals and that, of nine inoculated, two developed the disease with incubation periods 14 to 22 months. In a subsequent passage, they inoculated brain and spinal cord emulsion from sheep that had developed scrapie into other healthy lambs. Four out of eight sheep developed scrapie with an incubation period of one and two years. In further experimental studies, these researchers inoculated sheep by intracerebral, epidural and subcutaneous routes, all of which were effective. They further claimed to have transmitted the disease to goats, and showed evidence of experimental transmission of the disease. In their studies, they also demonstrated that the agent was small enough to pass through a fine porcelain filter, and that therefore scrapie was an infective virus disease. However, Bertrand et al (1937) attempted to repeat Cuillé et al's experiments, but were unable to transmit the disease, and disagreed that the agent could not be a virus.

Although the infectious nature of the agent was disputed at this time, the unfortunate mishap of accidentally inoculating several thousand sheep with louping-ill virus vaccine contaminated with scrapie agent (Gordon, 1946), and the data of Cuillé et al (1936; 1938), who had transmitted the disease, aroused a fresh interest in Britain. In 1938, an experiment was started using 788 animals to confirm the transmissible nature of the disease. After four and a half years, 60% of those inoculated intracerebrally, and 30% of those infected subcutaneously became clinically affected. The incubation period after intracerebral inoculation was the shorter, seven months compared to 15 months by other routes.

Wilson et al (1950) continued these experiments, attempting to overcome the difficulties of cross-contamination by injecting ultrafiltrates of pooled central nervous material from affected sheep into normal lambs, and discarding those that did not develop symptoms within a year, because they considered the average incubation period to be six months. They succeeded in transmitting the disease to 21 out of 83 seven month old Cheviot wethers, which developed symptoms between 5-10 months. Wilson et al also transmitted the disease from infected sheep to healthy sheep in a series of nine passages, and also confirmed the earlier findings of Cuillé et al, that the transmissible agent would pass a virus filter. They interpreted their results to mean that scrapie was caused by a virus infection of the CNS. Wilson et al believed that the agent was a transmissible virus, and, amongst other properties had the ability to survive boiling at 100° C for 30 minutes.

Inoculation of Non-Natural Hosts

In 1959, a new chapter in the history of scrapie was begun when Dr. Chandler reported the successful experimental transmission of the scrapie agent to mice inoculated with the brain and spinal cord homogenate suspension from naturally infected sheep. These experiments, beyond doubt, demonstrated the infectious nature of the disease. Subsequently, the disease was transmitted to rats and then serially passed from mouse to mouse. Inoculation was either by injection or feeding with brain and spinal cord homogenate. These results were soon confirmed in many other laboratories all over the world. The mouse model facilitated laboratory investigations and confirmed the transmissible nature of scrapie. Later, the disease was established in hamsters with a much shorter incubation period. Serially transmitted disease in hamsters (transmission from hamster to hamster) had an incubation period of 60 to 80 days, the shortest incubation period model of all species of animals. Through inoculation and selection studies in mice over the following few years, it became apparent that there are many different strains of scrapie agent characterised by the distribution pattern of lesions in the brain and by the length of the incubation period in mice by serial inoculation. Based on the length of the incubation period, strains of the scrapie agent have been broadly divided into short and long incubation period strains.

The disease has been experimentally transmitted, by oral feeding, to sheep, goats, mink and mice (Pattison et al, 1972; Fraser et al, 1994; Robinson, 1994; White et al, 1994). Now we have witnessed how feed, accidentally contaminated with the scrapie agent, has transmitted disease into a large population of cows. Another man-made accident, where several thousand sheep had been accidentally inoculated with scrapie-infective material in the 1930s, has already been referred to. On that occasion, the vaccine used was prepared from brains, spinal cord and spleen derived from sheep, and treated with formalin, and around 18,000 sheep were reported to have developed scrapie, including black-face, a breed in which scrapie seldom occurred.

In animal exposures, where infection has been documented after high doses of infected tissue feed, transmission has been irregular and the question arises as to whether the true portal was through the gastrointestinal tract itself or through areas of mucosal abrasions. Ulcerations in the lips, gums and intestines appear to play an important role. Studies of the effect of gum damage on the oral route of infection demonstrated that 70% of those without gum lesions compared with 100% in mice with gum damage, developed the disease and with a significantly shorter incubation time (Carp, 1982). In experimental scrapie, the oral route of infection is generally considered to be least efficient. Prusiner et al (1985) examined oral transmission, and compared the incubation period with that following direct brain inoculation. Hamsters developed clinical scrapie after 100 to 160 days following ingestion of scrapie-infected brains. The researchers attempted to shorten the incubation period and time of death, by the repeated feeding of scrapie-infected tissues. They concluded that infection by the digestive tract for the same period of incubation, may require about 10 to 100,000 time more of the scrapie-agent than by intracerebral inoculation. However, they did not find any significant reduction in the incubation period in animals which were repeatedly fed with the scrapie-infected tissues as compared with a single feed. These results suggest that, once a host has been infected, repeated doses of the agent are not required for the development of the disease. However, it is possible that a single episode, or even several of oral ingestion of the agent may not alone be enough to transmit SE. Further, it is likely that other factors play an important role, such as size of the dose of the agent, which would certainly influence the length of the incubation period.

Virus in other tissues and body fluids

It has been generally considered that muscle of scrapie-affected animals had not been examined for the presence of the agent. In 1962, Pattison et al reported their attempts to establish the distribution of the transmissible agent in scrapie-affected goats. The fluids and tissues examined included brain, sciatic nerve, cerebrospinal fluid, urine, blood, pituitary gland, adrenal gland, salivary gland and biceps femoris muscle, which they injected intracerebrally. A total of 140 goats were used in this experiment.

These animals were held under experimental observation for 30 months. During this period, scrapie developed in 13 out of 13 goats inoculated with brain tissue; 11 out of 14 with pituitary gland; 6 out of 13 with cerebrospinal fluid; 5 out of 14 with sciatic nerve; 5 out of 13 with adrenal gland ; 5 out of 14 with salivary gland; and 1 out of 14 with biceps femoris muscle. The remainder, which did not develop the clinical disease, were also killed and, therefore, it cannot be ruled out that some at least were incubating the disease. These results were indicative of what has now become the established relationship between the dose of the scrapie agent in a tissue, and the incubation period in a recipient animal injected with that tissue. In 1959, Stamp and colleagues, and many other researchers, independently demonstrated that the scrapie agent could be serially passaged into sheep and goats by inoculating spleen, or lymph glands or cerebrospinal fluid into experimental animals.

In their subsequent studies, Stamp et al (1959) demonstrated that the disease developed in Cheviot sheep inoculated with spleen, lymph gland and cerebrospinal fluid taken from animals affected with scrapie. However, similar Cheviot sheep, inoculated with pooled brains taken from 20 of their healthy companions, failed to develop the disease within 12 months of being inoculated. These experiments showed that many of the inoculated animals developed the disease after an incubation period of five to seven months, and that the disease could be produced in nine-month-old lambs, an age at which natural infection had never been observed.

Rapid blind passage in sheep

Stamp et al (1959) prepared a saline suspension of pooled scrapie sheep brain and inoculated 1 ml each into the brain of ten Cheviot lambs. Two months after inoculation, and before any obvious symptoms of scrapie had developed, these sheep were slaughtered and their brains, except for portions sent for histological examination, were pooled and injected in the same way intracerebrally to a further ten Cheviot lambs. This process was further repeated over four times. The final passage however, was made using 20 Cheviot lambs of which three developed scrapie within five to eight months of inoculation. Since the scrapie agent had been inoculated, from sheep to sheep blindly, at two-monthly intervals before clinical symptoms, through seven groups of Cheviot sheep, it would appear that the agent is in fact replicating during the two month incubation period. It would seem unlikely that at the end of their experiment, the original inoculum of 1 ml could have been present in sheep brains in sufficient quantity to cause scrapie to occur at a dilution factor of 10^{18}.

Since 1936, when the disease was successfully experimentally transmitted by inoculation, the view that it was a naturally infectious disease gained ground. There were a number of good reasons for regarding the causative agent as a virus: 1) it is filterable; 2) it is capable of replication; 3) it can be diluted out at an appropriate level; and 4) it can be serially transmitted to a large number of animal species.

The agent causing the disease is self-replicating. Gradually, the infective units increase in number and accumulate slowly over many weeks to months, in differing amounts in different organs, following the inoculation. Eklund et al (1963) found the earliest signs of illness in mice between 97 to 123 days, when inoculated with 1,000 fold dilution of brain suspension, and between 149 to 169 days when inoculated with 1,000,000 fold dilution of brain suspension.

In 1967, Eklund et al reported that, after mice had been injected by intracerebral or peripheral routes, the scrapie agent reached a high concentration in spleen and lymph nodes and later in spinal cord, lung, and the intestinal wall. Field (1968) reported the scrapie agent distribution throughout the tissues and, in a scrapie affected rat found it in lungs, liver, kidney and muscle. The virus also appeared in the brain four weeks later, after it had been found in the spinal cord (after subcutaneous inoculation in the thigh), suggesting it might have taken four weeks for the infection to have spread from the cord to the brain. Field et al (1968) found that the blood was infective soon after intracerebral inoculation, indicating that blood may have an important role in spreading the infection. In hamsters, after intraperitoneal infection by more sensitive methods, it has been possible to demonstrate a viraemic phase (virus in blood) which lasted for at least 40 days post-inoculation of the animals (Diringer, 1984).

Furthermore, scrapie of sheep and goat origin has been successfully transmitted to three out of ten cattle by all at once in the same animals, intracerebral, intravenous, intraperitoneal and oral dosing of the brain homogenates in the USA by Gibbs et al (1990). It is not clear why it was decided to infect the same animals by so many different routes. These results demonstrated the much wider than previously recognised host range for the SEs agent. Further, these results indicate susceptibility and the efficiency of transmission across the species barrier.

In experimental animals, regardless of the route of the infection, or dose of the agent, or the source of the agent, the infected animals develop the clinical disease, and the amount of the agent in terms of infectivity levels in the brain of sick animals are the same.

Concentration of the agent in body tissues

A number of studies have investigated the dose of the scrapie agent from a variety of organs. A known amount of tissue has to be homogenised and suspended in a known volume of saline (salt solution). The concentration of the infective agent is expressed in titre dose/units of infectivity in each gram of tissue. "Infective units" means the tissue by weight which can be diluted with saline water to produce disease (dilution, $1:10 = 10^1$; $1:100 = 10^2$; $1:1000 = 10^3$ and so on). For each inoculation about 0.02 ml of the final diluted solution is used to inoculate a mouse or hamster. With high titres, such as 10^8 to 10, therefore, one gm of tissue would be enough to inoculate and produce disease in 500 million and 5 billion mice and hamsters. The gradual dilution of the infective material increases the incubation period of the disease.

The more the tissue is diluted the longer the incubation period. Once the tissue has been diluted to a level where it just remains infective to produce the clinical disease, but with an extended incubation period, suggests that the agent takes time to replicate to levels of active infection. Although infective units may be low to begin with, once replication starts, the infectivity units increase with the incubation period, irrespective of the genetic make-up of the host. There are, however, relatively minor differences in the maximum amount of infective units present at the end of the incubation period, regardless of the animal species or their genetic make up.

In experimental animals the first units of infectivity are found in the spleen, lymph nodes and salivary glands, within four weeks of inoculation, increasing to a plateau of concentration of 10^4 to 10^5 titre of infectivity in these tissues during the first quarter of the incubation period of the clinical disease. Most of the other tissues, including bone marrow, intestines, placenta and muscles in some of the studies, have been shown to contain an infective dose of approximately 10^3. The scrapie agent has sometimes been found in spinal fluid. Blood from affected sheep and mice has also occasionally produced cases of scrapie suggesting a brief "viraemic" phase (virus in blood) during the incubation period. In one study, mice were inoculated and killed at various intervals starting with 30 min., 1 hour, 2 hours and blood from these mice was used to further inoculate other mice. This produced the disease, again demonstrating the presence of the scrapie agent in the blood being carried-over to the next cohort of mice.

When one considers contamination of soil by affected animals in fields, it is important to note that the scrapie agent has also been found in sheep stomach worm (Hourrigan et al, 1979), therefore it is possible that the infection from land can be transferred by these parasites to a new host.

Effects of Detergents on Infectivity

Experimental transmission of scrapie in mice, has allowed the large scale measurement of scrapie by the standard microbiological technique of titration to a limiting dilution to give an LD_{50}. In this technique, the highest dilution at which 50% of animals become sick is commonly known as LD_{50}. It was apparent from early studies that incubation periods extended as the amount of infectivity was reduced because of the dilution factor (Chandler, 1963; Mould et al, 1967). However, when all variables are kept constant, that is when the strain, the age of the mouse, the strain of the scrapie agent, treatment of inoculum and the amount are the same, then titre estimates and incubation periods are remarkably repeatable (Outram, 1976).

If some of the parameters for measuring scrapie infectivity are changed, then the picture changes. For example, varying the strain of the mouse, the age of the mouse, the strain of the scrapie agent and the route of infection can increase or decrease the incubation period for the same dose of the scrapie agent. Somerville et al (1983) compared the effect of certain detergents for example sodium dodecyl sulphate (SDS) on the infective concentrations of the scrapie agent, while keeping all other factors strictly the same. The addition of the detergent resulted in at least a 100-fold increase in the estimate of infectivity. This suggested that the amount of the scrapie in a sample, measured conventionally, may be an underestimate.

A number of ideas have been put forward to explain this increase of infectivity after detergent treatment. Since the increase in concentration is primarily due to a higher effective dose being present in the sample, it is more likely to be due to the fact that the scrapie agent is present in a large aggregated form, while the addition of detergent breaks-up the clumps, thereby increasing the number of free virus particles. Extensive homogenisation of the brain tissue and ultrasonication, break-up virus particle clumps resulting in 100 to 1,000 fold increase in infective dose (Rohwer et al, 1980; Narang, 1988). Somerville et al (1983) found that significant losses of infectivity can occur when inocula are left to stand for a period of 4 hours in a glass bottle or syringe before injection, suggesting that virus particles aggregate on standing.

Studies of experimental scrapie give the overwhelming impression of a disease which proceeds from infection to clinical signs with clockwork precision. The route and dose of infection significantly affect the outcome. Even with the development of diagnostic methods, and the demonstration of specific degenerative changes in the brain and spinal cord, precise knowledge of the exact means of transmission and pathways of the natural scrapie agent in sheep remains a mystery. Pattison et al (1961) demonstrated that the disease is readily transmitted experimentally by oral administration of infected tissue of scrapie sheep. In 1972, Pattison and co-workers used foetal membranes from six scrapie-affected sheep for experimental injection. The membranes from each affected ewe were used for the inoculation of four sheep and six goats. They inoculated two sheep and three goats by intracerebral injection as before, and two other sheep and three other goats were fed orally a suspension of the remainder of foetal membranes ranging in weight from 165 to 650 g. Thirty months later, scrapie developed in five sheep and three goats dosed orally, and in four sheep and one goat inoculated intracerebrally. While the clinical signs of scrapie reported varied somewhat among individual sheep, however, they did not notice any difference between ani-

54

mals dosed orally and those inoculated intracerebrally from the same donor.

Pattison et al suggested that since the scrapie agent is very resistant to adverse physical and chemical treatments, and because sheep might eat foetal membranes voided by other sheep at lambing time, scrapie could spread by the ingestion of contaminated material. Thus, natural transmission by the oral route remains an acceptable possibility. The simple infection hypothesis, however, leaves a problem to be explained, namely why the progeny of scrapie-infected mothers lambs should have a so much higher incidence of scrapie than those from apparently healthy mothers, although they graze on the same pasture. Concomitant venereal infection would seem to play some role.

Species barrier

Transmission of scrapie from one animal species to another is often associated with exceptionally long incubation periods when inoculated into a new host. The incubation period is much shorter when the same species of animal is used to provide both the donor and the recipient of the infected material. This phenomenon of a species barrier is highly relevant to the epidemiology of scrapie, CJD, BSE, Kuru, mink encephalopathy and other related spongiform encephalopathies. No animals, however, have been found to be resistant to the scrapie agent. An understanding of the mechanism of a species barrier has enabled researchers to isolate many different stable strains of the agent.

Kimberlin et al (1979) studied the pathogenesis of scrapie from hamsters and mice. They observed that the replication of the scrapie agent in the brain and spleen was delayed for 175 days. After this greatly delayed period of infection, the agent started to replicate and this phase lasted for 150 days. The delayed process "Zero phase" is used to describe the period of time when the agent, following inoculation, does not replicate but just remains latent. These researchers did not observe this "Zero phase" phenomenon in the second passage from mouse-to-mouse transmission, where replication of the agent occurred over the whole of the incubation period.

Although little is known about the cause of the zero phase, that it happens at all is of great importance in species barrier studies, in particular the study and understanding of BSE when assessing the infectivity concentration in different tissues of suspected cases. Negative results do not mean that on successive passage of the agent in the same species, the results will remain negative.

Factors Influencing Susceptibility

Wilson et al (1950) experimentally inoculated different breeds of sheep: Cheviot, half-breed, Grey-face and Black-face. All these animals developed clinical scrapie within an incubation period of about five months, except one Black-face sheep which had an incubation period of about 17 months. Differing breeds of sheep, strains of mice and hamsters are all uniformly susceptible to scrapie. However, marked differences are to be seen in the incubation periods, in the patterns of lesions in the CNS when same strain of scrapie agent is inoculated in different animal species. Differences in the incubation periods and the patterns of lesions in the CNS varies in the same animal species with differing strains of the scrapie agent. This phenomenon is not unique to scrapie, it is evident with many other common viruses.

The Effect of Developmental Maturity on Susceptibility

It used to be thought that, because of the long incubation period, establishing the infection experimentally would mean that the animals had to be inoculated during weaning. Younger goats and sheep appear to be more susceptible than older animals to naturally acquired infection. However, in mice it has been found that the older the animals when infected, the shorter the incubation period.

Contrary to normal expectation. newborn mice are more, rather than less susceptible to scrapie infections by an intraperitoneal route. It has been found that 50 to 500-fold less dose is required for adult inoculation by the intraperitoneal route compared to intracerebral inoculation. These experiments suggested that the peritoneal cavity of the adult is a much more favourable environment for the scrapie agent than the neonate. Passage from one species of animal to another, can effect the incubation period, making it longer or shorter.

Replication of the Scrapie Agent

One of the important aspects of scrapie in sheep to have remained unresolved is the route of infection that makes the disease contagious. What is the portal route of entry of the virus? Nor do we yet know precisely when infection usually takes place. From the limited studies, it would appear that under natural conditions of exposure, the infection with the scrapie agent starts from birth onward (Dickinson et al, 1974). The oral route seems to be an important route of natural spread of infection (Pattison et al, 1972; Hadlow et al, 1979; 1982). Hadlow et al (1982) found that in 8 out of 15 clinically normal lambs of 10 to 14 months old, the scrapie agent was detected in lymphatic tissues and intestine. However, the titres in these tissues were low, but it was detected throughout this period, while the nemavirus was also detected in the brain at the age of 25 months. In the course of time, the nemavirus spreads to most lymph nodes but rarely to other extraneural organs. The scrapie agent continues to replicate, or persists in moderate amounts, in intestinal and lymphatic nodes for many months, or even years, before becoming detectable in the CNS. Eklund et al (1969) previously demonstrated that the replication of the scrapie agent is found early in the incubation period of scrapie, first in the spleen and then in other lymphoid tissues.

In this subclinical infection phase, during which nemavirus replication continues or persists in moderate amounts in intestinal and lymphatic nodes for many months, or even years, the scrapie is shed to the outside world where it may then infect other sheep and contribute to horizontal transmission. Hadlow (1982) concluded that sheep can be infected carriers, most probably via the intestine, where virus replication begins, and he recommended that excretions and secretions of naturally infected sheep and goats be examined, more assiduously than they had been in the past, for more clues to explain the contagious nature of the disease. Strangely the nemavirus was not found in faeces, saliva, urine or milk even though it has been regularly detected in intestinal tissue and often in nasal mucosa (Hourrigan et al, 1979; Hadlow et al, 1982).

This discovery is in keeping with the occurrence of viremia in mice and hamsters infected with scrapie virus (Field et al, 1968; Casaccia et al, 1989), and in guinea pigs and mice infected with CJD virus (Manuelidis et al, 1978; Kuroda et al, 1983).

Pathology

A study of the literature shows the state of confusion which exists, not only over the aetiology of the disease, but also over its pathology. A very wide range of degenerated neurons may be present, and no consistent picture of a pathological entity, distinct enough to explain the often severe neurological signs, has hitherto emerged. No lesions have been demonstrated in any organ outside the CNS, although an increased amount of cerebro-spinal fluid in some cases has been observed. On microscopic sections, the brain not uncommonly shows some degree of hydrocephalus, which, in some cases, may be quite marked.

Cassirer, in 1898, was the first investigator to observe scrapie-affected sheep and found no obvious, significant changes in superficial or deep reflexes. He failed to find any microscopical changes in the CNS. However, Besnoit et al (1898) in the same year, by microscopical examination, described vacuolation in the anterior horn cells of the spinal cord and intense neuritis involving the smaller motor nerves. They called the disease "Nérrite périphérique enzootique du mouton".

M'Gowan published his monograph on the disease in 1914. He found no changes in the CNS, but found muscles in sheep to be heavily infested with a common parasite, called sarcocysts, which he thought produced itching and death. He believed that the site of the disease was muscles, and thus concluded that scrapie was due to heavy manifestation of the sarcocysts. In 1926, Stockman microscopically observed vacuolation in the medulla and spinal cord of the scrapie sheep, thus substantiating earlier observations of Besnoit et al (1898). Although this observation was very significant, Stockman (1926) did not consider the relationship of vacuolation specific to scrapie. Bertrand et al (1937), and Brownlee (1936-40) also made detailed microscopical observations of brain and spinal cord which revealed degeneration of neurons. These researches confirmed the presence of vacuolated cells in the medulla and spinal cord of scrapie infected sheep. Brownlee (1936-40) compared vacuoles, seen in louping-ill virus with those in scrapie. The vacuoles in the two conditions differed in that those of louping-ill virus were much smaller and occurred only in necrotic cells, whereas in scrapie, the cells containing the vacuoles appeared normal apart from vacuolation.

The vacuoles seen in spongiform brains are not artifacts, and their presence is not dependent upon fixation or histological preparation of the tissue. Vacuolation has been observed in human pathology in some conditions, for example, that after ultrasonic irradiation of the nervous system (Peters, 1949), and vacuolation was noted in chronic alcoholism (Buzzard et al, 1921), and was probably a specific response to injury.

Holman et al (1943) described neuro-anatomical arrangement of the medulla of sheep and showed that the distribution of vacuolated cells in scrapie-infected animals was selective for certain nuclear groups, especially the reticular formation, the medial vestibular and lateral cuneate nuclei. They showed vacuoles in the medulla of 75 affected sheep, while no similar vacuoles were seen in sheep dying of other disease conditions. Statistical examination of these results indicated the vacuoles were to be expected in not less than 94% of brains of scrapie cases, thus, for the first time, establishing a link between nerve cell degeneration and the disease of scrapie. Greig (1940), in his experiments on transmission, confirmed the disease by presence of vacuoles in neurons. In addition, Wagner et al (1954), independently confirmed these findings in Ohio, USA.

Over the years, the study of vacuolated neurons attracted a lot of attention and became of special interest. Since it's recognition as a characteristic change in scrapie in sheep, vacuolation has been used as a diagnostic criterion in paraffin section. Vacuolated cells may occur anywhere in the brain and spinal cord, in one case the neuronal damage being wide-spread throughout the central nervous system and, in, another, being very localised. The vacuoles may appear as single cavities within a healthy neuronal cell cytoplasm and these vacuoles, over a period of incubation, may increase in size and cause very extensive ballooning of the neurons, leading, in turn, to disruption of the cell membrane. In some cases, or even in the same case, there may be single or multiple vacuoles, as if a part of the cell cytoplasm has undergone degeneration. Usually the vacuoles appear empty, but may contain hyaline eosinophilic material with more staining granules embedded in them (Holman et al, 1943).

All parts of the CNS may not be equally affected. In natural scrapie, as a rule, most consistent lesions are found in the medulla, pons, and mesencephalon. There seems to be evidence to suggest that the lesions occur more constantly in the centres, along the midline of the neuraxis. Pattison (1957) reported the presence of vacuoles in nerve cells in the medulla of goats experimentally inoculated with materials from scrapie affected sheep. This vacuolation in experimental goats was far more intense than that observed in control animals. Zlotnik et al (1957) observed vacuolated nerve cells in clinically normal Cheviot sheep and they suggested as a possible explanation that: 1) the sheep were incubating scrapie; 2) the sheep were affected with a non-clinical form of the disease; or 3) that vacuolation of neurons is not directly connected with scrapie. Later, Zlotnik

58

(1957), on further examination of field cases of scrapie, discovered that vacuolation was more intense in a few cells in the control group of sheep. He concluded that there was a correlation between the vacuolation and scrapie, but emphasised the necessity for examining serial sections of the medulla before assessing the significance. He described the morphology of the vacuoles, and provided evidence that vacuoles were not artifacts. In affected animals, vacuoles were found particularly in the lateral cuneate nucleus, the lateral caudal part of the reticular formation, and in the papilliform nucleus with a bilateral symmetrical distribution. Zlotnik described various stages of neuronal degeneration associated with vacuolation, and attempted to classify vacuolated neurons morphologically.

Histological examination of the CNS may not be as distinct and exclusive as has often been made out in classical studies. Concern arises when the pathologist finds insufficient neuropathological microscopic changes to confirm the diagnosis. The spongiform changes may be hard to find in cases with typical clinical signs. That happens in clinically confirmed cases (Fraser, 1976), and difficulty multiplies in merely suspect cases. There are so many variations. Detailed study of the neuropathology of the natural scrapie is still to be investigated (Hadlow, 1982). Breed of sheep and strain of the scrapie agent, most likely, play a major role in the topographic distribution of the lesions.

There was a setback in 1956, when Bosanquet et al challenged the proposition that scrapie was essentially an infection of the CNS, and they described the discovery of widespread myopathic disease in sheep suffering from scrapie. They compared the similarities of the scrapie myopathy to the human disease, whose principal lesion is muscle degeneration, muscular dystrophies, and polymyositis. They did not accept that the vacuoles described in the CNS were the cause of scrapie. Subsequently, over the next few years, many more papers were published by Zlotnik,1957, 1958; and Palmer, 1957, 1958; confirming vacuoles and involvement of the CNS in the pathology of scrapie. It was confirmed that these specific changes observed in the brains and spinal cord were not found elsewhere in other disease conditions.

The CNS of sheep suffering from scrapie has been studied for a century. From the first description of neuronal vacuolation, it took nearly sixty years to recognise that these vacuoles are characteristic changes in scrapie of sheep and other spongiform encephalopathies. Now, vacuolation of the CNS is used as a diagnostic criterion by histological sections. Vacuolated cells may occur anywhere, but they are especially common in the medulla, among the large nerve cells in the brain and especially near the midline, where they are nearly always affected to some degree. These vacuolated lesions are common in the pons, thalamus and in the hippocampus, while in the spinal cord, anterior horn cells are frequently affected. Lesions are also seen in basal ganglia. It is important to point out that differences in the distribution and degree of the lesions are apparent in experimental sheep, as opposed to the natural disease condition. By experimental inoculation of different strains into mice, it became apparent that the de-

59

gree and distribution of lesions depended on the strain of the scrapie agent, the strain of animals, and the site of inoculation. These vacuoles in the CNS give the tissue a spongy appearance, and from this the name "spongiform encephalopathy" has been given to this condition. However, vacuoles are an important help in diagnosis, but probably also represent a response to starvation or injury of the tissue. The origin of the vacuoles has been sought, via electron microscopy, by Field et al (1964), who concluded that they might originate from more than one source, although these researchers did not think that extracellular spaces were a source of vacuoles.

Apart from vacuolation, many nerve cells in advanced scrapie show degenerative changes, with isolated neurons throughout the grey matter of basal ganglia appearing shrunken and hyperchromatic, or with hyalinised cytoplasm. Neuronophagia is not marked and glial rosettes or perivascular cuffing are noticeably absent.

Fig 1 Section of the cerebellar cortex from a typical case showing irregular vacuole (a) and extensive vacuoles (b). X 250.

Chronological Study of Pathology

In the CNS, in addition to vacuolation, other researchers observed additional microscopical changes. With the development of experimental models, additional pathological changes have became easier to interpret. There is general agreement that the earliest change to be observed is proliferation of astrocytes, a type of cell which has large processes, and that this is a cardinal feature of both natural and experimental scrapie (Fig 2). Hadlow (1961), in his careful study of experimental scrapie in the goat, emphasised the importance of astroglial activation, and pointed out that: "hypertrophy and proliferation of astrocytes could be the initial response to the injurious agent, rather than merely a reflection of primary damage to the nerve cell." In brains of normal animals, astrocytes and their processes are very pale and do not stain well. Once the animals are inoculated and the disease processes start, the first noticeable morphological microscopical change is the enlargement of astrocytes, their cell processes becoming prominent. The stain readily impregnates, making the processes stand out clearly (Fig 2). So precocious and characteristic are these processes that it gives them the appearance of "spiders", hence the common name "spider cells." The astroglial hypertrophy proliferation is quite out of proportion to any observable neuronal degeneration, and spreads to all parts of the brain and spinal cord. At this stage, the appearances of these cells, with their "sucker feet", give the tissue a very "wild" and "angry" look under the microscope. Astroglial changes have been considered as the cardinal feature of the scrapie process by several workers (Hadlow, 1961; Pattison, 1965; Field, 1969).

Fig 'I'c Electron microscope showing marked vacuolation

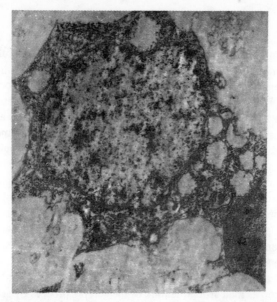

Section showing widespread astrocytosis. X 350
Fig 2

It should be pointed out that hypertrophy and proliferation of astrocytes could be an initial response to an injury, although the change occurs very early, or soon after, infection of the CNS, and this change is by no means a specific indicator of scrapie. Therefore, these factors cannot be used as specific markers. Astrocytes have been shown to line blood vessels and take part in myelination of some axons, the nerve fibres (Narang, 1978). These cells are believed to be concerned with metabolic transport in the nervous system, so that subtle changes might readily lead to biochemical interference with neuronal function before morphological changes are visible. The dissociation of morphological and functional disturbance might, thus, be referable to disturbed neuronal nutrition following astroglial overgrowth (Field et al, 1964). Pattison's (1965) studies supported this interpretation of the scrapie process, and emphasised the strict bilateral symmetry of lesions. For Pattison, such bilateral symmetry has always been an insuperable obstacle to acceptance of the concept of scrapie as being caused by an "orthodox" virus, with a primary pathogenetic action on the nerve cells. The primary changes in the astroglial make understandable the symmetrical distribution of lesions, since "sucker feet" dysfunction might result in changes in the blood brain barrier. The symmetrical distribution of lesions might be due to the systemic circulation conducting of the disease to the CNS.

Myelin sheaths are layers of protective membrane formed around axons which insulate and keep the neural electrolyte system physically apart from each other, in a similar manner to electric wires which are coated by plastic material to prevent short circuiting. According to many researchers, demyelination, in the usual sense of disappearance of sheaths of nerve-fibre tracts, does not occur in

62

scrapie (Stockman, 1926; Brownlee, 1940), while Wight (1960) found evidence of axonal degeneration especially in the medial part of the ventral funiculus, where myelin droplets were most frequent. Such degenerative changes have been considered to be secondary to neuronal deterioration (Field, 1969).

Localisation of Pathological Changes

In the advanced natural disease, changes are widespread in the grey matter, but, in cases examined at early stages, these may be patchy. In some cases, neuronal damage, vacuolation and degeneration are confined to the medulla and pons (Stamp et al, 1959), whereas, in others, lesions are widespread from the telencephalon to the medulla-cord junction. In the latter region, lesions have been seen in only 40% of the animals examined in the early stages of the disease (Field, 1969). In the medulla, the large neurons of the formation reticularis, especially near the middle, are nearly always affected to some degree, and all grey nuclei may contain some vacuolated cells. Lesions are common in the pons and in the medial part of the thalamus. Spinal cord anterior horn cells are frequently affected, especially those of the intermediolateral group (Wight, 1960).

In the experimental disease of sheep, lesions are usually less marked, and most damage is to be found in the pons and midbrain, but in the natural disease the heaviest lesions are commonly in the medulla and pons (Field, 1969). A detailed study of the distribution of lesions in the experimental scrapie of the goat has been made by Hadlow (1961), who found that despite clinical variations, ("scratchy" and "drowsy"), the distribution of changes was remarkably constant.

In the mouse, Pattison et al (1963) have examined the localisation of lesions as seen in a single cross section through the brain. Extensive involvement of the cerebral cortex is an outstanding feature of mouse scrapie, whereas, in the sheep and goat, the brain stem is more affected.

Hypothalamo-Pituitary Changes

Field (1969) found in experimental scrapie of the mouse and rat, the hypothalamic region is affected late in the disease. In some cases, it may even remain unaltered in the presence of advanced lesions in other parts of the brain. Beck et al (1964) claimed degeneration of the supraoptic and paraventricular nuclei, the hypothalamohypophyseal tract, and the neural lobe of the pituitary gland to be the primary lesions in sheep with natural scrapie, and these changes were reported to resemble those seen after pituitary stalk section. They are not related to obesity or wasting. Beck et al (1964) suggested that obesity, excessive thirst, a craving for salt, and instability of body temperature, observed in some of their animal specimens, may be related to hypothalamic changes. In a later study of semi serial sections through the hypothalamus and pituitary of sheep with experimental scrapie, no evidence of special local pathology or nerve cell damage was found (Field, 1969). It was concluded that hypothalamopituitary dysfunction is not a primary feature of the disease in the mouse, but may result from direct extension of the scrapie process at a relatively later stage (Field, 1969).

Electron Microscopic (EM) Observations

Electron microscopic observations have revealed that some disruption of the myelin sheath is more widespread than would appear from light microscopy (Chandler, 1968). Field et al (1972) found considerably increased numbers of dense-bodies and pleomorphic inclusions with a laminated internal structure in neurons of scrapie-affected mouse. The mitochondria of neurons in natural scrapie sheep showed degenerative changes, leading to the formation of elongated internal structures comprising a central core surrounded by a spiral, or stacked disks. Myelin figure inclusions made up largely of parallel membranes in the cytoplasm of the microglial cell were a common feature.

Plaques

Degenerating areas in tissue are termed plaques and can be seen by the microscope in histological sections. Some of the plaques in brains are considered to consist of a central core of fibrillary material, called amyloid, surrounded by clusters of abnormal degenerating cellular processes. Plaques are observed in a number of naturally occurring human diseases, in particular Alzheimer's disease, commonly known as senile dementia, and CJD (Fig 3, 4, 5). Often, plaques are observed in old age brains but in only small numbers. The origin and nature of these plaques remains unknown, but, because of their histological staining properties and appearance, it has been assumed that all plaques in different conditions are caused by a similar mechanism of origin. A detailed study of these plaques by EM, however, has revealed some major differences in the fine structure and composition in differing disease conditions. Plaques are more common in brains in some strains of experimentally induced scrapie mice, and less frequent in the brains of adult sheep affected by scrapie, although their number and distribution varies from region to region in the same brain. Plaques probably represent a response to some degenerative process, but they are not a diagnostic feature of spongiform encephalopathy. Some authors have considered the accumulation of this fibril material as aggregates of the scrapie agent.

Immunohistochemical Studies: By immunohistochemical methods two types of plaques can be demonstrated in brains.

i) amyloid ß-protein positive plaques are commonly seen in Alzheimer's disease (AD) and ii) Protease-resistant protein (PrP-sc) positive plaques are seen in CJD, kuru, and natural scrapie of sheep. The PrP-sc positive plaques have not been observed in AD or Down's syndrome. Plaques are described in detail in the CJD chapter.

64

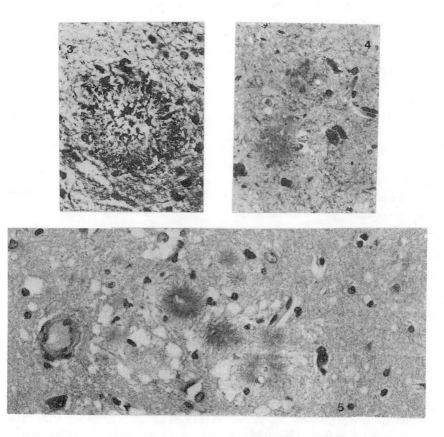

Fig 3   Cerebral cortex from a Alzheimer's patient showing large senile plaque.
        X 450
Fig 4   Cerebral cortex from a scrapie mice showing large kuru-type plaque. X
        450
Fig 5   Cerebral cortex from a "new strain" CJD 20 year old patient showing
        large kuru-type plaques surrounded by a zone o extensive spongiform
        changes. X 350.

65

Identifying Preclinical Infection

The importance of identifying preclinical infection would provide better epidemiological studies and a means to promoting a more effective control program. So far, there is no serological monitoring test known which can give any indication of SE and identify preclinical or clinical disease. Again, greater understanding of the nature of the agent might provide such a diagnostic test.

At present, MAFF have no way of identifying SE in either experimentally infected or naturally infected animals, or during the long incubation period. It is of vital importance that we have a means of detecting the virus at every stage of the incubation period, both at pre-clinical, sub-clinical, and at the clinical stage. The only way we have, as yet, of making a certain diagnosis is by detecting the virus in surgically accessible tissue under the microscope.

Since spongiform changes are a late event, histological examination of the brain tissue cannot be used in identifying preclinical infection. Animal inoculation bioassay has been used for identifying infected sheep, but it is expensive and may take months and years to reach a conclusion. Devising simpler, more precise ways of identifying pre-clinical and subclinical infected animals and humans is, therefore, a priority item for research. However, a recently developed "touch-technique" in the laboratory hamster model, which can be performed in a relatively short period of time, may help considerably and may permit specimens to be examined within a day. This method may be useful in identifying infected sheep during the preclinical stage.

Therapeutic Treatment of Spongiform Encephalopathies

Therapeutic treatment of SEs is frustrated because it is not possible to diagnose the disease in its preclinical stage and, furthermore, the clinical changes during development cannot be easily traced, making evaluation of therapeutic treatment difficult. For a physician or scientist to attempt treatment without knowing the nature of the agent or the cause of the transmissible SE is merely a shot in the dark, and unlikely to be successful. A question to be asked is, whether at any level the therapeutic intervention has been beneficial in treating the disease? Most of the pharmacological drugs have been tested using the experimental scrapie models. If any of these drugs had shown a true beneficial effect, it would have been of great help in the further investigation of the pathogenesis of the disease. However, unfortunately, none of the drugs known or tried have had any practical therapeutic role in the prevention, or significant curtailment, of the course of the disease.

Although many drugs have been tested, at present, no real therapy or vaccine is available for the cure of transmissible spongiform encephalopathies. The agents that cause the SEs have for a long time been considered by many to be closely associated with plasma membranes. Therefore, it is not surprising that some of the first therapeutic drugs studied were membrane-related. A vast variety of anti-infective and other drugs have been studied in animal models including

66

some with membrane-active compounds. A few of these have prolonged the course of infection, while others appear to have some temporary beneficial effect. However, no form of therapy has been effective when given after the disease has become clinically manifested. Because there is no laboratory test to detect pre-clinical infection, development of preventive treatment, as predicted, has been unsuccessful.

No humoral or cellular immune response in an infected host has ever been shown to appear, therefore it has not been possible to monitor the state of the disease. The infectious agent is considered to be a virus, or virus-like agent, by many workers in the field. Hence, many of the drugs tried were immunosuppresants, steroids, anti-lymphocytic serum and archis oil, immunomodulating drugs, interferon, interferon inducers, immunostimulants, vaccine virus, BCG, and bacterial polysaccharide. For viral infections, amantadine, cytosine and adenosine arabinoside, phosphonacetic acid, sodium butyrate, sodium thiocyanate and many other compounds have been used for this purpose.

Over the past several years, a number of other chemotherapeutic agents have also been used to treat experimental scrapie and CJD (Brown, 1990). In the trials were many drugs active against known parasites, for example, niclosamide, diiodohydroxyquin, chloroquin, metronidazole, the antifungals, amphotericin B, griseofulvin, sinefungin, antibacterials such as tetracycline, sulphamethoxy-zole, trimethoprim, thiamphenicol, rifampicin and many others. All these drugs tested have had no significant practical therapeutic effect on the course of the disease.

The antiviral drug, HPA-23, has been shown to be effective against several scrapie models, but does not seem to prevent the initial peripheral infection with scrapie and its replication (Kimberlin et al, 1979; 1983). Dextran sulphate can prevent scrapie, even when given a few days after peripheral infection (Ehlers et al, 1984). Significant activity against experimental scrapie infection in mice and hamsters was observed with amphotericin B, ouabain and several of the polyanionic compounds, which lengthened the incubation periods of the disease, or even, in some cases, prevented the disease when inoculated with very low doses (Ehlers et al, 1984; Farquhar et al, 1986; Pocchiari et al, 1987, 1989). It has been demonstrated that amphotericin B is the only drug to have some prolonging affect whereby the incubation times are influenced in scrapie-infected hamsters (Pocchiari et al, 1987, 1989). These results appeared to be related to dose and are interval-dependent between treatment and infection. The drugs appear to have no direct toxic effect upon the scrapie virus since they are equally active when administered together with, or separately from, the virus inoculum.

Pocchiari et al (1990) studied amphotericin B activity against experimental scrapie-hamster and scrapie infectivity titres in parallel with the amounts of PrP27-30. A different pattern was found in amphotericin B treated hamsters. The increase in the amount of PrP27-30 did not parallel the increase in the infectivity titres. They demonstrated measurable PrP27-30 after 52 weeks incubation period, when the infective titre was 7.6 log LD50/brain equivalent. This data suggested that PrP27-30 is likely to be a pathological byproduct rather than a component of the scrapie agent. If any of these drugs had shown a truly beneficial effect, it would have been of great interest to further investigate the pathogenesis of the disease. However, none of the drugs has any practical therapeutic role in the prevention, or significant curtailment, of the course of the disease.

Economic Loss from Scrapie

From the history of the disease, it is obvious that scrapie brings economic disaster for flock owners. Both directly in the death of valuable stock, and indirectly by depreciation of breeding stock, scrapie causes farmers an economic loss. However, there are no statistics to form a base for a detailed estimate of the annual loss in terms of value, but these losses must be enormous for some farmers. Sigurdsson (1954) estimated that after the introduction of the disease in Iceland from Halle, Germany in 1933, the disease gained momentum and became extremely destructive! Dickinson et al (1965) recorded a flock where half of one age group developed scrapie within one year, but such a high level is rare. They also deduced, by making allowances for the effects of commercial culling, that at least 1 in 4 of potential cases of scrapie are liable to occur after 4 and half years of age, at which time half the ewes have normally been culled (Dickinson et al, 1964).

It is said that during the 1950s, the annual loss from scrapie often equalled the total from all other diseases of sheep combined, and thus double the annual mortality-rate, which, in scrapie-free lowland flocks was considered about 5% of the breeding females. In the 1950s, pedigree sheep, mainly of the Suffolk and Cheviot breeds exported from Britain to various countries, for example Canada, USA, New Zealand and Australia, developed the scrapie at varying periods after arrival in the importing country. Sheep in these countries were reputed to be free of scrapie before this. This led to the imposition of a complete embargo by these countries on the import of sheep from Britain (Stamp, 1962).

Detergents

Scrapie virus is resistant to most of the bactericidal and virucidal disinfectants commonly used for inactivation of bacteria and viruses - including sodium deoxycholate and Tween 80. The infectivity of the scrapie agent decreases about 100 fold after treatment with Triton X-100. However, low concentration of SDS produces marked reduction in the titres and while Millson et al (1979) reported that treatment with 5% SDS often drops titres to undetectable levels. This, however, was not confirmed in many other studies with different disinfectants including SDS, which have often yielded inconsistent results. Treatment with 6 M urea virtually eliminated infectivity in the 22A strain of the scrapie agent injected by intraperitoneal route (Kimberlin et al, 1985).

68

Physical Inactivation of the Scrapie Agent

1. Heat: Stamp (1959) demonstrated that the transmissible agent is "unusually resistant" and that, among its other properties, it can survive heating at 100° C for half an hour, showing the high resistance of the agent to heat inactivation. Stamp et al (1962) also found that the scrapie agent could withstand a temperature of 95.5^O C for eight hours or more. The fact that the brains from sheep, which had developed scrapie following the injection of boiled material, were themselves in turn capable of transmitting scrapie when injected into further sheep, indicates that boiling does not effectively eradicate the agent and thus is not a toxin. Some researchers questioned validity of these sheep experiments on the basis that the sheep used in inoculation studies would have developed the disease whether they had been inoculated or not. Difficulties of obtaining sheep from guaranteed scrapie-free stocks was the main hindrance in starting these transmission studies.

The agent of scrapie has many remarkable properties. It is resistant to heat. However, it is important to note that a significant amount of infectivity in the tissue can be destroyed by heat treatment. If infected material is maintained at a temperature of 80° C for 60 minutes, it shows a negligible loss of infective titre, but Hunter et al (1964) have demonstrated that a considerable drop of infective titre of scrapie agent occurs following incubation at 100° C for 10 to 60 minutes. Remarkably, a subpopulation of about 10^3 still survives from an original infective titre of the order of 10^8 to 10. According to Hunter et al (1964), the critical temperature of rapid heat inactivation is 87.5^O C; at lower temperature inactivation is very slow, from which it was inferred that the bulk of the agent exists in a heat stable form that probably contains double-stranded DNA.

In several studies, no infectious virus has been detected in preparations following treatment in a steam autoclave for 30 minutes, or longer, at 121° C. However, some other studies have suggested that the scrapie agent is highly thermostable - even after exposure to 121° C for a period of one hour. After heating, most of the infectivity remains in the crude suspension, which is apparently in the coagulated larger particles of the tissue. Two porous-load experiments, which were conducted with the mouse-passaged 22A and 139A strains of the scrapie agent, showed that heat at 136° C for 4 minutes exposure inactivated the agent (Kimberlin et al, 1983). Some of the recent studies have, however, demonstrated that infectivity may survive even lengthy exposure to dry heat at 160° C or brief exposure at 240° C, and a small amount of infectivity still survived after one hour exposure to temperature as high as 360° C (Brown et al, 1990)

A revised DHSS Health Hazard Note (AD) 84, 16,1984, recommended that objects or materials contaminated with the SE agent should be disinfected with steam. The recommended autoclaving procedure, for inactivation of CJD agent, is a porous-load cycle at 134° C to 138° C for 18 minutes (DHSS, 1984), and this has been largely adopted as an appropriate decontamination standard for all the SEs agents. Steam at 132° C for an hour showed the highest level decontamination (Brown et al, 1986).

The results obtained by different researchers depend on the technique used for heat inactivation. In many of these studies, full protocols are not given, and it is also possible that cross-contamination of inoculum had occurred. It has been demonstrated that some of the scrapie agent strains are more thermostable than others, and it is also known that infected tissues from a single animal may contain more than one strain of the scrapie agent. It is therefore possible that some of these strains, which occur at low levels, may survive.

2. Chemical Inactivation: Many chemical disinfectants reduce, but do not eliminate, the levels of the infectious agent, and some residual infectivity usually survives.

3. Formalin saline: The major vaccine accident during the 1930s, detailed previously, was when formalised tissue of louping-ill virus vaccine caused a large number of scrapie cases in sheep flocks. Gordon (1946) and Greig (1950) demonstrated that the agent of scrapie survived a concentration of formaldehyde of 0.35% acting over a period of at least 3 months. Pattison (1965) found that scrapie goat brain could produce disease after treatment with 20% formalin for 18 hours at 37° C, while Field (1968) found that the infectivity survived an exposure to 20% for as long as 28 months. Several studies have demonstrated that formalin does reduce the infective titre by about 1.5 log (Brown et al, 1990). Taylor (1994) found that BSE-infected cow brains, immersed in 10% formalin saline for two years, produced disease after intracerebral and intraperitoneal injection into mice.

In many instances, where no fresh tissue was available, old formalin-fixed tissue blocks were homogenised, and these, when inoculated into animals, also transmitted the disease - and it was possible to confirm diagnosis.

4. Glutaraldehyde: Glutaraldehyde, a conventional disinfectant commonly used in the laboratory, is also not effective in inactivating the scrapie nemavirus (Brown et al, 1984). Brown et al (1990) have demonstrated that, although steam autoclaving greatly diminished or destroyed the infectivity, pretreatment of tissue with formaldehyde before steam autoclaving surprisingly, served to preserve the infectivity. From a practical stand point, autoclaving has no laboratory value for decontamination of pre-formalin-fixed scrapie or CJD tissue (Brown et al, 1990). Pretreatment with formaldehyde might produce rigidity from a molecular cross-linking effect in the protein, which in turn would make a shell and protect the nucleic acid from degradation by heat. We know that genes of other agents can be amplified by the Polymerase Chain Reaction (PCR) from 40 year old formaldehyde fixed tissues, thus demonstrating, that although proteins are fixed, genes can be biologically preserved and reactivated under controlled conditions.

Since it had been demonstrated that formalin and glutaraldehyde do not reduce infectivity, a way had to be found to handle tissues which are fixed for routine histological examination with these two fixatives. It has been established that steam autoclaving of formalin pre-fixed scrapie and CJD tissue do not significantly further reduce the infectivity.

5. **Formic acid:** Multhaup et al (1985), demonstrated inactivation of the scrapie agent in extracts of brains after 15 minutes exposure to concentrated formic acid. It was found that further treatment of pre-formalin-fixed diseased tissue with concentrated formic acid for one hour does greatly reduced the infectivity in tissues which have been pre-fixed with formaldehyde for histology,and which, therefore, would be relatively safe to handle in the laboratory (Brown et al, 1990).

6. **Sodium hydroxide (NaOH):** Brown et al (1990) found no infectivity after suspension of infected brain homogenate in 1M NaOH for 60 minutes at room temperature. However, Tateishi et al (1988) treated CJD tissue with 0.5M, 1M and 2M NaOH for 2 hours and observed a prolongation of the incubation period in animals inoculated with treated tissues, thus demonstrating a partial inactivation of infectivity of the CJD agent after 2 hours treatment with NaOH. They found that groups of animals, inoculated with tissues which has been treated with 1M NaOH, were comparable to groups of animals which had been inoculated with tissues, previously autoclaved at 120^{0} C for 30 minutes. That is, they found equivalent to a decrease of infectivity, approximately, 1 million doses per gram of tissue. Since the decrease by the two treatments was similar, they recommended NaOH retreatment as being a practical and being as effective procedure as autoclaving at 120^{0}C.

7. **Sodium Hydroxide plus heat:** Having found the weakness of the NaOH treatment, Tateishi et al (1988) found that a combination of 1M NaOH and boiling in 3% SDS for 10 minutes was a fully effective inactivating procedure. They found that there was no detectable infectivity in the CJD agent material after one hour exposure to 1M NaOH solution, followed by a 30 minute gravity-displacement autoclaving cycle at 120^{0} C. The majority of infectivity can be eliminated by autoclaving, and almost all by 1M NaOH at over 55^{0} C (Taylor, 1994).

Diringer et al (1989) demonstrated that the brains from scrapie-infected hamsters at the clinical stages contained nine to ten log infectivity, while dura from scrapie-infected hamsters contained seven to eight log infectivity per gm of tissue. In order to destroy bacteria and virus, a commercially available human brains the dura mater was treated with salt solution, hydrogen peroxide, and acetone for several weeks and was then irradiated with Cobalt-60 (25 KGy). Diringer et al (1989) demonstrated that treatment of hamster dura mater in this way lowered infectivity only 1 to 2 log. However, incubation of the tissue with strong alkali at room temperature for 60 minutes, almost completely destroyed the infectivity. Since 1 out of 40 hamsters developed the disease, although with an increased incubation period, they argued that treatment of tissues with alkali was a very efficient method of inactivating the CJD agent in the dura mater.

8. **Sodium hypochlorite:** Hypochlorite has been used for the inactivation of microbes for almost 200 years. Potassium hypochlorite was prepared by Be-

rthollet in 1789, and sodium hypochlorite was used as disinfectant in 1870 (Coates, 1985). Over the past 50 years, chlorine-active compounds, and hypochlorite in particular, have been widely used as disinfectants in hospitals, research establishments and the water industry because of their high effectiveness against a wide range of organisms including bacteria, fungi and viruses.

The effectiveness depends on the rate of diffusion of hypochlorite molecules into the cell and the degree of interaction with the cellular components. These properties, in turn, depend on pH (Fair et al, 1948). In addition to pH, various environmental factors and, in particular, the presence of organic material and fat can determine the effectiveness of free available chlorine (Coates, 1985). Kimberlin et al (1983) evaluated the effect of sodium hypochlorite on two strains of the scrapie agent, and found that exposure to solutions of sodium hypochlorite containing 13,750 or 16.500 parts per million of available chlorine, for a period of up to an hour, achieved inactivation of the scrapie-infectivity.

9. Sodium dichloroisocyanate: Unlike sodium hypochlorite, sodium dichloroisocyanate formulation has only recently become available. It has the definite advantage that it is available in powder and tablet form, and, therefore, is more stable (Hoffman et al, 1981). In addition, the required dilutions can be prepared safely and accurately. The microbial activity of solutions, prepared from sodium dichloroisocyanate formulation, may be greater than using sodium hypochlorite because the pH of the former solution is lower, and activity increases with acidity (Coates, 1985). There are, however, no reports of sodium dichloroisocyanate formulation being tested against the agent of spongiform encephalopathies.

10. Alkylating agents: Exposures of homogenates of the scrapie tissue to the action of acetyl ethyleneimine for a period of time, exceeding by 50% what is required to inactivate completely most known viruses, proved ineffective for the scrapie agent. Ethylene oxide both at ambient and high temperature and pressures, was also found ineffective in inactivation of scrapie virus infectivity. A concentration of 0.2 to 1% ß-Propiolactone in some of the studies produced a reduction of 2 log titre of infectivity (Haig et al, 1968; Stamps et al, 1959).

11. Organic solvents: Ethanol (50 to 70%), and fluorocarbons have little, if any, effect on the infectivity of the scrapie virus. Many solvents including acetone, ethyl ether, acetone-ethyl ether and butanol-chloroform at various concentrations reduce infectivity but never by more than 2 logs. Phenol and chloroform 80% solution of 2-chloroethanol produced a remarkable reduction in scrapie titres of the order of around 5 logs. Several studies have demonstrated that treatment with 90% aqueous phenol often removed all detectable infectivity titre.

12. Halogen compounds: Among the halogen compounds tested, the limited data indicates that cesium chloride (2.5 M), sodium iodate (0.01M) and sodium periodate (0.1M) reduce titres by the order of 1 to 2 log. In some of the studies, it has been shown that a solution of 0.3% iodine in 70% ethanol did produce a marked reduction in the infectivity titre of scrapie agent but these results

were not confirmed by another study. Potassium permanganate (0.024M), and urea (3-6M) solutions were not very efficient for inactivation, while 8M urea has been reported in one study to reduce infectivity of the scrapie agent markedly (Hunter et al, 1969).

13. Acids and bases: The scrapie agent was found to be stable at pH varying from 2.1-10.5 at room temperature for 24 hours. It has been demonstrated in a number of studies that NaOH 1M is one of the most potent chemicals, for inactivation of both scrapie and CJD agents.

14. Radiation: The scrapie agent also differs from other viruses in that it is not affected by UV radiation. It should be pointed out that such resistance is also shared by small plant viruses called viroids which cause natural plant diseases such as potato spindle tuber disease, chrysanthemum stunt disease, citrus exocortis mottle and cucumber pale fruit disease. Viroids are composed of naked, single-stranded RNA and are 70 to 90 times more resistant to UV radiation than conventional viruses. A comparison of viroids with scrapie suggested that the scrapie agent might contain a nucleic acid of the order of 150,000 Dalton which, like viroids, would survive UV radiation. It is also known that a highly purified viroid nucleic acid of molecular weight of 100,000 becomes totally resistant to UV radiation when mixed with clarified plant sap, thus making it appear that non-specific proteins can protect nucleic acid from degradation. It has also been shown that a crude preparation of the scrapie agent is more resistant to UV radiation than the purified agent, demonstrating that the presence of proteins protected it from the UV radiation. Heating of the host double stranded DNA, or its exposure to UV radiation, causes the two strands of the DNA to separate, a phenomenon called melting.

Most of the previous studies did not consider the presence of a single-stranded DNA in the scrapie agent, which, like viroids, can tolerate UV radiation and much higher temperatures than double-stranded DNA. Single-stranded DNA does not melt since the covalent bonds between the bases would have to undergo disintegration with consequent decomposition of the compounds, and for this the energy requirement would be very high. The infectivity of the scrapie agent would not be destroyed by treatments with protease, RNase or DNase. Again it has been demonstrated that, although viroids contain naked RNA, the presence of proteins in the suspension protects the RNA from digestion by RNase. The possibilities that a protein is present associated with the scrapie agent, as may be the case, or that nucleic acid might be protected by a protein coat have never been considered. Negative results, however, should not be taken as proof that no genetic information exists in the scrapie virus.

Handling of Spongiform Encephalopathy Materials

In a microbiological laboratory, precautions and techniques used for handling "hepatitis" virus probably provide the best protection against risk of possible infection from the scrapie agent. Workers should be aware of the potential danger of self-inoculation, either direct or through a cut. Gloves of good quality should be worn at all times and especially careful handling of all materials contaminated with tissues and spinal fluid is required. Laboratory benches should be cleaned, where appropriate, with the recommended concentration of either NaOH 1M or sodium hypochlorite solution (5.25% diluted fresh) and it is recommended that the exposed surfaces should be treated for at least one hour.

A revised DHSS Health Hazard Note [(AD) 84, 16, 1984] recommended the disinfection of all material, possibly contaminated with the infectious agent, by steam treatment using one of the following autoclave procedures:

A)   A single cycle 121-124° C (15 lb psi) for 90 minutes holding time at temperature (HTAT).

B)   A single cycle 126-129° C (20 lb psi) for 60 minutes HTAT.

C)· A single cycle 136-138° C (30 lb psi) for 18 minutes HTAT.

D)   6 separate cycles 136-138° C (30 lb psi) for 3 minutes HTAT.

It should be noted that, in many cases, treatment of unfixed tissue for 30 minutes at 134° C may not achieve total inactivation of infectivity, and there is no absolute certainty that the agent has been destroyed by a single treatment. The risk of partial inactivation of infectivity always exists, and the danger cannot be over stated.

Disposable equipment, broken glass, needles, blades etc. should be very carefully packed in rigid, leakproof containers during transportation. Contaminated organs and animal carcasses should be wrapped in double plastic bags. These should be incinerated with careful adherence to the usual precautions being essential. Cortical biopsies are now rarely performed for the diagnosis of CJD. Current guidelines in the UK require neurosurgical instruments to be destroyed after use on a suspected case of CJD.

Autopsy procedures

A "high risk" autopsy room is desirable, but not essential. Access must be restricted to the autopsy room during the procedure and only essential fully trained medical and technical staff should be present.

An open body bag should be used to minimise contamination of the autopsy room.

Disposable protective clothing to be worn and with disposable instruments to be incinerated on completion.

All disposable equipment, temporary bench coverings, contaminated fluids, and tissues to be incinerated.

Nondisposable instruments should be autoclaved or decontaminated.

Working surfaces, after completion, to be decontaminated by trained staff with sodium hypochlorite containing 20,000 ppm chlorine.

Decontamination

Heat-stable equipment and nondisposable protective clothing Porous load autoclave:

A single cycle $134^{\circ}C$ (+4/0) (30 Ib psi) 18 min (holding time at temperature).

Six temperature cycles $134^{\circ}C$ (+4/0) (30 Ib psi) 3 min (holding time at temperature). Nondisposable, nonheat stable equipment and work surfaces to be cleaned
with sodium hypochlorite containing 20,000 ppm available chlorine for at least 1
hour exposure with repeated wetting if required.

Exposure to 2M NaOH with repeated wetting

Nature and Properties of the Scrapie Agent

"The great tragedy of science - the slaying of a beautiful hypothesis by an ugly fact" T.H. Huxley.

Nature of the Scrapie Agent

Scrapie in sheep, BSE in cattle, and kuru and CJD in humans have long baffled farmers, veterinarians and doctors. The nature of the causative agent has remained elusive and, even with the development of biological techniques in the mid-20th century, scientists are still at odds. Our knowledge of the properties of slow viruses is largely based on the study of the scrapie agent. In earlier studies, the long incubation period made it difficult for the disease to be established in laboratory animals, and, for many years, the only available hosts were sheep, goats and primates which were considered susceptible and acted as indicators. Later, cats, and then guinea pigs, were also found to be susceptible to the agent of SEs. The virus was eventually adapted to mice (Chandler, 1961), and, thereafter, to hamsters (Kimberlin et al, 1975).

It is important to distinguish between hypothesis (theory) and fact. Hypothesis is an idea as yet unproven. Only after scientific proof does it become fact. Over the last 50 years, an impressive array of data has accumulated which indicates that the SE agent is of replicating and infectious nature and it has been found to be a type of virus. Many of the features of SE diseases are not typical of a viral infection. In particular, unlike other viral infections, there is no detectable antibody production by the host. Since 1980, research undertaken on the subject has been very extensive, and almost all research articles concerning the nature of the agent of SEs contain introductory remarks along the lines: "the nature of the transmissible agent that causes SEs still remains controversial." It is because of the extreme properties such as resistance to inactivation by physical and chemical treatments, and the apparent lack of immunological response (Gibbs, 1967), which has made this group of slow viruses "stand-out" as being entirely different from all other known viruses. The precision of SE-host interactions has been one of the important factors which has provided the opportunity to establish reliable details about its pathogenesis, while the nature of the agent responsible for these diseases still remains uncertain. Any understanding of the pathogenesis of the disease in the clinical phase is limited. Most of the time, hypotheses are being misquoted and stressed as facts. Since the public and the media have joined in the debate, the issue has become very complicated, and therefore it is important to distinguish between hypothesis and fact.

Since 1945, a remarkable series of discoveries along the way have been made which include : (1) - the transmission of the scrapie disease of sheep to mice; (2) - Kuru, an epidemic neurodegenerative disorder was shown to share pathological similarities with scrapie; (3) - Kuru can be experimentally transmitted to primates; (4) - the neuropathological similarity of scrapie to CJD and BSE has been established; (5) - CJD and BSE can also be transmitted to susceptible host

76

species; (6) - subsequently, familial CJD has also been in turn successfully transmitted to susceptible host species. The considerable amount of experimental work that has already been conducted on scrapie, kuru and CJD is now being applied to BSE.

In the laboratory, most studies have been directed at understanding the virus-like properties and pathogenesis of disease. The precision of scrapie agent-host interactions has been one of the important factors which has provided the opportunity to establish reliable details about disease pathogenesis. From the knowledge accumulated, the majority of scientists still believe that the infection is caused by a slow virus. As would be understood from the terminology the SE agents replicate slowly. The titre rises- up to 10^{10} to 10^{12}/gram of the brain tissue. This titre is 4 to 6 logs (10,000 to 1000,000 times) more than any other commonly known viruses. Replication is slow in the sense that clinical symptoms develop only after a long incubation period. Otherwise SEs follow a course which is just as regular as the course of other infections. In the infected animals, many of the organ tissues of the hosts' body show no histopathological changes at all. However, these apparently normal looking tissues may be highly infectious. The SE agent appears to multiply by replicating slowly with a very long asymptomatic incubation period of months or even years and with a protracted clinical course. Subsequent to the long asymptomatic incubation period, suddenly the terminal clinical signs appear! Within a short time of appearance of the first clinical signs, symptoms progress leading to serious disease, followed by death. Because of the long asymptomatic incubation period the SEs disorders, Sigurdsson (1954) was the first one to apply the term slow viral infections. The term "slow" has to be carefully distinguished from "chronic" disease, although infection in both may appear to spread over a long period of time. Furthermore in some "chronic" diseases, infection can persist but may eventually clear. In a slow virus the course of infection in a given species of animal follows a regular course as in acute infection, but on a long time scale. The slow viruses do not lie dormant in host's body but constantly replicate, unlike latent virus which may lie dormant at same time in host's body. In other words, a slow virus continues to replicate all the time.

Once the animals are infected there is a period of incubation. The incubation period of slow viruses does not vary within very wide limits in the same animal species but appears to be related to the dose, the route of infection, the strain of the SE agent and the age of the host at the time of infection. At the end it could be summed up in all respects as catastrophic, since a devastating, fatal disease ultimately declares itself. Originally it was considered that to establish the disease experimentally, because of the long incubation periods, the animals had to be inoculated during weaning. Subsequently, further experiments have demonstrated that the incubation period is related to the hosts age at inoculation, for example, the older the animals when infected, the shorter the incubation period. Since knowledge in this field is still limited, it would be potentially dangerous

77

to assume and predict categorically that there is no danger of infection from the handling of uncooked meat or from eating the cooked food.

Physical and Chemical Properties of the SE Agent

After many years of research, the nature of the agent responsible for SE diseases still remains controversial. So far with regard to physical and chemical properties, there are two important known facts which should be considered: 1) SE is a transmissible replicating agent; 2) it is resistant to a variety of chemical and physical treatments.

Stamp et al (1959), showed by straightforward dilution experiments, that scrapie affected sheep brain can be diluted-out between 10^5 to 10^9, a dilution one might expect to obtain with a biologically active agent. Wilson et al (1950) used gradocol membranes measuring 410 micrometers to confirm earlier findings of Cuillé et al (1938) that the transmissible agent could be passed through a virus filter. They interpreted their results to suggest that scrapie was caused by a virus infection of the CNS with an incubation period of 18 months to 5 years. Stamp (1962) suggested that the agent is a particulate and observed that the active agent would not pass through a 27 micrometer gradocol membrane. He repeated his experiments using boiled material at each stage in serial passage studies, which demonstrated that the active portion of the boiled material like that of the unboiled, will not pass through a 27 µm gradocol membrane.

The enormous resistance to inactivation by UV radiation, and the total lack of host antigen response to a highly infectious virus has led to speculation that these are the unique microbes without a nucleic acid - without a non-host protein - and composed of a host derived protein. The SE agent remained viable after scrapie-infected hamster brain was mixed with soil and packed into perforated petri dishes, embedded within soil-containing pots which were then buried in a garden in the Washington DC area for at least 3 years (Brown et al, 1991). From this study, however, it should not be concluded that the agent cannot survive longer than 3 years in the soil. Because of its biological properties, its resistance to nucleases, irradiation with ultraviolet light and hydrolysis, and the degree of its physiochemical stability, (such that a remarkable amount of the infective dose can often survive a heat of $132^{\circ}C$ for half-an-hour) the term "unconventional viruses" was used to distinguish and separate the slow virus group from the rest of the other infectious microorganisms (Gajdusek, 1985). However, the majority of infectivity can be eliminated by autoclaving, and almost all by 1M NaOH at over $55^{\circ}C$ and also by hypochlorite treatment (Taylor, 1994). Successive determinations of the size of the SE have given progressively smaller estimates (Field, 1969). The agent will pass through a gradocol membrane of about 100 nm, but not through 20 nm pore size, demonstrating the virus-like properties of the agent (Gajdusek, 1985; Narang, 1994). However, these atypical SE infectious diseases differ from other known conventional viral diseases of humans and animals, in that they do not initiate a virus-associated anti-

78

body immune or inflammatory response (Porter et al, 1973). With these unusual properties it is evident that the SE agent is very different from all other known viruses of animals, plants and also viroids. Many researchers have spent their whole working life on the organism and been much embarrassed by the agent's stubborn refusal to reveal itself in any morphologically visible form and therefore they have proposed unorthodox hypotheses.

Route of Infection and Replication of the SE Agent

After all the years of research, some of the important aspects of scrapie in sheep and CJD in humans, which have remained unresolved so far, are the route of infection, means of transmission and the nature of the causative virus that makes the disease so contagious. How does the agent replicate and spread within the host's body? So far in studying the natural infection of sheep and in experimental animals, there has been very little information from which to draw any firm conclusions. What is the true nature of the agent causing the SEs? We need to know answers to all these questions and many more. This information and preclinical diagnosis is crucial to controlling the spread of the disease.

What is the natural route of infection that makes these diseases contagious? This feature appears to be no different in the spread of BSE. What is the portal route of entry of the slow virus? We do not yet know precisely when infection in these animals usually takes place. From the studies in sheep, it would appear that, under natural conditions of exposure, the infection with the SE-agent starts from birth onward (Dickinson et al, 1974). The oral route of infection has been considered to be one of the important routes (Pattison et al, 1972; Hadlow, 1979; 1982). Hadlow et al (1982) found that in 8 out of 15 clinically normal lambs of 10 to 14 months old, he detected the SE-agent in lymphatic tissues and intestine. However, the titres levels of infectivity in these tissues were low, but it was detected throughout the infection period, while the virus was detected in the brain at the age of 25 months. In the course of time, the virus spreads to most lymph nodes and in low amounts to other extraneural organs. The agent continues to replicate, or persists in moderate amounts in intestinal and lymphatic nodes for many months or even years before becoming detectable in the CNS.

As the infective titre (dose) reaches up to 100,000 to 10 million doses/gm of brain tissue, This infective titre 10,000 to 100,000 doses/gm is more than any other commonly known viruses. Apart from brain and spinal cord, in other tissues of the body, it remains constant in the order of 10,000 dose/gm. The replication is slow, in the sense that clinical symptoms develop only after a long incubation period. Otherwise symptoms of the disease follow a course which is as regular as in acute-infections. With scrapie, in tissue-culture studies, it has been found that the amount of the agent increases until a monolayer forms which inhibits further cell division (Haig, 1970; Clarke et al, 1970). Therefore, it has been suggested that the replication of the agent in tissue-culture is related to the cell division cycle but this can not be true in the host brain where cells do not divide. It is more likely that tissue-culture cells infected with the scrapie agent remain constant because, in tissue culture, the fluid media is regularly changed, which keeps the titre dose constant.

Effects of Immunological Parameters on Replication of the SE agent

Although it was shown in 1936 that scrapie could be transmitted to healthy sheep by inoculation of CNS tissue from an infected sheep (Cuillé et al, 1936), the earliest published attempt to detect an immune response in infected animals did not appear until 1959 (Chandler,1959), with negative results. These first efforts were a harbinger of things to come. Since 1950, every conceivable type of test with antigens derived from SE tissues and also repeated with almost monotonous regularity ever since, failed to provide a positive result (Clarke et al, 1966; Gabizon et al, 1988; Marsh et al, 1970). No inflammatory response whatsoever has been detected either locally, in the brain or cerebrospinal fluid, or systemically, in lymphoid tissues or circulating blood. In fact, the absence of inflammatory signs was originally a major reason for considering these diseases in terms of a degenerative, rather than infectious, process. The failure to demonstrate any specific antibody in these diseases led us to believe there is no immune response.

Attempts to detect cellular immunity, by a wide range of tests, have also failed to identify any responses. Infected animals have been shown to have functionally normal splenic and peritoneal macrophages (Michel et al, 1987). Animals with congenital absence of the thymus gland (Fraser et al, 1978) or a deficiency in B-cell maturation (Kingsbury et al, 1983), respond to the infection in exactly the same way as do genetically normal animals. Numerous attempts to alter the course of disease by immunomodulating procedures such as irradiation (Fraser, 1979), or the administration of interferon (Field et al, 1969; Gresser et al, 1983), or by interferon inducers or inhibitors (Allen et al, 1977; Gresser et al, 1983) and a variety of other immunostimulating and immunosuppressive drugs (Outram et al, 1974; Worthington et al, 1971) have, for all practical purposes, proved unsuccessful. These studies strongly suggest that the immune system does not appear to play a role in the suppression of the SE diseases. So far there is no evidence for any type of antibody response to the agent (Carp et al, 1991; Clarke et al, 1966). In recent studies the levels of IgA immunoglobulin were found to be lower in the plasma of SJL strain of mice injected with the 139A scrapie strain, than were the levels in mice injected with normal mouse brain homogenate, whereas the level in ME7-injected mice were not significantly different (Carp, 1994). In fact no consistent immunologic response occurs in scrapie disease. Immunoassay therefore has no value as diagnostic aids for SE disease conditions.

There appears to be no cellular response, and there is no effect on T-cell responsiveness (Kingsbury et al, 1981; McFarlin et al, 1971). It is also possible,

80

if immunity does develop at all, that we do not have the means to detect it or current tests are inadequate. Perhaps scrapie has to some extent eliminated its own species alien specificity in the immunological sense? The disease seems to progress unhampered for long periods of time until animals die or are killed for humanitarian reasons. Splenectomy increases the incubation period in mice (Fraser et al, 1970). In intact mice the concentration of the scrapie agent in the spleen is known to increase relatively rapidly to a maximum soon after injection and subsequently maintains this plateau level for the remainder of the incubation period (Dickinson et al, 1969).

With the benefit of 40 years of extensive cumulative research, we might well pause to consider and evaluate the possible explanations for this massive failure to identify an immune response in the SEs. There are a number of possibilities:

(1) Antigens of the SE agent are not present in sufficient purity or concentration in infective tissue preparations to be able to detect antibody. (2) Cellular and immune responses are of a type that cannot be identified by the particular tests employed. (3) Antigens of the SE agent do not come into contact with the host immune defence system. (4) In fact, the infective agent has been shown to be in very close contact with immune defence elements almost from the moment they enter the body, first replicating in lymph nodes and spleen, and persisting in these organs throughout the course of the disease (Kuroda et al, 1983). (5) The SEs are caused by the agent that induce a state of immune tolerance.

The question is, why should the infective agent not be antigenic? This problem concerns the lack of degradation of the complex core formed during interaction of the host protein and viral coded proteins. The degradation of the complex protein to it s core fragment is an obligatory step in its catabolic pathway and recognition of antigenic sites for the production of antibody.

Misinterpretations:

(1) Heat does not destroy infectivity ---while it is well known that a considerable (1,000 to 10,000 dose/gm) infectivity survives at a temperature of 100^0 C for 10 to 60 minutes.

(2) "Prion" protein (PrP) is the agent - it is a hypothesis and not fact. PrP is derived from a normal host protein 33-35 kDa. The most important discovery in this work was that the protein is encoded by a host DNA. Furthermore there are number of facts which the prion hypothesis cannot explain, for example the existence of different strain which "breed true".

(3) Mutation in the protein causes the disease. Mutation in the PrP gene has been found in some familial cases while sporadic CJD cases, which form the majority, do not have these mutations. To support the hypothesis, there is negative and indirect evidence. Presence of a replicating agent has been demonstrated by transmission studies from all animals suffering with SEs including familial CJD cases with or without mutation. It is obvious from a very large number of transmission studies that the agent, like other viruses, is replicating in the

81

brains of all CJD cases and other animals incubating the disease. True genetic diseases are not infectious, an explanation is needed as to how a genetic disease can be infectious.

Extraordinary features have hindered progress in many ways, and researchers have often followed wrong clues, and taken a wrong path of research and have left the track. Rather than treating research discoveries as tentative findings, they are accepted as established facts about the disease, and have become part of the scrapie dogma.

Conflicting Theories on Structure and Nature of the Agent

The failure to identify typical virus particles consisting of nucleic acid and protein in scrapie infected brains and the unusual resistance to procedures that normally inactivate nucleic acids, has forced some radical rethinking about the nature of the scrapie agent and other slow viruses. Several hypothetical structures have been proposed, involving every major class of macromolecules as possible components. Examples include: a small DNA virus (Kimberlin, 1967); replicating abnormal polysaccharide within cellular membranes (Gibbons et al, 1967); a replicating polysaccharide on its own (Field, 1967); a naked nucleic acid without a protective protein coat (Diener, 1972); or nucleic acid surrounded and stabilised by a polysaccharide coat (Adams et al, 1967). It has also been suggested that the agent is exclusively composed of a protein (Prusiner, 1982). So far the structure of the agent has proved both unusual and difficult to define. Nevertheless, some experimental studies have suggested that the SE agent behaves as a good old-fashioned neurotropic virus (Field, 1969). This view is further strongly supported by Dickinson et al (1979), and Fraser (1979) who have demonstrated strain variations of the scrapie agent which produce different incubation periods and distribution of the lesions. Nevertheless, it has been known for some years that the agent is an independent pathogen exerting control over a number of characters (Kimberlin, 1982).

From these investigations, four major hypotheses on the nature of the scrapie agent have emerged. They are : 1.- The viroid hypothesis which suggests that the agent is composed of naked nucleic acid of low molecular weight (Diener, 1972); 2.- The virino hypothesis, claims that the agent consists of a nucleic acid which is protected by a host derived protein (Dickinson et al, 1979). This nucleic acid does not code for the protein, but might have regulatory functions within the cell analogous to those proposed for viroids; 3.- The Prion hypothesis, proposed by Prusiner (1982), considered that the infectious agent is composed of a protein molecule(s) and has no nucleic acid; 4.- The agent is related to the "scrapie associated fibrils" (SAF) (Merz et al, 1981). 5.- The agent is a virus termed Nemavirus particles (NVP) (Narang et al, 1972; Narang, 1992). These hypotheses will be discussed in turn along with their significance in detail.

The Viroid Hypothesis

The viroid hypothesis suggests that the agent is composed of nucleic acid species of low molecular weight and is naked without capsule (Diener, 1972). Although there are a number of claims that there is no nucleic acid which is associated with the scrapie agent, a number of kinetic irradiation- inactivation studies have suggested that the scrapie agent may contain a nucleic acid genome equivalent in size to a small virus (0.75×10^6 daltons single-strand virus or 1.6×10^6 daltons double-strand virus) (Rohwer, 1984). It has been demonstrated that protein is an essential part of the SE agent. These studies therefore consider that the SE agent is composed of only naked nucleic acids as in viroids. Known plant viroids, when compared to the scrapie agent, differ in their sensitivity to various physical and chemical inactivation procedures. Further, viroids contain RNA which does appear to code for protein, but some protein appears to be an integral part of the SE agent. For these reasons it was considered that the SE agent is unlikely to belong to group of viroids which are RNA structures.

The Virino Hypothesis

The virino, a tenuous hypothesis, is that the agent has a nucleic acid and might have a regulatory function analogous to those proposed for viroids (Dickinson et al, 1979). A virino is constructed of a low molecular weight scrapie specific nucleic acid and protected by protein which is host-derived. The nucleic acid has no coding capacity for the coating protein. The nucleic acid acts by inducing the disease, and replication of the infective nucleic acid is accomplished exclusively with the help of host enzymes. The virino hypothesis appears very attractive and explains many of the unconventional properties of the agent, such as the difficulty in purifying the agent, its resistance to UV radiation and absence of an immunological response in (susceptible) infected animals. Recently two dimensional fingerprinting analysis to compare fractions prepared from healthy hamster brain and scrapie-infected hamster tissue, by centrifugation gradients have demonstrated that the RNA from infected hamsters contained oligonucleotides that were not present in the RNA isolated from healthy hamsters (German et al, 1985). There is no other experimental work to support this hypothesis.

Scrapie Associated Fibrils Hypothesis

A new era of the molecular biology of SEs was ushered in by the discovery of abnormal fibrils designated "scrapie associated fibrils" (SAF) from scrapie infected brains, by negative contrast staining techniques and electron microscopy (EM) (Merz et al, 1981) and thereafter SAF have been consistently observed in other SEs, natural scrapie-infected sheep, from patients with kuru and CJD, including BSE (Merz et al, 1984; Narang, 1992; 1994; Narang et al, 1990). The morphological structures consist of twisted filaments of about 16 nm diameter, with a nodal periodicity of 40 to 60 nm (Fig 6). SAF are recognisable struc-

83

tures, and they are considered as excellent candidates for the SE agent, or a form of infectious agent (Merz et al, 1981; 1984; Rohwer, 1984; Carp et al, 1985) or that SAF represents component(s) of the agent (Somerville, 1985). SAF have been found only in scrapie and related SE diseases caused by unconventional viruses (Merz et al, 1981; 1984; Somerville, 1985) and not in normal tissue, nor in a variety of other human and animal diseases exhibiting similar histopathological and ultrastructural features such as Alzheimer's disease and multiple sclerosis (MS). It was also shown that SAF were the only abnormal structures seen by electron microscopy. Demonstration of SAF by EM has been commonly used as a confirmation of SE.

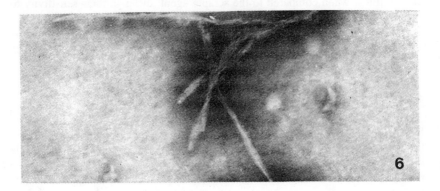

Fig 6   SAF from cerebral cortex from scrapie hamster brain . bar =100 nm.

Further, the occurrence and number of SAF have been shown to parallel the increase in infectivity with a high degree of co-purification between SAF and infectivity in relation to protein concentration. The physiochemical properties and infectivity have been determined only on crude, or partially purified extracts of SAF fractions which may have contained up to 10% impurities. The apparent infectivity of fibrillary material may be due to coincidental co-purification of the agent. Biochemical analysis of highly purified SAF preparations were shown to consist of a single major polypeptide of 27-30-kDa, commonly known as protease-resistant protein (PrP-sc) (Bolton et al, 1982), which is derived from the full-length of 33-35 kDa, normal host precursor sialoglycoprotein (Oesch et al, 1985). The biochemical and immunological evidence so far also has demonstrated that the SAF and PrP-sc cross-react antigenically (Diringer et al, 1985; Bolton et al, 1982; Prusiner et al, 1982).

The importance of these fibrillary structures was quickly appreciated within a few years when, in 1984, their major molecular structure was identified. This discovery has profoundly changed research on transmissible SE disorders. They were analysed serologically and biochemically and shown to consist of a polypeptide of 27-30 kDa molecular weight, similar to the "prion" PrP27-30 kDa

84

molecular weight proteins, associated with scrapie infectivity (Prusiner et al, 1982). The main differences between the prion and SAF hypotheses, appear to hinge on the exact chemical composition of the structures. Since both have the same 27-30 kDa molecular weight polypeptide which cross-react antigenically, they are the same proteins. Because the protein was found to be comparatively resistant to protease enzymatic digestion, it was termed protease-resistant protein (PrP or PrP-sc). It has been demonstrated that PrP-sc molecules aggregate to form "prion rods" (SAF) and aggregate to form plaques (DeArmond et al, 1985; Prusiner et al, 1983). A number of later studies (Narang, 1991; 1994; Narang et al, 1988), have demonstrated that PrP-sc molecules do not aggregate to form "prion rods"/SAF during purification steps as suggested previously (DeArmond et al, 1985; Prusiner et al, 1983. As soon it was realised that both SAF and the PrP-sc "prion" are composed of the same protein, virtually the whole of the work on the molecular biology and genetics of the SEs has since been directed to characterising the origin, activity and chemical structure of this protein under the name of "prion".

Prusiner's Prion Hypothesis

1. Essential backbone of Prusiner's hypothesis: Prusiner (1982) considered that the individual prion is the agent and suggested that protease-resistant protein (PrP-sc) is the sole component of it. He also argued that the prion is too small to contain a nucleic acid. Prusiner's prion hypothesis has been based on two major points (i) there is no demonstratable nucleic acid in infectious PrP-sc preparation and (ii) resistance of the scrapie agent to harsh procedures (Bolton et al, 1984). There is a great deal of published work promoting "prion" as the agent with remarks, such as "There is now very persuasive evidence that the transmission agent for SEs such as scrapie, consists of a modified form of the normal host protein PrP-sc, devoid of any nucleic acid". However, there is no direct evidence to point to the "prion" as the agent. Whether prions are composed only of an abnormal isoform of the prion protein or they contain some additional molecules is uncertain. Prusiner (1996), however, has modified his original statement, "They are largely, if not entirely composed of a protein designated as the scrapie isoform of the prion protein." On the other hand, there are many different strains of the scrapie agent with different biological properties, such as incubation period, which can be propagated in animals homozygous for the PrP gene. This suggests the requirement of a nucleic acid, however small, as an essential component of the agent. It is more likely that formation of PrP-sc is a secondary pathological change and the infectivity is associated with some other factor as well as SAF.

2. Evidence for PrP-sc hypothesis: Prusiner et al (1982) attempted to purify the agent from scrapie- infected hamster brains. They used detergent and enzyme treatment, polyethylene glycol and ammonium sulphate precipitation,

followed by density gradient ultracentrifugation and claimed a 100 to 1,000 fold purification of the scrapie agent associated protein. Further, sodium dodecyl sulphate (SDS) gel electrophoresis appeared to increase this from 1,000 to 10,000 fold purification (Bolton et al, 1982). Analysis of these partially purified fractions by polyacrylamide gel electrophoresis (PAGE) revealed a diffuse-protein-band with a molecular weight of 27-30 kDa (PrP-sc), which had not been seen in control preparations and this they considered to be the agent or part of the agent (Prusiner et al, 1982; Bolton et al, 1982). Since the infectious purified preparations of SEs were considered predominantly to contain a single protease-resistant protein, Prusiner (1982) proposed that the infectious agent is composed of molecules of protein(s) which have no nucleic acid. Chemical analysis later revealed that both the prion and SAF were composed of the same major sialoglycoprotein of molecular weight of 27-30 kDa and are one and the same. Therefore, they are synonymous terms (Bolton et al, 1982; McKinley et al, 1983; DeArmond et al, 1985). Antibodies were raised in rabbits by injecting the SAF and the 27-30 kDa polypeptide from both hamster and mice preparations cross-react (Bendheim et al, 1984).

There are two major lines of indirect evidence in favour of the protein-only hypothesis. (1) With PrP-sc, scrapie infectivity copurify (Diringer et al, 1983; Bolton et al, 1982; Prusiner et al, 1982; 1983), no specific nucleic acid has been detected in highly purified PrP-sc preparations (Kellings et al, 1992; Meyer et al, 1991; Oesch et al, 1988). (2) Genetic evidence indicates that there might be a possible intimate linkage between the PrP disease and Prn-p, the gene which is considered to control the incubation period (Carlson et al, 1986; Hunter et al, 1987). Here, there are two assumptions, either the PrP-sc must bind to a specific host DNA sequence and act as a depressor, or the prion must violate part of the central dogma of molecular biology, and so the genetic information must be transferred indirectly from nucleic acid to proteins (Prusiner, 1982; 1984, Kimberlin, 1982). Researchers from the wide variety of independent disciplines including protein chemistry, molecular genetics, immunochemistry, neuropathology and neurobiology, all strongly suggest PrP might have a central role in pathogenesis but it is not the agent by itself.

Evidence for the prion concept has come largely from the fact that infectivity in hamster brain homogenates is resistant to a variety of treatments expected to destroy nucleic acid but some of the infectivity is abolished only by certain protein-specific reagents (Prusiner, 1984). This clearly demonstrates that, apart from any other classes of macromolecules, protein is an essential part of the SE agent. This property is not unique to the scrapie agent because all conventional viruses normally depend on a protein coat for their integrity and infectivity. Also, all other micro-organisms such as bacteria and mycoplasmata contain proteins and any interference with their protein coat destroys them. Many of these arguments have been based on the assumption that a nucleic acid of SE is unprotected, free of a protein coat as observed in viroids.

Structure of the Protease-Resistant Protein

Two independent studies have produced data that the 27-30 kDa "prion" protein is in fact a product of a normal cellular gene which is expressed (produced) to the same extent in brains of infected and uninfected animals (Chesebro et al, 1985; Oesch et al, 1985). The protein is also expressed at a lower levels in other organs of healthy animals (Oesch et al, 1985). Since 1985 it has been accepted that the PrP is encoded by a normal cellular gene and not by a putative nucleic acid carried within the prion (Oesch et al, 1985). The question has to be asked, why a normal protein acts as the infective agent? Several other important observations were made during this period. Studies, where brain tissue homogenates were not treated with proteinase K (PK, an enzyme which digests proteins), revealed a cross-reacting protein of 33-35 kDa. This protein migrated more slowly than the prion protein during the analytical procedures. On the basis of this evidence, these researchers suggested that PrP27-30 kDa was probably derived from the normal precursor protein, PrP33-35 kDa. The modified PrP27-30 kDa protein is antigenically related to the PrP33-35 kDa protein in that it was partially resistant to PK digestion. These findings explained that although both normal and scrapie-infected brain homogenates contain PrP33-35 kDa protein, the purification procedures reveal PrP27-30 kDa, in scrapie-infected brains, but not in normal uninfected hamster brains, where there was no PrP-sc recorded (Prusiner et al, 1982; Bolton et al, 1982). Since these original observations, it has been demonstrated that the PrP 27-30 kDa protease-resistant protein is derived from a PrP33-35 kDa precursor protein which is coded by a normal single copy chromosomal gene which is located on the short arm of chromosome 20 in humans and in mouse chromosome 2 (Robakis et al, 1986; Liao et al, 1986; Sparkes et al, 1986). The PrP gene coding for the complete translated precursor protein of 254 amino acids has been sequenced from a number of mammalian species (Basler et al, 1986; Goldmann et al, 1991). The sequence of the peptide itself does not differ in a healthy animal from that encoded by a cDNA from scrapie-infected animals (Basler et al, 1986). Furthermore, the PrP gene has been identified in numerous vertebrates and possibly even in nematodes and Drosophila (Westaway et al, 1986). Therefore, we can consider it a natural product found in many animals who do not suffer from SE.

From purified extracts of scrapie-infected hamster brains, the PrP sequencing techniques have determined its amino acid structure (Prusiner et al, 1984; Multhaup et al, 1985). The amino acid sequence has been translated into DNA structure, and oligonucleotide probes corresponding to short amino acid segments of the corresponding peptide were then used to retrieve a 1900 base nucleotide from a scrapie-infected hamster brain cDNA library (Oesch et al, 1985). The nucleotide was found to begin coding considerably upstream from the N-terminus of the 27 kDa protein. Subsequently the sequence was found to extend to another 33 nucleotides upstream, yielding what is now considered to be the complete translated precursor protein of 254 amino acids. This protein has an apparent molecular weight of 33-35 kDa (Robakis et al, 1986). The composition of several regions of this protein has been confirmed by direct sequencing of protein extracted from scrapie-infected hamster brains (Bolton et al, 1987).

The amino acid backbone of the complete protein has some interesting chemical features (Fig 7). A comparative backbone amino acid sequence of precursor proteins from different animal species shows the same basic structure. However, there are in places different amino acids. The significance of these amino-acid differences in different species remains to be determined. In its basic structure, the PrP sequence can be divided into eight domains A-H (Fig 7). Domain A contains 34 amino acids with triple repeats of Pro Gly Gly, and domain B contains 32 amino acids with quadruple repeats of 8 amino acids in order of Trp Gly Gln Pro His Gly Gly Gly, while the next domain C of 12 amino acids show Gly Gly Gly repeats of B domain. In the next D-H domains, a number of repeats are also observed, beside some homology among domains. The N-terminal string of 22

Met Ala Asn Leu Ser Tyr Trp Leu Leu Ala Leu Phe Val Ala Met Trp Thr Asp Val Gly Leu Cys
1

A   Lys Lys Arg Pro Lys (Pro Gly Gly)[1] Trp Asn   Thr Gly Gly Ser Arg Tyr Pro Gly Gln Gly Ser
    (Pro Gly Gly)[1]   (Asn Arg Tyr Pro)[2]   (Pro Gly Gly)[1]   Gly Gly Thr

B   (Trp Gly Gln Pro His Gly Gly Gly)3   (Trp Gly Gln Pro His Gly Gly Gly)3
    (Trp Gly Gln Pro His Gly Gly Gly)3   (Trp Gly Gln Pro His Gly Gly Gly) 3
    Trp Gly Gln   Gly Gly Gly Thr

C   His Asn Gln Trp Asn Lys Pro Ser Lys Pro Lys
    Thr Asn Met Lys His Met (Ala Gly Ala)4 Ala Ala   (Ala Gly Ala)4

D   (Val Val Gly)5 Gly Leu Gly Gly Tyr Met Leu Gly Ser Ala
    Met Ser Arg Pro Met Met His Phe Gly Asn Asp Tyr Gly Asp Arg

E   (Tyr Tyr Arg)6 Glu Asn Met (Asn Arg Tyr Pro)2 Asn Gln Val
    (Tyr Tyr Arg)6 Pro Val Asp Gln Tyr   Asn Asn Gln
                                                 Asn Asn Phe Val His Asp Cys Val Asn

F   Ile Thr Ile Lys Gln His Thr Val Thr Thr Thr Thr
    Lys Gly Glu Asn Phe Thr Gly Thr Asp Ile Lsy Ile Met Gly Arg

G   (Val Val Gly)5 Gln Met Cys Thr Thr Gln Tyr Gln Lys Gly Ser Gln
    Ala Tyr Tyr Asp Gly Arg Arg Ser---Ser Ala Val

H   Leu Phe Ser Ser Pro Pro Val Ile Leu Leu Ile Ser Phe Leu Ile Phe Leu Met Val Gly

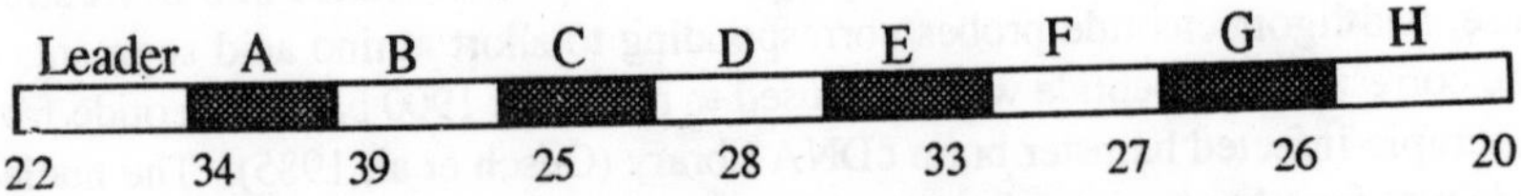

Fig. 7 Amino acid sequence of PrP precursor protein with schematic representation from hamster. The segments of amino acid are aligned without breaking the order to show similarities (no) or underlining in the domains A-H. Numbers shown underneath are amino acids in each domain.

amino acids is very hydrophobic and exhibits the characteristics of a single protein.

The first stretch of 67 amino acids, which have a strongly hydrophilic, predominantly coiled and turned character, is nearly half composed of the four-time repeated octapeptide sequence (Fig 7). The protease-resistant PrP 27-30 core protein beginning at position 68 has alternating hydrophobic and hydrophilic domains that more or less corresponds to a protein which forms a helix and ß-strand or sheet configuration. The C-terminus string of 19 amino acids, is like the N-terminal, very hydrophobic.

Originally, the possibility was considered that the C-terminal hydrophobic string of 19 amino acids constituted a membrane anchor for the cell membrane. However, the amino acid composition of the native protein accorded better with a termination at position 213 (Oesch et al, 1985). This alternative to amino acid anchoring is being increasingly recognised as a widespread phenomenon, exemplified by membrane proteins as mammalian acetylcholinesterase and the variant surface glycoprotein (Low & Saltiel, 1988). Questions mainly remain to be answered concerning the precise identity and arrangement of sugars and their influence on the tertiary structure of the folded protein.

The PrP, a Normal Host Gene: Its Role in Pathogenesis

The additional findings of multiple transcription initiation sites and a promoter region which are rich in guanine and cytosine just upstream from the short 5' exon, are reminiscent of many ubiquitous 'housekeeping genes'. All these studies have demonstrated that the PrP is a product of a normal cellular gene. The protein is predominantly found on the surface of neurons attached by a glycoinositol phospholipid anchor (Hay et al, 1987; Prusiner, 1991). The precursor peptide is synthesised on the endoplasmic reticulum and Golgi apparatus and then transported to the cell membranes. Further studies have determined that, although the gross structure of the precursor protein gene is similar, there are minor nucleotide differences which are seen within the coding region in different host species, and also different strains of the same species. As might be expected for a host-specified protein, nucleotide differences also produce variant amino acids in different outbred species, including the closely related rat and mouse. The significance of these amino acid differences remains to be determined (Robakis et al, 1986; Liao et al, 1986, 1987).

Function of Protease-Resistant Protein

To differentiate between the two types of protein, the terms for normal PrP33-35 kDa (PrP-c) and scrapie PrP27-30 kDa (PrP-sc) have been commonly used. Questions have to be asked: 1) - What is the true function of the normal PrP-c protein? 2) - How does a directly operating protein or gene-messenger-protein product system go awry to produce PrP-sc in a condition with characteristics of an infectious disease? 3) - What is the prime mover that initiates the process of malfunction? While the function of normal PrP 33-35 kDa is unknown, several observations have suggested that it might be involved in receptor sites for scrapie virus. PrP-c is bound to the external surface of the cell membrane (Fig 8). It is important to differentiate between primary and secondary changes in the PrP 33-35 kDa protein. There is general agreement that the gene is expressed in messenger RNA to the same extent in brains of infected and uninfected animals, giving rise to the same primary translation product both in normal and scrapie-infected brain (Chesebro, et al, 1985; Oesch, et al, 1985). When normal tissue is extracted with proteolytic enzyme, most, if not all of the precursor protein is completely degraded; whereas when infected brain tissue is similarly extracted, apart from the precursor protein, variable quantities of converted, protease-resistant protein PrP-sc, is detected (Meyer et al, 1986). Because there is no other detectable chemical difference between the precursor proteins extracted from normal and infected brain, the observation of different protease sensitivities has been interpreted to indicate that the protein must exist in two distinct conformational isoforms.

Are there really two different "isoforms" of the precursor protein? Knowledge of the precise relationship between normal PrP-c and scrapie PrP-sc and SAF has been marred by uncertainty about whether in vitro (outside the body) analysis of brain extracts accurately reflect the in vivo (inside the body) situation. Questions asked are: (i), is PrP-sc an artifact rather than the pathological process. (ii), is SAF similarly an artifact of the purification procedure? The PrP, 27-30 kDa core protein is usually considered not to occur in normal brains. In other experiments, SAF extracted in the presence of protease inhibitors were nevertheless found to consist of multiple molecular weight components, including both the 27-30 kDa and 33-35 kDa protein species (Hope et al, 1988). In other studies it has been demonstrated that NVP were consistently observed on negatively stained impression grids prepared from scrapie-infected hamster brain (Narang et al, 1987; 1988). Since SAF was demonstrated in the centre of intact NVP with the use of a detergent rather than protease this suggests that SAF is not an artifact of protease treatment of proteins at the purification step. These results also confirm that SAF/PrP-sc is protected by a thick outer coat, and that tubules release typical SAF after exposure to detergent.

What is the role of this normal host protein? Is it a major component of the infectious agent? Prusiner et al (1982, 1984) reiterated their belief in the involvement of the protein in the infectious process and introduced the term "Prion" for the scrapie agent. These researchers considered that the SE agent consisted solely of protein with no nucleic acid whatsoever (Prusiner, 1984). The most important discovery in this work was that the protein was found not to be encoded by a foreign DNA. From these studies it was concluded that the host-encoded, non-pathogenic PrP-c precursor is converted into the modified infectious form as a consequence of the introduction of PrP-sc into a new host. This implies that the introduction of PrP-sc into a host both elicits the pathological processes and gives rise to more PrP-sc than the amount used for inoculation. The above mechanism suggests that the PrP-sc acts as the infectious agent, by converting PrP-c into PrP-sc. If PrP-sc acts as the infectious agent, however, it is obvious from the mechanism that this conversion process is not replication by itself. PrP-sc molecules aggregate to form SAF, protease-resistant protein, and if this linking is a continuous process, how does the titre increase?

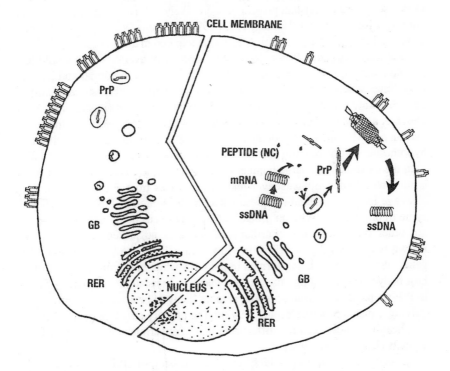

Fig 8 A schematic representation of a cell showing endoplasmic reticulum (ER) Golgi body (G) showing synthesis of PrP 33-35, and *Nemo corrupta* (NC) is coded by ssDNA. When molecules of PrP33-35 make contact with the NC molecules, the later interacts either as an enzyme, or has very similar receptor site as cell membrane. They act against each other and join head to head and tail to tail position to form a protease-resistant protein, morphologically seen as SAF. The ssDNA is wrapped around to form nemavirus. The part of the cell membrane which receives a continuous supply of PrP33-35 (left side) and the opposite side (right) because of trapping of PrP molecules a slow disruption in the infected cell causes gaps and weakening of cell membrane. Weak cell membranes reach a breakage point and vacuolation follows and clinical symptoms become evident.

Although it is evident that prions do not multiply, the mode of replication therefore seems fundamentally different. In technical terms, this conversion process of PrP-c into PrP-sc is not replication by itself as seen in virus replication. How could this transformation of the host PrP 33-35 kDa be triggered? Is it a direct or indirect action? Since PrP-sc molecules aggregate to form SAF, a protease-resistant morphological structure, an explanation is also needed for how PrP-sc molecules, once they have assembled as SAF, break up to form monomers in a new host. These findings suggest that post-translation conversion of PrP-c to PrP-sc, protease-resistant protein, is more likely to be a secondary process involving a fusion protein (Narang, 1992; 1996). Prusiner's group now also have concluded that another protein than PrP-sc, is required in the process.

One might envisage PrP-sc initiating a cascade of events, which would lead to conversion of PrP-c to PrP-sc form. The PrP-c found in normal and infected host tissue differs from PrP-sc in its physical properties and its susceptibility to PK. Probably this is due to post-translational modifications (Basler et al, 1986; Oesch et al, 1985). The post-translational modification process leads to the formation of SAF which does not appear to be a reversible process. Models which hypothesise involvement of the protein as the only agent, are in direct conflict with the existence of a large number of distinct scrapie strains. However, there is no direct evidence whatsoever that PrP-sc arises from PrP-c by proteolytic cleavage leaving outstanding questions as to the source of this proteolytic enzyme in brain cells. Why do proteolytic enzymes selectively modify PrP-c and not other brain proteins? Furthermore, there is no proteolytic enzyme yet known which will digest PrP-sc in vitro. All cells of the body contain a PrP gene. Why is PrP-sc being formed in the CNS while not in other tissues of the host body? These findings also suggest that post-translation conversion of PrP-c to PrP-sc, protease-resistant protein, is more likely to be a secondary process involving a fusion protein (Narang, 1992). The primary structure of the PrP gene in a healthy animal does not differ from that in experimentally scrapie-infected animals (Brown et al, 1992).

A recent study into the interspecies transmission of BSE to mice revealed that, although all of the mice injected with homogenate from BSE-infected cattle brain exhibited neurological symptoms and neuronal death, more than 55 percent of the mice had no detectable PrP-sc (Lasmezas et al, 1997). However, during serial passage of the BSE agent from mice to mice, PrP-sc appeared after the agent became adapted to the new host. It is obviously clear that the BSE agent is virulent enough to replicate in the new host. This may account for the exceptional ability of the BSE agent to cross the species barrier effectively both by inoculation and oral routes. The study demonstrates that PrP may be involved in the species adaptation but it is not the agent itself. The result of adaptation suggests that the transmissible agent is closely associated with the PrP-sc.

Role of Mutations in the PrP Gene

In humans it is estimated that only about 10% of CJD cases occur in family members, while almost all Gerstmann-Sträussler Syndrome (GSSS) cases appear to be familial. GSSS is considered to be inherited. After twenty three years, however, the revelation that familial as well as sporadic varieties of SEs could be transmitted to experimental animals, shows the infectious nature of the disease (Ferber et al, 1974). Transmission studies demonstrate that the infective agent is present in the patient's tissue. Therefore, we are faced with the problem of explaining how a genetic disease can be infectious. If infective agent is present alongside inherited features, this would suggest that there is vertical transmission in these cases. In a pure genetic disease without involvement of the agent, tissues would not have these transmission properties. Often with familial cases there is a problem in separating the effects of inheritance and shared environment. It should be stated here that there is no direct evidence to support familial CJD or GSSS being genetic diseases, except that a few cases have occurred within in the same family.

Surprisingly, the PrP protein isolated from normal individuals does not differ in biochemical or immunological features from the protein isolated from affected individuals (Basler et al, 1986). Therefore, the mutations observed in CJD cases are not caused by the SEs agent. Once it was realised that the PrP molecule was host derived, molecular genetics entered on the scene. A search began for mutations in the corresponding PrP human gene, amongst affected families. In some of the familial cases several amino-acid mutations have been discovered in the precursor protein of 254 amino acids of the PrP gene. Since there is linkage between mutation and GSSS and both a base substitution (Haiso et al, 1989), and an insertion in the PrP gene (Owen, et al, 1989; Collinge et al, 1989), it has been suggested that, in man, mutations in the PrP gene may cause the disease. The first mutation was found in codon 129, then in 102, and subsequently in codons 117, 178, and 200. In addition, there are reports of other mutations in codons 51 and 118 (Owen et al, 1989). In fact, no affected family is known to exist that does not carry one or another mutation. New ones are being discovered every year. It has been suggested that one of the two unique mutations (102 or 117) in the PRIP open reading frame segment of the PrP gene in some patients with familial CJD and GSSS, differentiates the familial cases from sporadic CJD cases (Owen, et al, 1989; Goldgaber et al, 1989). This mutation (102) is common in GSSS while in CJD cases no such mutations have been found.

Initially, it was thought that a specific mutation was frequently associated with a particular clinical and neuropathological presentation (Hsiao et al, 1990). Currently, these mutations have been classified into four groups according to the disease phenotype. Group I, express heterogenous clinical and pathological type (Brown et al, 1991; Baker et al, 1991; Owen et al, 1990). In phenotypes that are consistent forms of GSSS, the mutations occur at codons 102, 117, and 198 (Prusiner, 1991; Hsiao et al, 1991). The mutation at codon 102 segregates with

93

the ataxic form while the encephalic form is linked to mutation at codon 117. Neurofibrillary tangles type has been linked with the mutation at codon 198 (Hsiao et al, 1991). The fatal familial insomnia cases are linked to a mutation at codon 178 (Medori et al, 1992). Prusiner (1996), considers that the precise chemical causes are now known. But - what are they. He does not explain them in his paper and apparently no one knows these chemical causes. If the exact function of the normal PrP gene still remains unknown how is it possible to predict role of mutations in the PrP gene? It is one of many assumptions without any scientific evidence. There are thousands of genes in a host, any one of them or a combination of them might be influencing the incubation period. However, an increasing number of exceptions are being found in the PrP gene mutations and even in a single family with a particular PrP mutation, different clinical and neurological manifestations have been observed (Hsiao et al, 1989).

There are a number of other family members who have the same mutations, but do not develop the disease. How many unrelated normal individuals have been examined for point mutations in the PrP gene? No one knows. Does that mean that sometimes mutation causes the disease and other times it does not? Is there another component or explanation? Apart from variable point mutations, some of these mutations have been seen in a number of first degree relatives of affected patients who are still healthy into their 60s and even mid 70s (Brown et al, 1991). Based on these findings, it is important to question the significance and relationship of mutations in the PrP gene. What role if any do they play in the disease process? Is this role direct or indirect? The best explanation is the involvement of a virus which produces the disease as revealed by transmission studies. This view is further supported by the fact that sporadic CJD cases, which form the majority, do not have these mutations. These and other findings do not support the idea that the mutation seen in GSSS is the agent or that it is directly responsible for the disease. Further, it is also important to stress that since tissues from these inoculated GSSS patients transmitted the disease into laboratory animals, the tissue must contain an infective agent. Under these circumstances we must explain how a genetic disease can be infectious and hereditary at the same time?

It is important not to ignore the fact that there is no gene mutation of any type to be seen in any of the sporadic cases of CJD, while many of the relatives of the familial cases with the mutation do not develop the disease. According to Brown (1994), in spite of the great temptations of molecular geneticists, the heyday of mutation hunters has probably come and gone. It is unlikely that the next dozen mutations will add very much to what we have come to appreciate from the first dozen. One should also look at the vast diversity of animal species with the PrP gene. After single inoculation these animals develop the clinical disease. These transmission studies strongly suggest that a different genetic make-up of the PrP gene does not mean resistance to the infection from the SE agent.

94

If PrP gene sequence is playing a primary role then the incubation period should not be different in the same strain of mice with different strains of the scrapie agent. However, at first sight, a discovery of a mutation was welcomed as an aid in the diagnosis of the disease. The absence of these mutations in the PrP gene in some familial and all sporadic CJD patients might be important for two reasons: i) that the mutation reflects an increased susceptibility or ii) that mutation has occurred in patients subsequent to infection. It is a well established fact that in experimental animals the primary structure of PrP encoded by the gene of a healthy animal does not differ from that encoded in scrapie-infected animals. These studies conclusively demonstrate that infection in life does not cause mutation in the PrP gene. Since the PrP gene segment can be found in normal healthy lymphocytes and in AD, HIV and MS patients, it is unlikely that isolation of the PrP gene alone can be used as a diagnostic test for SE.

Furthermore, it has for some time been known that PCR technique used in DNA synthesis can generate 3 to 5% misreading. Since PCR has been used to prepare the DNA from lymphocytes, a 3 to 5% misreading could create an artifact in the reading frames of the PrP gene, thus recording an artificial mutation. Since in these studies, results of mutations are based on the PCR method, some of the recorded mutations might just be artifacts of preparation techniques.

Certainly, full length PrP33-35, the normal primary structure, apart from being longer in length as compared to the scrapie PrP27-30, displays no amino acid change (Basler et al, 1986; Chesebro et al, 1985). Samples taken from the same animals before inoculation and after the clinical disease developed, so far have shown no structural difference between the normal non-infectious and the scrapie infectious modified form of the PrP gene. The agents of these so-called unconventional slow virus diseases, neither spontaneously create a mutation in the PrP gene nor do they copy any mutation in the PrP after being infected from familial cases or any other source. If PrP is the agent which is present in all animals, surely one does not need the same protein from another host to infect yet another host of same or another species. If the infection is dependent on such a common protein, hundreds of blood transfusions being carried out daily should carry a very high risk of developing CJD. However, at present the incident rate is nowhere near to suggest transmission of the disease through blood transfusion.

Several ingenious hypotheses have been devised in which a protein might accumulate by virtue of being involved in the regulation of its own synthesis (German et al, 1983; Bolton et al, 1988; Wills, 1989). Most of these hypotheses fall short of being comprehensive explanations, the most interesting of which invokes a frame-hopping misreading mechanism at the level of messenger RNA translation (Wills, 1989). This hypothesis emphasises the concept that a population of biological molecules always includes some "incorrect" minor species variants, together with the "correct" major molecular species which are formed in the host. Proof of the hypothesis requires the demonstration that in fact

95

a misreading of messenger RNA actually occurs; and that the primary structure of the precursor protein, synthesised in disease, is indeed different from the normally translated protein. It is evident from transgenic mice studies that human PrP-c is being expressed 4- to 8 -fold higher in level compared with normal level mouse PrP-c and yet the mice with higher levels of human PrP-c compared to their own failed to develop human PrP-sc or human -mice hybrid PrP-sc. These studies suggest that minor and major amounts of specific PrP-sc expression do not appear to control either the final post translation modification into PrP-sc or the disease process.

The crucial points, however, concern infectivity. Infectivity is separable not only from SAF (Gabizon et al, 1987) but even from the protein itself (Prusiner et al, 1983; Manuelidis et al, 1987). Further, neither the gel-purified PrP protein nor the *in vitro* translated and modified synthetic protein have proven to be capable of transmitting disease when inoculated into susceptible hosts. Since the protein model specifically relies exclusively on a normal host encoded protein, we must first explain why the disease does not occur in everyone; then we must explain how it can be transmissible; in the sense of a process involving both molecular replication and the transfer of information.

The protein model must also account for a number of typically viral features seen under various experimental conditions: 1) - agent strain differences seen in the same strain of host inoculated with different pathogenic isolate; 2) - agent strain competition, the ability of one strain of the agent to inhibit replication of a different strain later inoculated into the same animals; 3) - host strain differences , either in susceptibility to disease, or in different disease characteristics in different host strains; 4) - species barrier effect, resistance to disease transmission between different species; 5) - adaptation, gradual change on early serial passage in a new host species; 6) -mutation, unpredictable sudden change on passage in a single host strain. A further requirement for a satisfactory molecular model for the SEs is to be at least consistent with the pathogenesis and pathology of the disease.

A most important issue is the requirement of an explanation for the presence of multiple stable strains of the scrapie agent. The PrP hypothesis must establish the mechanism of propagation of the agent with a protein-only information molecule while retaining true strain property. Several explanations of scrapie strains, in the context of the PrP theory, have been put forward. However, as further knowledge about the biochemistry and molecular biology of the PrP has become available, most theories have been abandoned. The PrP hypothesis is that PrP can assume various tertiary structures and that these different structures can imprint upon the normal cellular infecting PrP molecule. Two approaches have been used to address the possible relationship between PrP tertiary structure and the dual requirements of the SE agent: replication and maintenance of the strain identity. The first involves serial passage of material derived from different brain areas. The second approach is to determine the putative role of the tertiary structure of PrP to treatment with PK which will denature the protein, followed by an analysis of the scrapie strain characteristic (Carp et al, 1994). Preliminary results of these studies, in which PrP extracts from scrapie-infected mice, and hamster brain were tested, show that the PrP is PK sensitive and the effect was made apparent on the various scrapie strain characteristics by using the method (Carp et al, 1994).

Another corollary of this example, proved in a number of transmission studies, is that the propagation of the infectious agent occurs after inoculation of a new host species, which has a different genetic make-up of the PrP (amino acid sequence) as compared to the original host. Monkeys or chimpanzees inoculated with human-infected tissues have no PrP gene mutations similar to those seen in human brain material infected with CJD, kuru or BSE. Tissues from CJD patients with the 102, 117, 178 and 200 codon mutations have been transmitted to monkeys and chimpanzees. These inoculated monkeys and chimpanzees developed a scrapie-like disorder, their PrP33-35 protein being modified into PrP27-30, containing PrP not of man or cow (donor) but of monkey or chimpanzee (host). None of the point mutations are copied in the new host PrP gene or its product PrP-sc. The clinical infectious disease develops and the scrapie agent replicates maintaining its specific strain characteristics. The inoculated host animals do not carry any of these point mutations, nor does the PrP made in these experimentally infected hosts contain these point mutations as recognised in CJD patients (Gajdusek, 1990). Further, when BSE tissue containing the agent and bovine PrP27-30-bo is inoculated into sheep, the affected host sheep modifies own PrP33-35-sh into PrP27-30-sh. Similar results are obtained by inoculating BSE tissue containing PrP27-30-bo into mice, pigs and goats, where host PrP33-35 modifies into, respectively host PrP27-30-mi, PrP27-30-pi, PrP27-30-go (Fig 9). It is fairly certain that the strain of the agent "breeds true", retaining its original properties during the passage from one animal species to another while the basic PrP changes with host change.

It has been accepted in general that the susceptibility and the incubation period in a new host to SE infection is co-determined by the interaction of the strain of the agent and host genotype. It is known that a host always produces the same specific host PrP-sc when inoculated with any one of SE strains, while keeping it's original strain characteristics of the agent in the same strain of animals. These findings clearly demonstrate that strain specific genetic information is not controlled by the PrP molecules or any other gene in the host. Therefore the host gene, with or without the PrP gene, is not the agent directly responsible for the disease. As found in these studies, to sustain true strain characteristics, there must be a nucleic acid which serves as the information bank DNA. The remarkable diversity and stability of SE strains demonstrated in a large number of studies makes the issue of explaining genetically stable strains with the "prion" theory, with or without tertiary structure, very problematic. It is not yet possible to reconcile all experimental findings with the PrP hypothesis.

97

TRULY INFECTIVE AGENT BREEDS TRUE

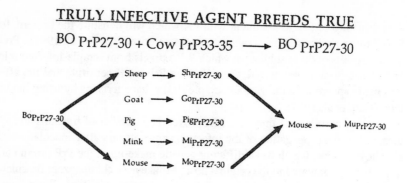

Figure shows On Interspecies Transmission PrP27-30 does not breed true

Fig 9. BSE brain extract used to inoculate Sheep, goat, pig, mink and mouse and then passaged into mice. In the respective of the source of infection, normal host precursor protein PrP 33-35 modifies into respective host PrP27-30.

The Species Barrier

Usually viruses of one animal species do not infect another animal species. However, when common viruses are transmitted from one animal species to another, the clinical disease often develops only after a very long incubation period, if at all. On serial passaging in the new host species, the incubation period may decrease dramatically and then stabilise. There are exceptions to this rule, for example, rabies can infect a large variety of mammals. It is not known if there is any change in the incubation period when rabies crosses from one species to another. In some cases clinical manifestations can be very severe. This so-called species barrier is also observed in scrapie, when scrapie is transmitted from one animal species to another. Like other viruses, scrapie usually develops but after a long incubation period. Primary transmission from any species infected with SEs to a different new host species might affect only a minority of the inoculated animals and only after a prolonged incubation period. This species barrier may disappear on one further passage in the new host and the incubation period is usually shortened. Kimberlin et al (1987) encountered a large species barrier in the mouse-to-rat passage incubation period, when the average of 128 days went up to about 589 days. From rat-to-rat, it stabilised at about 192 days. The average incubation period observed at the mouse-to-hamster passage increased from 118 days in mice to 378 days in hamsters, stabilising at 122 days on subsequent passage from hamster to hamster. During the passage of the rat-to-mouse and reisolation into mouse, the incubation period was at 174 days, stabilising at 115 days. However, during passage of hamster-to-mouse, the incubation period increased from 178 days to 449 days. It stabilised at 215 days on subsequent passages in mice. Often the interspecies barrier may result in isolation of a mutant strain or selection of a strain from a mixture of strains. This may be associated with no change in the properties or a permanent change in the scrapie genome due to selection of a mutant or even host protein which forms a functional part of the infectious agent.

A comparison of primary transmission from scrapie sheep and BSE into four strains of mice revealed a reduction of the incubation period in BSE cases compared to scrapie (Fraser et al, 1990). From a case of BSE they isolated a short incubation period 116+1 days not previously observed. There was a marked reduction in the incubation period at the subsequent sub-passage in mice. There is no known experimental way to test whether the new strain isolated represents a mutation in the SE agent or a strain of the virus with a short incubation period which existed in the scrapie sheep brain, nor we can be certain if it was selected during the passage through the cow brains. The number of uncertainties in the properties of the new strain and the species to species transmission would largely be determined by the dosage and route of inoculation. It is natural to presume changes in properties of the agent from the donor species, from sheep to cattle to man although these cannot be predicted. Accidental occupational inoculation is likely to contain high enough titres of the SE agent to present a greater statistical risk of transmission. These differences might increase or decrease the effective virulence of the species barrier. The risk to man will remain unknown for some 20 to 30 years or more.

Role of Transgenic Mouse Lines

It has been shown that in transgenic mice the "species barrier" for transmission of the SEs agent can be abrogated by expression of the host gene. To answer some of these questions a number of transgenic mouse lines have been produced by insertion of a non-host PrP gene (hamster or human), one group with foreign normal PrP, and another with PrP gene with mutation (Scott et al, 1989). Since the SEs agent can be transmitted to a wide variety of hosts with great ease, it is therefore important for the phenomenon of the "species barrier" to be considered in the light of a change in the incubation period from first to subsequent passages. The founder transgenic mice F1 were then mated to yield first generation transgenic mice. The first generation of mice were mated and provided a second generation. Neither transgenic mice with the foreign PrP gene, nor non-transgenic mice, developed SEs or any other clinical neurological disorder.

When the transgenic mice were later inoculated with a known dose of the SE agent, only a few of the inoculated animals developed SE. The incubation period in these experiments on transgenic mice was 75 days, similar to that seen in hamster inoculated with hamster scrapie, while in nontransgenic mice the incubation period extended to over 400 days (Scott et al, 1989). These results were not consistent from one experiment to another. Long inconsistent incubation periods were observed in the second and third experiment. The incubation time following inoculation with a known dose of the mouse scrapie agent in transgenic mice which developed SEs was between 156 and 174 days, while in nontransgenic mice, the incubation period was shorter, between 134 and 151 days. It is strange that these results are the opposite of the first experiment and therefore hard to explain. The most important finding of the comparison of these incubation periods between transgenic and nontransgenic mice, is that irrespective of PrP gene make-up, there is still a need for an infectious agent. These studies show that an unknown putative agent is present in the PrP preparations to cause the disease.

In general, overall results of the transmission studies and incubation periods are variable and disappointing. Often these results have been used selectively by these researchers to illustrate the points they wished to make. In 1995 Prusiner's group published the results of their comparative studies in some detail (Telling et al, 1995). Originally, the impression was given that when transgenic animals are used, they all become susceptible to human CJD. It is strange to find now when transgenic and nontransgenic mice are inoculated with the SE agent, only 10% in each group develop the clinical disease (Telling et al, 1995). Therefore the two groups are no different in susceptibility to the SE agent. However, some differences may exist in the length of the incubation period, in varying by several days in some of these experiments.

It should be pointed out, and it is important to stress, that genetic differences do not protect the animals from developing the clinical disease in their life span. Experiments revealed that using the same strain of the agent, the incubation period can vary in different strains of nontransgenic mice where no genetic alterations were carried out. The issue here is that all different strains of mice, irrespective of genetic make-up, develop the clinical disease with a different length of incubation period. Based on these experiments, it is unlikely that humans with an average life span of over 70 years can draw any comfort from not developing the clinical disease. Since transgenic mice involved in the above experiment had PrP gene from hamsters as well as their own, they were susceptible to both mouse and hamster derived scrapie agent. Although there might be some difference in the incubation period, they all eventually develop the clinical disease. Subsequent passages in a homologous host show a single incubation time that is characteristic for a particular species (Gibbs et al, 1979). These findings suggest that a normal PrP gene by itself is not the agent, but may alter the susceptibility and the incubation period using a mechanism for creating receptor-sites on the cell surface, in this way overcoming the species barrier.

PrP-Null-Mice

It has been suggested that the PrP gene is either identical or closely linked to genetic locus *Sinc* (in mice) and *Sip* (in sheep) gene which controls the incubation period. Mice have been experimentally produced in which the PrP gene had been deleted. By further breeding, homozygous mice with disrupted *Sinc*/Prn-p gene (Prn-p-o/o mice) have been generated. Although there is no detectable PrP in the brains in these mice, they developed without physical or behavioural defects and reproduced normally (Büeler et al, 1992). According to Prusiner (1996), PrP does not seem to be essential for normal development, at least in young mice, since disruption of the PrP gene has not caused any detectable abnormalities in the nervous, musculoskeletal or lymphoreticular system up to 9 months of age (Büeler et al, 1992). The original study was published in 1992, and 1996. Prusiner, emphasised this point-that PrP gene disrupted mice remain well up to 9 months of age, although he suggested that perhaps the absence of PrP will result in abnormalities later in life. What seemed strange is that after four years his information had not changed.

With the introduction of PrP-null-mice it became possible to study the response of Prn-p-o/o mice with the SE agent. In comparative studies, using mice carrying a single Prn-p allele (Prn-p-o/+ mice) and of Prn-p-o/o mice reconstituted with Syrian hamster PrP genes, it was revealed that only one *Sinc*/Prn-p-o/o mouse developed the disease after inoculation with heat inactivated (80°C for 20 minutes) mouse scrapie agent, while the rest remained alive and free of symptoms up to 13 months. Surprisingly. however, the unheated samples inoculated in the same Sinc/Prn-p-o/o mice caused the typical scrapie symptoms and death in all six animals 204 ± 14 days postinoculation (Büeler et al, 1993). It is strange that all six Sinc/Prn-p-o/o mice developed the disease from the unheated inoculum. The results of these studies suggests that somehow the scrapie agent has gained entry into the brain cells and PrP molecules on the surface of cell act as receptor sites. The receptor sites are entry sites for the virus which act like key and lock mechanisms. In experiments carried out by Büeler et al (1993), in which PrP-null-mice were inoculated with heat inactivated inoculum, the mice were free of symptoms up to 13 months post inoculation. This might be due to a considerable drop of the infective titre, since it is known that a considerable drop of titre of the scrapie agent occurs following heating at 80°C-100°C for 30 minutes. It is also possible that a co-factor in the unheated inoculum contained crude protein particles which helped the absorption of the scrapie agent into cells. Moreover, heterogygous Prn-p-o/+ mice showed enhanced resistance to scrapie. After introduction of Syrian hamster PrP transgenes, Prn-p-o/o mice became highly susceptible to the hamster-derived scrapie agent, but showed a long incubation period to mouse scrapie agent (Büeler et al, 1993).

To understand these points further, transgenic mice expressing chimeric PrP genes derived from Syrian hamster (SHa) and mouse (Mo) were constructed (Scott et al, 1993). One group had two substitutions designated MHM2 PrP (at position 108 Leu to Met and position 111 Val to Met) and the second group contained five amino acid substitutions designated MH2M PrP (additional three substitutions were Ile to Met at position 138, a Tyr to Asn at position 154 and Ser to Asn at position 169) (Scott et al, 1993). Transgenic mice expressing these chimeric PrP molecules were inoculated with Syrian or mouse derived strain of the scrapie agent. It was found that MH2M PrP mice were susceptible to both hamster and mouse scrapie agent. However, transgenic mice MHM2 PrP which produced 2- to 4-fold more PrP-c per microgram of total brain protein than normal hamsters, were resistant to the hamster strain of scrapie, while those which produced normal amounts of PrP-c were susceptible (Scott et al, 1989). Some lines of animals developed the disease with 306 to 448 days incubation period, compared to 134 days in MH2M PrP line.

It is strange that in some of these studies transgenic mice expressing chimeric human PrP have been shown to express 4- to 8-fold higher levels of normal human PrP-c and yet, upon inoculation with the human strain of the agent, they failed to develop the disease more frequently than transgenic mice expressing low levels of normal human PrP-c (Telling et al, 1995). Results of these experiments- combining transgenic and Prn-p-o/o mice "knock-out" animals, with a range of further crossed and back-crossed mouse strains and gene copy numbers, have become almost as difficult to interpret as the classical scrapie agent strains, which has made the story even more complicated. Without experimental evidence, the same authors suggest that PrP is the agent while the possibility remains that the infectious agent is something other than PrP-sc.

Most of the experiments, however, strongly suggest that the PrP molecules on the cell surface may act as receptor sites for the agent and absence of such sites would prevent entry of the scrapie agent into the cell, thus making the animals resistant to infection (Narang, 1994). This hypothesis can only be resolved by further experimentation, particularly using the BSE agent, where the incubation period is an interaction between the host and the strain of the scrapie agent and not just influenced by the genetic make-up of the host PrP gene (Narang, 1996). Since transgenic mice produced in the above experiment contain hamster PrP gene as well as their own, they are susceptible to both mouse and hamster derived scrapie agent. These facts demonstrate that the disease is not a genetic disorder, but favours the view that SEs are infectious diseases involving a non-conventional scrapie nucleic acid genome. These and other findings suggest, that a normal PrP by itself is not the agent.

Down's Syndrome Mice

Experimental Down's syndrome mice have been produced. The view that PrP is not the scrapie agent is further supported by inoculation of the scrapie agent into this trisomy 16 (Ts16)<--->diploid (2n) chimeras model of human Down's syndrome mice which were developed by mating doubly heterozygous Rb [16.17] 32 Lub/Rb, [11.16] 2H males with BALB/c females, and then aggregating preimplantation embryos of this cross with C57BL/6 preimplantation embryos (Prusiner et al, 1990). The scrapie infection susceptibility study in chimeras and control group mice revealed that the first symptoms of scrapie in the Ts16<--->2n chimeras appeared at 137.8± 4.3 days, a reduction of 17 days compared with the control group's 154.0 ± 2.2 days. The time between inoculation and death was reduced by 30 days. The Ts16<--->2n chimeras died within 3-4 days (at 140.5 ± 4.3 days) rather than 15 days of the control mice (at 170.9 ± 1.6 days) (Prusiner et al, 1990). Contrary to the findings with transgenic mice, neither PrP nor the genes known to   control the scrapie incubation period, can be implicated. The likely possibility is that the Ts16 neurons are developmentally immature relative to the control group, which may cause shortening of the incubation period. GSSS patients should be examined with the knowledge that there is another underlying disease condition, whereby these patients are more susceptible to infection or the incubation period is short.

Evidence For and Against a Nucleic Acid

Prusiner's hypothesis is largely based on negative results. A large body of biological and virological evidence indicates that the agent contains a nucleic acid. There are several objections to the prion hypothesis; 1) the rational appears incompatible both with the existence of at least 20 distinct genetically stable strains of scrapie, (Dickinson et al, 1979; Bruce et al, 1987); 2) host variation and the adaptation of the agent from one host species to another by repeated passage as shown by a reduction in the length of incubation period; 3) In experimental serial propagation, scrapie strains breed true and infective titre increases with incubation period. This implies that there must be a precise copying process to ensure stability of strains of the agent (Dickinson et al, 1979; Bruce et al, 1987; Kimberlin et al, 1987; Gibbs et al, 1979).

Evidence for the prion concept has come largely from the fact that the scrapie agent has been found to resist inactivation by harsh procedures that specifically hydrolyse or modify nucleic acids, a feature which argues that SEs are devoid of polynucleotides. Consideration also must be given to the fact that the nucleic acids of the scrapie genome, apart from being small in size, might be very well protected where binding of the protein to DNA is related to its structure. Ultraviolet and ionising radiation inactivation studies have not concluded a nucleic acid to be absent but, rather, have suggested the presence of small sized nucleic acid (Rohwer, 1984). It is unwise to use evidence of the failure of UV light inactivation of the scrapie agent as proof of the absence of nucleic acid, since a similar resistance spectrum to UV action can be demonstrated in a number of other microorganisms (Latarjet, 1979). However, Prusiner's own group (Kellings et al, 1992) have demonstrated the presence of nucleic acid molecules of heterogeneous population in preparations of PrP which had extensive hydrolysis treatment with Zn^{2+} ions and nuclease. These PrP preparations do contain a heterogeneous population of nucleic acid which may be the genome of the scrapie agent. Furthermore, Prusiner et al (1991) state "prions contain little or no nucleic acid" which is a confession that PrP 27-30 preparations are not free of nucleic acid, but contain some.

For nearly 20 years it has been well established that nucleic acids have a high degree of resistance and remain biologically active after harsh chemical treatments, as observed in the routine preparation of plasmid DNA. For example, in PCR, DNA is heated 40 times or more to over 90°C. PCR is the method employed to make more copies by Police Laboratories in genetic fingerprinting and does not destroy DNA. It is also important to realise that nucleic acids are resistant and can retain biological activity after harsh chemical treatments as the routine in the preparation of plasmid DNA. We boil, treat with NaOH, SDS, and many times with phenol and chloroform but still find it biologically active (Sambrook et al, 1989). Furthermore, DNA has been amplified after tissue has been fixed with formalin and blocked for over 40 years (Shibata et al, 1988). Most proteins cannot withstand such drastic treatment. Prusiner (1984) assumed the individual prion is the agent, and that it was too small to contain nucleic acid. Therefore he presumed there to be no nucleic acid. He further supported this view by the failure to detect any scrapie specific nucleic acid in highly infectious preparations. However, it has been well established that the NVP contains a ssDNA wrapped round the SAF/PrP-sc and protected by an outer protein coat (Narang et al, 1988).

Differential Cleavage Susceptibility of DNA and RNA

Differential cleavage susceptibility of dsDNA, ssDNA and RNA to Zn^{2+}ion: Unwinding and rewinding of double-helical DNA by heating and cooling has been observed in the presence of copper (II) ions and zinc ions (Shin et al, 1968). Differential susceptibility of DNA and RNA to cleavage by metal ions has shown that polyribonucleotides (RNA) are readily degraded by heating in the presence of various metal ions while negligible damage occurs to DNA with or without zinc (Shin et al, 1968; Butzow et al, 1975). Recently Prusiner's own group (Kellings et al, 1992) have demonstrated the presence of nucleic acid molecules of heterogeneous population <80 nt to 240 nt in preparations of PrP which underwent extensive hydrolysis treatment with Zn^{2+} ions and nuclease. Thus it would appear that the PrP preparations treated extensively with Zn ions used as inoculum contained enough nucleic acid to account for the infectivity (Kellings et al, 1992).

Photochemical inactivation of viruses by psoralen derivatives depends on a number of factors including properties of the viral nucleic acid, genome size and interaction from psoralen cross-links which, in turn, depends on the existence of single or double strandedness and secondary structure 'fold backs' in a nucleic acid (Hanson et al, 1978). Inactivation of dsDNA is far more rapid than that of single-stranded RNA virus by psoralen derivatives and this is very obvious from the electron micrograph of DNA fragments, by strand separation (Hanson et al, 1978). In their study, many of the small closed circular molecules of single-stranded DNA from fd bacteriophage, included for the purposes of length calibration, appeared to have stayed intact even after 30 min of treatment with psoralen derivatives (Hanson et al, 1978). Thus, the properties of a RNA and ssDNA virus would appear to be very different from those of dsDNA, while Prusiner

104

(1982; 1991; 1993) over the years has presumed them to be same. Some additional evidence that nucleic acid is present, is the relative resistance to photochemical inactivation after treatment with psoralen and resistance to treatment with 0.5 M hydroxylamine (McKinley et al, 1983).

Effects of DNase and RNase

Consideration must also be given to the fact that the nucleic acid of the scrapie genome, apart from being small, might be well protected in the same way as the lac gene, where binding of the protein to DNA is related to the dyad symmetry which protects DNA from DNase digestion. It is also difficult to detect and the binding protein appears to resist UV radiation. Recently, it was demonstrated that after nuclease digestion, up to 4 kb polyadenylated sequences have been detected in CJD infectious fractions (Akowitz et al, 1990). Ultraviolet and ionising radiation inactivation studies have not led to the conclusion that the nucleic acid is absent, but rather suggest that it must be small; of the order of 0.75×10^6 for ssDNA and 1.6×10^6 for dsDNA virus (Rohwer, 1984). It is unwise to use negative evidence of the failure of UV light inactivation of the scrapie agent as proof of the absence of nucleic acid, since a similar resistance spectrum to UV action can also be demonstrated in a number of other microorganisms (Latarjet, 1979).

Evidence that the Scrapie Agent Contains Nucleic Acid

Inoculation of non-natural hosts: In the 1960s, a new chapter in the history of scrapie was started when Chandler reported the successful experimental transmission of the scrapie agent to mice inoculated with the brain suspension from naturally infected sheep (Chandler, 1961). These experiments demonstrated beyond doubt, the infectious nature of the disease. Subsequently, the disease was established in rats, hamsters and in over 20 other animal species, suggesting a very wide range of host susceptibility (Gajdusek, 1985). Further transmission experiments, involving both parenteral and intracerebral infections, show the diversity of animal species that can be infected with scrapie agent, either directly or indirectly. One can conclude that almost every mammalian species can be affected by the scrapie agent to produce SEs. Clinically the disease appears in a wide range of host species, while the host's genetic make-up may influence length of the incubation period. The time scale of the disease in different species is characteristic. The incubation period usually has a relationship to the average life expectancy of the host.

Strain Variations

There are many distinct strains of the scrapie agent, identified by their relative incubation periods and neuropathological properties in relation to distribution of the lesions within the brain (Bruce et al, 1987). The number of field strains of scrapie based on these features can be only guessed. The differences in mouse-host strains, however, also effect the rate of development of the lesions, their distribution and the intensity of the vacuoles which is characteristic of each specific strain of the scrapie agent.

Based on an assessment of the incubation period, the symptoms which appear in the clinical phase, and the interval between challenge and death, there are two basic strains. One, with a long incubation period in mice, often running to 400 days or more; the other, with a short incubation period in mice, running to about 150 days. However, if the passage conditions are changed, the properties will also change in a predictable manner. Scrapie strains have been grouped into three classes. In class I, the strains are stable in their properties, irrespective of the mouse strains used to inoculate. In class II, the strains are stable in the strains of mice in which they were originally isolated, but gradually change, during serial passage, into another genotype of mice until a new set of stable strain with stable properties is achieved. In class III, the strains showed a sudden, discontinuous change in properties when passaged at high dose, even in the genotype from the strain that was originally isolated, and once again become stable in properties.

Bruce et al (1987) considered the changes associated with stability of Class II and Class III to be due to mutations in the informational molecules of the scrapie strains involved, followed by host-controlled selection of mutants. However, Bruce et al (1987) have considered that six Class III stability isolates consistently behave like a mixture containing both long incubation period strain, and, in smaller amounts, a short incubation period strain. These researchers suggested that the minor component is derived by a mutation from the longer incubational period strain isolated originally by them. They also considered the possibilities that one strain is a breakdown product of the other, or that two strains of the scrapie agent are already present as a stable mixture in the naturally affected sheep. It has been established that a long incubation period strain can block the subsequent pathogenesis of a short one, or vice versa, probably by blocking the receptor or replication sites, or both sites. However, this has been observed when two strains are injected a considerable time apart; it has not been demonstrable when the strains were mixed in the same inoculum (Bruce et al, 1987). The considerable strain diversity, together with the mutations shown by Bruce et al (1987), suggests strongly the presence of an independent nucleic acid.

By mouse passage from a range of infected sheep and goats over 20 different strains of the scrapie agent have been identified. For more than 20 years, Dickinson and his colleagues have characterised these strains in their laboratory by serial passage under specified conditions of mouse strain, route of infection and dose of infectivity. There are a number of genetic markers of scrapie strain differences and these are manifested in different organs and in different host functions including behaviour, metabolism and immunology (Carp et al, 1994). Scrapie strain differences have been described in several species; mice , hamsters, mink and in natural scrapie in sheep and goats (Bruce et al, 1987; Carp et al, 1994; Dickin-

106

son et al, 1979; Pattison, 1966) and in tissue culture systems (Carp et al, 1994). When scrapie strains are serially passaged in mice under specific conditions, regulating the amount of dose, route of inoculation and strain of mice used, their properties are then predictable. These distinct strains of the scrapie agent have been identified on the basis of their disease characteristics in experimentally-infected animals, in particular, relative incubation periods and neuropathological properties in relation to distribution of the lesions within the brain (Bruce et al, 1987). Consistently, the different strains, have either long or short incubation periods. Fraser et al (1973) found that the properties of these different strains were stable, and independently confirmed this using quantitative pathological criteria, in particular the graphical distribution of vacuoles in different parts of the brain. The clinical disease infection develops and the scrapie agent replicates, maintaining its specific strain characteristic, while PrP-sc changes to that of infected-host species. This clearly demonstrates that these strain differences cannot be contained within the host-coded PrP molecules which do not "breed true". Different strains of the scrapie agent in different host species have different incubation periods, exemplifying the influence of both host and agent interaction. There still remains the requirement of an explanation for the presence of multiple stable strains of the scrapie agent.

A large body of biological and virological evidence indicates that the agent contains a nucleic acid. There are a number of objections to the prion hypothesis; the notion appears to be incompatible both with the existence of distinct genetically stable strains of scrapie and with host variation and the adaptation of the agent from one host species to another by repeated passage. This has also been shown by a reduction in the length of incubation. The hypothesis that the agent replicates, with the help of a conjectured normal host nucleic acid serving as a coprion, also fails to explain how normal host nucleic acid in the same strain of mice produces a different incubation time and distribution with different strains of scrapie. Fraser et al (1968) suggested that with a single strain of the scrapie agent, after an identical challenge, the distribution of lesions during and at the end of the incubation period, is under the influence of a host genotype. The established fact, that many predictable, stable strains exist, and further, that there is considerable evidence that mutation can occur, indicates strongly that the scrapie agent has its own independent replicating nucleic acid genome.

The "species barrier effect" in the scrapie agent resembles that found with other viruses, although, with exceptionally long incubation periods at the first passage in the new host, compared to subsequent passages. Some transmissions fail, or when successful, have extremely long incubation periods at the first passage in the new host compared with the subsequent passages. Often the interspecies barrier may result in isolation of a mutant strain or selection of a strain from a mixture of strains.

Pattison et al (1968) studied properties of the "Chandler" isolate which is now designated "139 A" strain. Five times serial passage of this strain in Wistar

107

and white rats, then reisolation in mice, produced a permanent alteration of properties which included loss of vacuolation in the cerebellar white matter. These researchers considered that this alteration was due to the induced differences in the transmissible agent by mutation. It seems likely that there was a selection of a single strain from a preexisting mixture in mice. Kimberlin et al (1987) isolated a variant strain by mice-to-hamster-to mice inoculation which had twice the incubation period and suggested that this was a mutant strain that arose directly or indirectly from 139A, after passage.

Hadlow (unpublished) observed that the agent when passed in mink retains its ability to infect goats, but loses it s ability to infect mice. This adaptation of the scrapie agent to different species and strains of animals would suggest that the scrapie agent behaves like other viruses with an independent genome which modifies and acquires a protein shell from the host cell during replication, which influences the host adaptability to yet another a new host.

Result of inoculation of different strains of mice with the same strain of the scrapie agent and also inoculation of single strain of the scrapie agent to different strain mice revealed that there is an agent - host interaction. This knowledge of scrapie-host interaction has provided the opportunity to establish that there is input from both host and agent. This phenomenon is regularly observed in other viral infections. Scrapie strain differences have been documented in several species, for example goat, sheep, mice, hamsters, mink and tissue culture systems (Carp, 1994). Reproducible differences in the incubation periods from different strains, in different host species, with different genetic make-up, indicates an interaction of some host genetic basis for these differences (Carp et al, 1994; Dickinson et al, 1969; Fraser , 1979). There have been numerous studies on scrapie strain differences which affect the rate of development of the lesions, notably the distribution and intensity of vacuoles. This appears to be characteristic of each specific strain of scrapie agent. However, it has been observed that the damage can sometimes be affected by the length of the incubation period, the route of inoculation, or by the strain and passage history of the scrapie agent used. This distribution of lesions during incubation has been shown to be very similar to the distribution at the end point, differing only in intensity. Scrapie strains also differ in a number of other respects, for example in the extent of cerebral amyloid produced in the brain (Bruce, 1976). This phenomenon has been demonstrated repeatedly using scrapie isolates from six different natural cases in five different breeds of sheep (Bruce et al, 1987). Scrapie strain - specific differences in PrP concentration have been detailed in different brain regions of scrapie infected hamsters (Hecker et al, 1992) and in mice (Casaccia-Bonnefil et al, 1993).

All these previous studies have demonstrated that the scrapie agent must have a strain-specific informational molecule which determines disease characteristics. The only possible way the scrapie agent could retain its identity on passage through different host species is in a genome (Bruce et al, 1992). Although the molecular nature of this informational genome is still a matter of dispute, it is most likely to be a nucleic acid.

There are a number of genetic markers of scrapie strain differences that do not readily fit into any of the above categories. One involves the differential effects of amphotericin B on the incubation period (Xi et al, 1992). In this study, the incubation period of the 263K strain was extended by approximately 70% by the addition of amphotericin B, whereas similar treatment with amphotericin B of animals infected with 139H strain of hamster adapted scrapie did not affect the incubation period (Xi et al, 1992). In another experiment, a number of mouse-adapted scrapie strains were passaged into hamsters (Kimberlin et al, 1981; 1989). All strains showed the typical "species barrier" phenomenon in which the initial passage in the new species had an extremely long incubation period. Subsequent passages showed reduction in the incubation period which by second and third passage had reached a plateau that remained relatively constant for all the following passages. In contrast three strains 139 A, 22C and ME7H exhibited markedly different incubation periods and lesion profiles upon reinoculation into mice. Another important difference in these strains is that on subsequent reisolation and passage in mice the strains differed in their characteristics; some strains showed original characteristics while others were markedly different.

Competition between Strains of Scrapie

Dickinson et al (1972; 1975) have shown that competition between agent strains can occur if an operationally slow agent is injected first and then, after an interval of weeks or months, a quicker agent is injected. However, when two strains of widely different incubation times were injected in a mouse simultaneously, the mouse developed scrapie at the time predicted for the operationally quicker agent (Dickinson et al, 1979).

Host Genetic Factors (HGF)

It is clear ,from the earlier studies of scrapie in different breeds of sheep naturally infected with the disease, that the genetic background of the sheep played a major role in the course of the disease (Gordon, 1966). Further experimental studies have demonstrated that HGF of sheep and mice make the animals either more susceptible or more resistant to the scrapie agent, both in natural scrapie of sheep and experimental scrapie in mice (Dickinson et al, 1979). In experimental studies, it has been demonstrated that HGF are influenced by the strain of virus, dose of virus, and route of infection. The pathogenesis of experimental scrapie appears to be controlled by a precise interaction between the strain of the infectious agent with the host's independent genome. The resistance offered by genes in sheep and mice is far from clear, but it is mainly expressed as an increase in the length of the incubation period. It is possible that the onset of the clinical disease is delayed, apparently beyond the economic life span of these animals which is commonly far less than the natural life span. The same principles of the agent strain interaction may apply with other host genotypes of animals or humans. The role of host gene has been discussed in detail under the section "strain variations." The genetic factors controlling susceptibility to the scrapie agent have not been identified.

Influence of Host Gene on Incubation Period

It is obvious that inoculation of the same strain of the scrapie agent in different strains of mice gave different incubation periods and distribution of lesions. The numerical data, the precision and reproducibility of the incubation period in different strains of animals, all demonstrate agent-host interaction (Dickinson et al, 1979; Fraser, 1979; Bruce et al, 1985). Meanwhile, observations that the genetic backgrounds of sheep flocks profoundly influenced their susceptibility to scrapie, also raised the possibility that scrapie might be genetically controlled. Furthermore, the results of many experiments show that either a single gene or closely linked genes determine incubation periods. Using direct methods with the limitations of experimental size and time factors imposed by the type of disease, it has not been possible to distinguish between very closely linked genes or a single gene. Classical genetic analysis studies suggest that a *Sinc* gene in mice and *Sip* gene in sheep exert a major influence on the incubation period (Dickinson et al, 1968). Later the *Sinc* gene and *Sip* gene have been described as Prn-i (Carlson et al, 1986). It is because PrP gene was the most studied gene that it has been suggested it was either closely linked or identical to genetic locus *Sinc* and *Sip* gene, which control the incubation periods in mice and sheep respectively (Hunter et al, 1994).

Although the basic backbone of the PrP amino acid sequence is the same, there are striking differences among the mammalian PrP gene sequences. A great deal of allelic complexity in both PrP coding regions, and in flanking regions in the sheep have been observed (Hunter et al, 1994; Laplanche et al, 1993; Ryan et al, 1993). It has been widely appreciated that at least some biological aspects of scrapie and CJD, including susceptibility to infection and length of incubation period, vary according to the strain of the infected host animal (Bruce et al, 1987). Based on their response to the scrapie challenge, sheep *Sip* genotype are divided into "positive" (susceptible) and "negative" (resistant) lines, depending whether they develop the clinical disease or not (Hunter et al, 1994). In different strains of mice the allelic s7 is considered to have shorter incubation period, while that of p7 is longer. Mice with the s7s7 genotypes at the *Sinc* locus have been considered to have a relatively shorter incubation period than the ME7 strain of scrapie (145 days in C57BL, whereas the ME7 incubation period in mice with the p7p7 genotype was 252 days). F1 hybrid crosses of s7s7 X p7p7 mice yielded an intermediate incubation period of 200 days. It should be pointed out that the pattern for ME7 and 22A strains of the scrapie agent differed dramatically in hetrozygotic animals: for ME7 the incubation period for the s7p7, F1 mice fell between the incubation periods for the two parental mouse strains.

110

It has been suggested that the PrP gene plays a major role in determining the susceptibility and incubation period of all the diseases caused by SE agents (Brown et al, 1992). Dickinson et al (1971) suggested that there was only a short biochemical pathway between the *Sinc* gene and scrapie replication and that replication is largely autonomous, once it has started in a tissue. However, there is no direct evidence that PrP *Sinc* and *Sip*/ Prn-i gene control or influence the incubation period: it has been just an assumption. It has been realised that a very generalised character such as incubation periods might be expected to give scope for variation, due to many host genes including major genes, but in the wide survey of mouse strains which has been made, only minor modification of the *Sinc* has been found.

Sinc/*Sip* Gene have no Influence on the Incubation Period with the BSE Strain of Agent

Mice and sheep of different *Sinc* /*Sip* genotypes were inoculated with brain extracts collected from natural scrapie sheep and BSE cattle. These comparative experimental transmission studies unexpectedly revealed different patterns in incubation periods, between transmission of BSE and sheep scrapie to mice and sheep (Narang, 1996). Both the "positive" (susceptible) and the "negative" (resistant) lines of sheep developed the clinical disease through both inoculation and oral transmission of the BSE agent (Narang, 1996). More important was the finding that, in this experiment, there was no difference in the incubation period by the i.c. and oral transmission between the two "positive" (susceptible) and the "negative" (resistant) lines of sheep. These comparative studies clearly demonstrate Prn-i synonymous *Sinc* /*Sip* genes play no role in the outcome of susceptibility, nor have any influence on the incubation period with the BSE agent. Therefore it is obvious that the incubation period in BSE is preferentially being influenced by the strain of BSE agent which has a major influence on the outcome. A similar feature has been observed with the SEs agent isolated from domestic cats, tigers and some exotic species of ruminants in zoos. However, different strains of the scrapie agent in different host species have different incubation period which exemplify the influence of both host and agent interaction.

Since the emergence of BSE, numerous experimental results have revealed that the BSE agent is a novel major new strain of pathogen (Narang, 1996). The BSE agent is naturally transmitted with food from one species to another, jumping species barriers. The BSE strain of the agent, within a few years has infected domestic cats and 16 other exotic zoo animals (Narang, 1996).

Prospect for a BSE Vaccine

Dickinson et al (1972, 1975) have shown that competition between SE agent strains can occur if an operationally slow agent is injected first, then after an interval of weeks or months, a quicker agent is injected. This phenomenon is analogous to "interference" which has consistently been demonstrated in the inoculation of mice, first with a long incubation (600 days+) strain of the scrapie agent followed by inoculation a few weeks later with a short incubation (150 days) strain into the same mice. Inoculation first with the "long" strain inhibits replication of the "shorter" strain and vice versa. Competition has been demonstrated using the intracerebral (Dickinson et al, 1972) and the intraperitoneal (Dickinson et al, 1975) routes of injection. The interference phenomenon, demonstrates that only one dose of infection is required to produce the clinical disease. In experimental serial propagation the scrapie strains breed true with a precise replication process to ensure stability of strains of the agent within a fixed host (Bruce et al, 1987).

However, when two strains with widely different incubation periods are injected into a mouse simultaneously, the mouse develops scrapie at the time predicted for the operationally quicker agent (Dickinson et al, 1979). The evidence shows that competition is not due to a protracted immunological process. The site occupied by the first operationally slow-strain becomes unavailable to the faster strain injected later with the result that the effective dose of the latter is reduced and the incubation period is prolonged. Total blocking has been achieved by increasing the interval between the injection or increasing the dose of the first strain. Both steps will increase the amount of the agent occupying sites and thus reducing the chance of the second strain entering the cell and infecting it (Dickinson et al, 1979). Competition provides direct evidence that the number of entry sites on the cell surface is restricted. These studies were independently confirmed by inoculating two different strains 105 days apart. Since both steps would increase the amount of the virus, more of the number of replicating sites would be occupied, suggesting a complex virus-host protein interaction.

The interference phenomenon could be a blessing in disguise if humans have been eating scrapie-infected tissues. Because of the long incubation period of the scrapie agent the clinical disease may not develop in their life span. Meanwhile, the scrapie infection would block the BSE agent from establishing and therefore, humans might not develop CJD due to eating BSE contaminated tissues.

Unified Theory of Prion Propagation

Recently the transmissible and mutable nature of the agent led to a proposal of a new hypothesis; that the agent replicates, with the help of a conjectured normal host nucleic acid which serves as coprion (Weissmann, 1991). This hypothesis combines the essential features of both the "protein only" and "nucleoprotein" hypotheses and proposes that the infectious agent consists of two components - protein as "prion" and a host derived nucleic acid, termed coprion nucleic acid. The proposed mechanism requires that nucleic acid of this type is present in uninfected host cells. When "prion" enters the cell, it may react with the cellular nucleic acid which serves as coprion. The replication of the coprion nucleic acid is stimulated by normal cell enzymes. Weissmann (1991) is not suggesting selective protein expression of a gene, "coprion nucleic acid", he is proposing replication of host's nucleic acid. No selective replication of host gene has been demonstrated and this is a new phenomenon in biology. No such coprion nucleic acid has been ever demonstrated. The hypothesis that the agent contains only a protein (Prusiner, 1982) or the hypothesis that the agent replicates with the help of a conjectured normal host nucleic acid (Weissmann, 1991), which serve as coprion, cannot explain the phenomenon analogous to "interference". The hypothesis that the agent replicates with the help of a conjectured normal host nucleic acid serving as coprion also fails to explain how normal host nucleic acid in a single strain of mice produces a different incubation time and distribution with different strains of scrapie. Weissmann (1991), proposed and goes to great length to explain that this type of nucleic acid associated with "prion" is host derived. Strange, that he does not say it could be non-host, viral nucleic acid. All transmission experiments with the SE agent suggest that the donor host PrP sequence is not copied in a new host species. The host's own precursor PrP is modified to form the protease-resistant protein (Fig 3). So far there is no direct evidence to support PrP being an infectious protein and its role in pathogenesis remains unclear.

Evidence that PrP is not Essential for Infectivity

A number of studies have suggested that SAF/PrP-sc is the infective agent or that infectivity is associated with it (Merz et al, 1984). However, a number of other studies have suggested that infectivity can be separated from both SAF and protein itself and that PrP is not an essential component of the infectious agent (Sklaviadis et al, 1989). Aiken et al (1989) investigated the level of infectivity copurification with mitochondria during the course of a scrapie infection. The infectivity of 5% suspensions of crude brain homogenates, purified mitochondria and mitoplast were almost the same during the preclinical and clinical course of the disease. Given the high infectivity of the mitochondrial preparations to determine whether levels of the PrP correlated with the infectivity, they separated mitoplast into mitochondrial and synaptosomal fractions and compared them with SAF preparation. They found typical pattern of PrP in SAF and identical PrP in synaptosomal preparations, but not in mitochondrial preparations which had infective titre of $10^{8.5}$/ ml. This strongly supports the evidence that PrP is not the agent; rather some other factor present in the preparations is responsible for infectivity and that infectivity copurifies in the synaptosomal fraction. There are other reasons for believing that it is not the agent since, (1) Infectivity has been demonstrated in the absence of prion rods (Meyer et al, 1986). (2) SAF/PrP-sc can be demonstrated in brains of infected mice and hamsters, but not in their spleen which has a similar titre of infectivity (Czub et al, 1986). (3) In some patients with "prion" disease PrP-sc is barely detectable or even undetectable (Brown et al, 1992; Medori et al, 1992; Hsiao et al, 1990). The evidence so far presented supporting the concept that the scrapie agent is composed solely of protein is far from conclusive (Narang, 1991; 1992; Narang et al, 1987; 1988;

Kimberlin, 1987) and Prusiner (1982; 1984) himself also considers that the scrapie agent might contain some nucleic acid as well as protein.

"Prion Diseases" : A Misleading Term?

The term "prion disease" is a hypothesis, it is not established fact that prions are the SE agent. The term "Prion" first coined by Prusiner (1982), meant that the proteinaceous particle was an essential component of the agent of the possible models; (i) protein surrounding coding nucleic acid (ii) Protein with non-coding nucleic acid, (iii) protein with no nucleic acid, Prusiner favours (iii). Apart from it's still unproven assumptions, the "prion" theory has been put forward - that the aetiological agent is an unusual proteinaceous infectious pathogen. To this day, most researchers agree that PrP is involved in the SE disease process, but remain uncertain as to its role in the disease. It has been argued that scrapie pathology is due to intrinsic neurotoxicity of PrP-sc rather than depletion of PrP-c because PrP-deficient mice develop normally (Büeler et al, 1992). It is still unknown if the scrapie pathology comes about by neurotoxicity of PrP-sc, acute depletion of PrP-c, or some other mechanism. It has been demonstrated (by taking embryonic telencephalic tissues from transgenic mice) with over production of PrP and grafting into PrP deficient mice that high expression of PrP alone cannot induce neurological necrosis (Brandner et al, 1996). These researchers suggest that PrP-sc is probably only toxic when it is formed and accumulated within the cell, but not when it is located outside cells. Alternatively, it may be that PrP-sc is pathogenic when presented from outside, but only to cells expressing PrP-c, because it initiates conversion of PrP-c to PrP-sc at the cell surface. These studies demonstrate that it is highly unlikely that PrP-sc is the SE agent or the primary cause of the disease.

It has further been demonstrated in a number of studies that PrP does not correlate with infectivity titres in a biochemical setting. In mice inoculated with the agent of CJD, the infectivity is dissociated from PrP and accumulates nearly 100-fold during the first two weeks in salivary glands (Miyamoto et al, 1994). Spleen also showed a rapid increase of infectivity soon after inoculation while no PrP was demonstrated. These findings suggest that the primary sites of the CJD agent are salivary glands and spleen rather than brain. Xi et al (1992) and Czub et al, (1988) demonstrated similar dissociation in brain tissue of scrapie-infected mice treated with amphotericin B, where the infectivity titre *in vivo* does not correlate with accumulation of PrP-sc. These findings indicate that PrP-sc accumulation is due to secondary changes and that the "prion" is unlikely to be the SE agent.

There are no antibodies available which distinguish antigenically between normal protein PrP-c and pathological PrP-sc protein. In BSE cattle immunological demonstration of PrPBo is dependent on many variables, particularly tissue fixation, epitope demasking pretreatment and primary body characteristics. Wells et al (1994) devised a protocol to optimise immunological detection of Pr-

PBo in routinely fixed and processed bovine central nervous tissue. Immunoreactivity in BSE was not found to be disease specific and it identified PrP within the neuronal cytoplasm of normal cattle (Jeffrey et al, 1992). While in BSE, most immunostaining had no clear cell association, some was closely related to the surface of neurons (Jeffrey et al, 1992). However, particulate immunoreactivity in grey matter neuropil was diagnostic of BSE. The density of neuropil immunostaining was inconsistent with the severity of vacuolar changes. This method cannot be used in diagnosing of BSE. In a number of studies it has been demonstrated that PrP-sc is not detectable until brain titres reach levels of 10^6 per g (Manuelidis, 1994), and therefore demonstration of PrP-sc for diagnostic purposes in asymptomatic animals would be extremely difficult.

Once the protein had been identified, the prion hypothesis was put forward. The critical role of PrP in pathogenesis of the disease still remains unresolved, however, our imagination, based on assumptions, has run as far as our experimental techniques will carry us. It is time to put behind us the "protein only" hypothesis and think of the participation of a nucleic acid. Prusiner's group has put forward the view that since they have not yet identified a nucleic acid, there is no need to look for one. On the contrary, the major scientific evidence suggests there must be a nucleic acid which regulates the strain specific characteristic. Working from the basic principles of science this is an important issue. Approaching the matter from a scientific basis, we cannot ignore this issue of nucleic acid on such flimsy evidence. If Prusiner's group has not found a nucleic acid, we can always start again in another direction. If we look back some years, when our studies at the molecular and cytological level of the pathological findings led us nowhere, it is time to consider the possibility of a NVP as the causative agent. From the evidence, now we can see that the SAF/PrP-sc involvement is of a secondary nature and is not primary in the process of pathogenesis. As for pathology, NVP the one particulate structure that must somehow be incorporated into the framework of any molecular solution to the disease.

Tubulofilamentous Particles, Nemavirus

Since the original observations of intracellular NVP, "virus-like" particles have repeatedly been seen in brains of animals with scrapie and CJD (Fig 10, 11) (Narang, 1972, 1975), this particular type of tubulofilamentous particle has featured most frequently on EM examinations of tissues (Narang, 1972; 1974; Narang et al, 1980; 1987). Many of the particles are circular and are occasionally seen as short tubulofilaments. The overall diameter of both forms is 23-26 nm and the true nature of these scrapie-associated particles is not understood. In some publications, tubulofilamentous particles have been referred to as tubulovesicular structures (Narang et al, 1987; Gibson et al, 1989; Liberski et al, 1990). Large arrays of loosely packed NVP have been demonstrated in natural scrapie of sheep and all species of experimentally scrapie-infected animals. Most frequently these particles have been observed in the nerve-endings, termed post

115

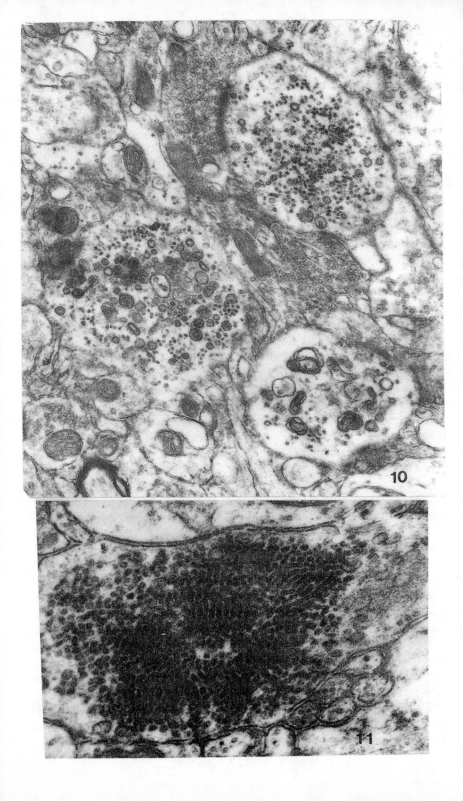

10

11

Fig 10, 11. Electron micrograph of a thin section from cerebral cortex of the brain of a mouse terminally ill with scrapie showing a array of nemavirus in postsynaptic terminals. bar = 100 nm.

synaptic terminals (Fig 10, 11). A detailed examination of these particles reveals that they are tubulofilamentous forms, and in sections they appear circular. Large vesicular bodies are frequently found in association with these particles. In some sections there is evidence that these NVP have swollen head vesicular bodies.

Further detailed studies using different methods demonstrate that they are long tubular structures, therefore, it is appropriate to term these tubulofilamentous particles Nemavirus (Nema=filamentous) (Narang, 1990). NVP seen in earlier stages of incubation are less densely stained and often loosely packed. With increasing incubation time, the number of particles increase and they are more elongated. In some strains of scrapie with a long incubation period, the number of NVP becomes so large that they get packed quite densely. Also, the number of NVP inclusions appear to be much higher compared to strains with shorter incubation periods.

Similar particles have been independently reported by other workers in experimental and natural scrapie (Baringer et al, 1979; 1981; Gibson et al, 1989). Prusiner (1982) and Carp et al (1985) in some of the original studies could not demonstrate the particles and therefore they were thought to be absent from brains of hamsters with experimental scrapie, in which the highest concentration of the agent had been reported to occur (Marsh et al, 1975). The researchers did not consider the scrapie-associated NVP to be the infectious agent or even a consistent component of the pathology of SEs (Baringer et al, 1979; 1981). However, in subsequent studies these particles have been observed in scrapie-infected hamster brains and all SEs including CJD and BSE-cattle (Narang et al, 1987; Liberski et al, 1987; 1991). The presence of these NVP in natural CJD (Narang, 1987) and BSE (Liberski, 1990) is unlikely to be due to the blind passage of a carrier virus as may be the case in experimental animals, and consequently these particles can no longer be dismissed as incidental to the disease process. Failure to demonstrate the NVP in hamsters in previously reported studies might have been due to difficulties in sampling, or because the studies had been carried out early in the incubation period rather than at the peak of the disease, which normally occurs after the long incubation period of 70 days in hamsters and up to seven months in mice. Similar NVP have been observed in the brains of naturally infected sheep (Narang 1974), and in mice and hamsters inoculated with different strains of scrapie agent. Recently, these NVP have also been observed in thin sections from BSE brains of (Liberski, 1990). A careful search in sections of brain from normal and sham inoculated animals has failed to reveal similar particles. These NVP can be readily distinguished from normal structures. Apart from their size and different configuration ultrastructurally, the scra-

117

pie-associated particles resemble the nucleoprotein capsid of measles virus suggesting that the NVP in scrapie might also be helical. However, in measles, alignment of nucleoprotein occurs under the membrane of infected cells to form budding virus particles (Narang, 1981). In scrapie, no such alignment of the Fig scrapie-associated particle was observed, and it may be that the scrapie-associated particles represent the complete infectious unit. Further evidence comes from the fact that aggregates of the scrapie-associated particles are found in cell processes termed synaptic terminals and the enriched fractions of synaptic terminals have the highest titres (Narang et al, 1972).

Development of the Touch Technique

The progress in characterising these particles, or investigating their relationship to the elusive aetiological agents of the SEs, has been impeded by failure to identify them except in embedded plastic sections, where they are inaccessible for studies other than morphological analyses. It was important that these particles should be identified by a negative staining method (without fixation) with the goal of obtaining such particles in a state in which they could be concentrated, purified, and their structure and function determined. In repeated trials, a majority of the studies failed to find scrapie-associated particles in various suspensions of brain tissues. A simple method by negative staining for EM of brains infected with the agent of scrapie and other SEs, has been developed (Narang et al, 1987; 1988). The method involves taking a piece of fresh brain tissue and making a simple impression on a grid from the sample tissue. The process of preparation can be accomplished in any laboratory with or without an electron microscope. Specimens can be prepared in one laboratory and examined elsewhere with electron microscope facilities.

Examination of the water moistened grids prepared from fresh scrapie-infected hamster brains revealed 50 nm NVP, often over 1 μm long, with 5 to 20 particles present on some grid squares while other squares had none. The NVP were distinguishable from normal microtubules which were usually straighter, thinner with clear outline and measured about 40 nm across. The grids treated with very low SDS concentration (1 part in 1 million) revealed NVP with a central core of a twist fibril (Fig 12), while at higher SDS concentrations, the outer coat of these twisted fibrils were seen at various stages of marked fragmentation of surface material (Fig 12). The fibrils ultrastructurally resembled SAF, and were often seen singly and in groups of two to five. Often a large cluster of them was seen. These fibres measured 16 to 20 nm in diameter narrowing every 90 to 100 nm. Many of the SAF were short, about 200 to 300 nm long. NVP or SAF were not seen in any of the preparations from normal brains. The grids which were not treated with SDS did not show SAF or SAF-like structures.

118

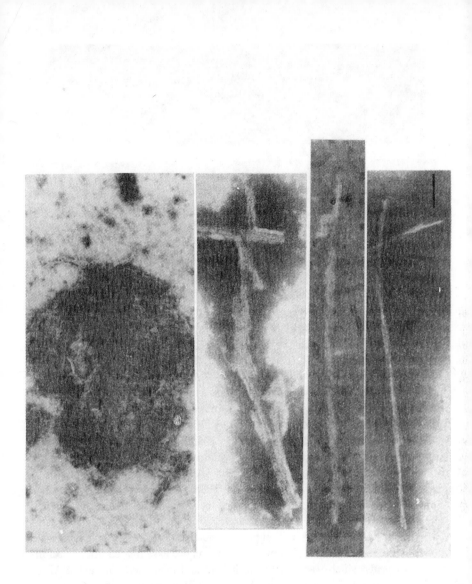

Fig.12. EM of negatively stained cerebral cortex from a scrapie infected-hamster. (A) grids prepared soaked in water showing a clumps of typical nema-virus particles some with swollen ends. (B) grids treated with solution of SDS showing nemavirus with SAF fibril in the centre (C,D) fragmentation of surface material.

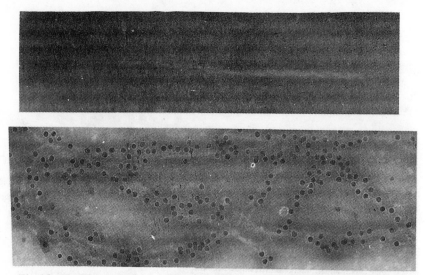

Fig 12. (E) EM exposed for 30 min proteinase K and then to mung bean nuclease. Note typical SAF fibril with clear background. Fig 13. Stained with an immunogold labelling technique. Note typical SAF. Grid bar=100 nm.

The grids treated with with proteinase K for periods from 30 to 120 min at 37°C revealed abnormal tubules of similar length measuring about 30 nm in diameter, while on these grids no SAF were seen in this preparation. No SAF were observed on grids incubated at 37°C with RNase or DNase only, or when the grids were first treated with proteinase K and then with RNase. However, when the grids were first treated with proteinase K and then with DNase, or mung bean in recommended buffers, typical SAF identical to those produced by exposure to SDS were seen (Narang et al, 1988). The most marked difference found was that following enzyme treatment there was little or no fluffy material on the grids compared with SDS treated grids (Fig 12). On the other hand, incubation of grids with DNase and mung bean nuclease, where essential ions were not added into the buffers, did not show SAF on protease treated grids. Examination of grids which were treated with SDS and incubated with anti-SAF or anti-PrP showed gold particles distributed over filaments with little nonspecific adherence to the background (Fig 13), while no gold labelling of SAF was observed with anti-tubulin. Specific decoration with gold granules was not observed in those grids which were not treated with SDS. Specific decoration marker with gold granules was used to identify the fibrils obtained by touch preparation (Fig 13), and comparison with the previous method of preparation confirmed that these fibrils seen by touch method, were in fact scrapie-associated fibrils. It became evident from some of these studies that scrapie-associated fibrils form the core of the NVP.

120

Blind Touch Technique

Syrian hamsters were inoculated intracerebrally on the right side of the brain with 0.02-ml aliquots of scrapie-infected or normal brain 10% suspension as previously described (Narang et al, 1987, 1988). Scrapie-inoculated animals had ataxia between 60 to 70 days later, and all died with severe wasting and immobility by 80 ± 7 days postinoculation, while controls remained well. In this blind study, one scrapie-infected and one normal hamster were killed for brain studies at intervals of 3, 5, 7, 10, 14, 18, 21, 24 and 28 days following inoculation. Their brains were removed and divided into right and left. Examination of grids prepared from both left and right side of the brain after 3, 5, and 7 days revealed no NVP or SAF from either side. However, examination of water moistened grids prepared from both left and right from 10 days scrapie-infected hamster brains, from the right side only, revealed NVP, often with 1 to 3 particles present on some grid squares while other grid squares had none. On the grids treated with SDS the outer coats of these twisted fibrils of SAF were seen. The fibrils ultrastructurally resembled SAF, and were often seen singly or in groups of two to three. At this stage, large clusters of them were not seen. The NVP and SAF were observed from 18 days in both sides of the scrapie-infected hamster brains. Replication of the agent appears to start from the site of inoculation. This view is supported by the fact that the length of the NVP and SAF appeared to increase with incubation period, this was evident from the twists observed in the SAF. The appearance of NVP in the infected brains from 10 days after inoculation and their replication, is consistent with the gradual increase of infective titre in the brain tissue. It appears that the formation of NVP and SAF as early as 10 days postinoculation is not consistent with the proposal that aggregation of PrP involves a nucleation event, analogous to the seeding of a crystal, as suggested by Come et al (1993).

Abnormal tubulofilamentous structures were consistently observed on negatively stained impression grids prepared from the brain tissues of animals with SEs. In scrapie-infected hamsters, these structures have been demonstrated by negative staining at 20 to 31 days which precedes the appearance of other neurological changes (Narang et al, 1987) and in mice, about half way through the incubation period, before vacuolation is apparent in the thalamus (Narang, 1988). The number and the density of the NVP increase during subsequent weeks until the particles are readily seen which correlate with infective titres (Liberski et al, 1990; Narang, 1988). It has also been established that the appearance of NVP in experimental CJD and scrapie precedes the onset of clinical disease (Liberski et al, 1990). The presence of these NVP in natural CJD, scrapie sheep and BSE is unlikely to be due to the blind passage of a carrier virus, as may be the case in experimental animals. Consequently, these particles can no longer be dismissed as incidental to the disease process. These particles are readily distinguishable from normal cellular structures.

121

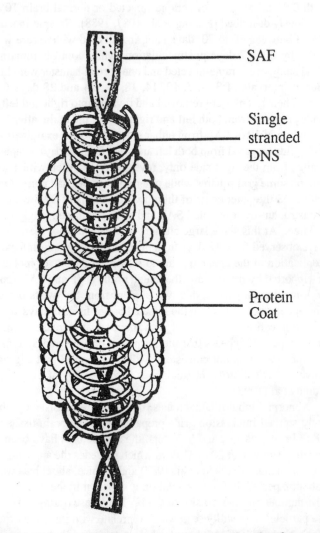

SAF

Single
stranded
DNS

Protein
Coat

Fig 14.   Nemavirus from cerebral cortex from a clinically ill brain of a scrapie
hamster along with a model of nemavirus, showing ssDNA coiled around the
SAF as a spring protected by an outer protein coat.

122

Relationship of NVP to SAF/PrP-sc

Tubulofilamentous particles have been regularly observed on negatively stained impression grids prepared from scrapie-infected hamster brain and all other brain materials examined from other SE disorders. Furthermore, treatment of grids with different concentrations of SDS (without proteinase K) have confirmed that the NVP have a twisted filament core. Only after disruption of the outer coat of the NVP was it possible to stain SAF both by anti-SAF and anti-PrP. These observations offer the real explanation for the fact that SAF are not visible in cells because they are disguised in additional molecular coats. No SAF or SAF-like structures were seen in normal animals. It is a strange coincidence that SAF/PrP-sc, once considered to be the agent or part of the agent, forms the core of the abnormal NVP as seen in preparations from scrapie-infected hamster, mice and human CJD brains (Narang, 1992; Narang et al, 1987; 1988). Since SAF/PrP-sc were demonstrated in the centre of intact NVP with the use of a detergent, rather than protease, SAF/PrP-sc is not an artifact of protease treatment of proteins at the purification step. In contrast to the morphology of common viruses which have a two layer structure, a nucleic acid protected by an outer protein coat, tubulofilamentous particles have a novel three layer structure with the ssDNA lying sandwiched between two layers of protein, the inner being the host derived protease-resistant protein PrP (Fig 14). The nature of the outer protein coat still remains to be determined, but it appears to be very hydrophilic (Narang et al, 1988). It is most likely that the outer protein coat with ssDNA is the infectious agent which co-purifies with the SAF/PrP-sc fractions in various amounts as fluffy fragments.

Purification of Nucleic Acid

The cardinal rule of studies on involvement of a DNA molecule in the scrapie disease is that without seeking, you shall not find one. Various unsuccessful attempts have been made to purify a nucleic acid. Meyer et al (1991) have recently conducted a search for a putative scrapie genome using a refocussing gel electrophoresis method which failed to produce a specific nucleic acid, but the researchers state that they cannot rule out the existence of a small nucleic acid, or alternatively the molecules exist in variable lengths.

Important differences exist in the preparation of the nucleic acid in my study as compared to previous studies (Wietgrefe et al, 1985; Diedrich et al, 1987; Duguid et al, 1988; Bellinger-Kawahara et al, 1987; Gabizon et al, 1987). Since it was apparent from the "touch" technique, that the ssDNA lies wrapped round SAF/PrP-sc protected by a protein coat (Narang, 1991; Narang et al, 1988), a new method was devised to purify the nucleic acid whereby no detergents are used to disrupt the tissue. Purification of nucleic acid was carried out using clinically-ill scrapie-infected hamsters as previously described in detail (Narang, 1990; 1993). By this method of differential centrifugation from brain homogenate, host nuclei which contain the bulk of the host nucleic acid are removed, selectively. Once the background nucleic acid is removed, enriched preparations of mitochondria/NVP with a infective titre of $10^{8.5}$ per/g of tissue are isolated and used for further purification of DNA.

Further analysis of nucleic acid purified from both infected and the equivalent fraction of uninfected brain, run on an agarose gel, revealed a striking difference in mtDNA from scrapie-infected as opposed to uninfected brains. In scrapie-infected brain tissue, mtDNA was present in multimeres of high molecular weight as well as in normal monomers that did not differ in size or amount from monomeric mtDNA of control uninfected tissue. Complex forms of mtDNA of high molecular weight have been known for some time in cancer tissues (Hudson et al, 1967; Nass, 1969; Smith et al, 1973). The mtDNA dimers and higher multimeric forms of mtDNA have been previously reported, particularly in established mammalian cell lines, such as HeLa (Hudson et al, 1967) and mouse fibroblast L-cells (Nass, 1969), as well as in certain tumor cells (Smith et al, 1973). Complex forms of mtDNA generally appear to be a minor species in normal cells formed under conditions of stress, while in certain cancerous cells larger amounts of complex mtDNA have been observed.

When purified preparations of DNA are treated with mung bean nuclease which specifically digests ssDNA and RNA they showed a marked difference after treatment. The apparent disappearance of the slower migrating mtDNA band after incubation of the preparation of scrapie-infected tissue with mung bean nuclease, suggests involvement of ssDNA with the slow migrating mtDNA. Aiken et al (1989) purified mitochondria by density centrifugation and suggested that scrapie infectivity was associated with the mitochondria.

Further analysis of nucleic acid purified from both infected and the equivalent fraction of uninfected brain, run on an alkaline agarose gel under alkaline conditions, revealed an unusual DNA band of about 1.2-kb which stained only with ethidium bromide from scrapie-infected brain (Narang, 1993). The specific ssDNA from scrapie-infected hamsters was only found because ethidium bromide was first added by mistake while running an alkaline gel analysis of the nucleic acid preparations. Ethidium bromide binds to DNA by intercalating in the double strands of DNA, since under alkaline conditions all types of DNA become single stranded. Under these conditions, there should be no binding of ethidium bromide. Staining of the ssDNA band with ethidium bromide under denaturing conditions suggested an unusual nature of the ssDNA band which might have a very high base pairing property. The repeat multi-palindromic sequence obtained with a uniform symmetry was anticipated. Palindromic sequence features are common to many recognition sites for regulator proteins. In some clones the sequence TACGTA started with the reading TATATATATACGTA, the short TATA region is also a palindromic sequence and may reflect the head or tail part of the sequence. Because of the unusual multi-palindromic nature, under normal physiological conditions, ssDNA would base pair and coil in a very complicated fashion. Thus, in purified nucleic acid preparations, the molecules of ssDNA may base pair within the same molecule or with other molecules, forming a long chain. It is difficult to imagine how this nucleic acid exists *in vivo*, but once it has been disrupted, the molecules would form a heterogeneous population. This was further evident from an experiment in which NaOH-treated DNA was diluted to lower the concentration of NaOH to 100 mM NaOH and also from DNA samples treated with NaOH and formamide, and then run in alkaline conditions in which it remained stained with ethidium bromide but with reduced intensity.

An unusual palindromic six base $(TACGTA)_{10}$ repeat sequence was also obtained in BSE infected brains (Narang, 1996). In three out of ten CJD cases, both C and T were missing from one of the palindrome reading frames (Fig). These changes in the sequence could account for the scrapie agent strain variations. These results demonstrate that each NVP ssDNA molecule consists of multiple copies of $(TACGTA)_n$ with intermediate segments (yet to be sequenced) spaced along the length of the ssDNA.

It is evident from this self-pairing property within the same molecule and with other molecules why most of the previous studies have failed to reveal a specific nucleic acid by subtractive hybridisation methods; a) subtractive hybridisation of cDNA libraries which failed to identify a scrapie-specific nucleic acid (Wietgrefe et al, 1985; Diedrich et al, 1987, Duguid et al, 1988). b) Cloning residual DNA and RNA molecules present in highly purified infectious fractions. Neither of these approaches have identified a scrapie-specific nucleic acid (Oesch et al, 1988). It also became apparent, after alkaline gels analysis, that synthesis into dsDNA from this ssDNA would present problems. It was obvious from the results from alkaline gels that many of the strategies described for molecular cloning would not work for the sequencing of scrapie-specific DNA. For this reason, synthesis of double-stranded DNA failed using the self-priming method as in Klenow fragment of *E. coli* DNA Polymerase I at 15°C. Further, it was not possible to link synthetic DNA linkers or adapters. Attempts to link scrapie-specific ssDNA by terminal transferase to plasmid DNA were also unsuccessful. Synthesis of cDNA by using Taq Polymerase at high temperature appeared to be the best method.

It appears that the six base palindromic sequence repeat has been disadvantageous in the dideoxy sequence reaction by competing by self annealing. Although a 38 base sequence consisting of a six base repeat was readable by the dideoxy sequence reaction, analysis of the PCR product by restriction enzyme suggested that, in the insert, there was repetition of these six bases over 20 times. These results suggest that 1.2 kb molecules consist of multiple copies of $(TACGTA)_n$ spaced along the length of 1.2-kb ssDNA with a preceding sequence of TATATA. It still remains to be seen if there is another sequence linking TATATA and TACGTA. The repeat sequence of TACGTA encodes three possible diamino acids (Thr, Tyr)$_n$, (Arg, Ile)$_n$, or (Tyr, Val)$_n$ peptide and with the preceding TATA region there is an additional amino acid.

If this palindromic sequence is part of the scrapie genome one can see the reasons why many searches for a putative scrapie genome revealed no specific nucleic acid. The property of this high base pairing as demonstrated by alkaline gel electrophoresis might have a direct bearing on the binding capacity of receptor protein molecules, which might in turn affect the protection of the nucleic acid against methylation, UV or DNase degradation (Lewin, 1988).

The morphological relationship between the PrP, ssDNA, the outer protein coat and NVP is obvious (Fig 8), while the involvement in the disease pathogenesis, or its relationship to the agent, remains to be determined. In all animal species, normal PrP 33-35-kDa precursor protein PrP-c is an essential housekeeping component, normally found on the cell surface (Prusiner, 1991). Conversion of PrP-c to protease-resistant protein/SAF is considered to be a post-translational process. Since it has been suggested that an abnormal form of cellular protein PrP-sc is the only major and necessary component of the SEs agent, it implies that a simple interaction of PrP-sc with the normal PrP-c brings about the post-translational modification in the normal isoform of the protein. This has been the main theme of Prusiner's hypothesis. Recently Prusiner's group (Telling et al, 1995), following a number of experiments on transgenic mice, have concluded that another macromolecular protein, other than PrP-sc, is required in the post-translational process. They proposed "another" X protein which interacts with the cellular PrP-c and modifies it into the protease-resistant protein PrP-sc. This is the first independent confirmation and admission by Prusiner's group that another macromolecule other than PrP-sc is required in the pathogenesis. If this were true then PrP-sc is not the agent of SE disorders. Is this "another X" protein macromolecule, a host derived or a non-host protein? There are two requirements for this process to occur. (1) To code for "another X" protein macromolecule a DNA is required. (2) Since all hosts have the PrP gene, to code for "another X" protein macromolecule, the DNA has to be non-host. However, if the second DNA were host DNA, all animals should develop the disease. Further it would also be difficult to explain strain variation in the scrapie agent. It is most likely that the DNA which codes is a non-host, which would explain the strain variation in scrapie. In previous studies it had been demonstrated that this macromolecule is coded by the ssDNA of the NVP (Narang, 1992, 1994).

It has been suggested (Narang, 1992) that in the infected cell, the ssDNA wrapped around SAF/PrP-sc codes for a non-host peptide, an "accessory" protein which has an enzyme "double action" bifunctional property, to cleave and cross-link (bind) precursor PrP-c into a chain and become protease-resistant protein/SAF. This modification and fusion of precursor protein 33-35-kDa, possibly occurs in a similar mechanism as in Willebrand factor (vWF) peptide, a plasma glycoprotein which exists as a single type homomultimeric unit (Verweij et al, 1988). The bifunctional "accessory" protein may have a very similar receptor site for PrP as on the cell membrane where PrP33-35 would lose

126

the leader segment. Once the leader segment of a protein is lost, it will not reach its target site on the cell membrane (Fig 7, 8). After cleavage of the leader segment, the pro-peptide segment of PrP33-35 is converted into an active protease enzymes and these, once generated, act against each other. This phenomenon has been well illustrated by chymotrypsinogen, which is converted by cleavage of a single peptide bond into an active enzyme fragment called π-chymotrypsin, then "self acts" against other π-chymotrypsin molecules. This cleavage would explain the reduction in the size of the precursor protein from 33-35-kDa to 27-30-kDa scrapie PrP (PrP-sc). The non-host "accessory" protein has a cutting and linking function. For this "double action" it would be appropriate to designate a term *Nemo corrupta*. The reason that this newly formed chain of PrP-sc and peptide is not recognised by the host as non-protein, is most likely that being protease resistant protein it cannot be degraded by macrophages. Immunological response is not recognised and therefore no antibodies are produced by the host.

As the PrP-sc molecules are added into the chain, the morphological assembly of protease resistant SAF takes place while ssDNA wraps around SAF and, after acquiring a protein coat, forms the NVP. As PrP-c molecules are consumed to form SAF, while cell membranes are being deprived of the PrP-c molecules, this results in a gradual starvation of cell membranes (Fig 8). As the incubation period progresses, the process of replication of ssDNA and the accessory protein formation accelerates, more and more of the PrP-c molecules are diverted to form SAF and the weak cell membranes reach breakage point. Vacuolation occurs and some of the cells are lost. The clinical symptoms appear as a result of accumulative vacuolation of a large number of cells which become evident after a long incubation period. In some hosts infected with a low dose of SE agent, the breaking point of cell membranes may not be achieved in the life span of the host and the disease remains subclinical. It is concluded that PrP-c, a normal protein, plays a role in the pathogenesis of SE, and is closely associated with the ssDNA which is securely anchored to SAF/PrP-sc. The genomic information is held in this ssDNA and mutations in the ssDNA would explain the strains variation. The role of SAF/PrP-sc is that it is being used as a convenient protein for holding and protection. This explains the true breeding of the strain of scrapie while the PrP-sc changes in a new host.

Bovine Spongiform Encephalopathy of Cattle

In 1985, BSE was simply an isolated curiosity among the 11 million cattle in Great Britain. For the scientists it was just a new disease in a new species. The novelty in reality turned out to be a nightmare which brought a great deal of headaches to politicians. As media publicity spotlighted BSE in headlines with photographs of burning animals in fields, the cattle disease for the ordinary man in the street, unwilling to tackle the somewhat tongue-twisting name, and reflecting the image so often seen on the TV screens, BSE rapidly and universally became known all over the world by the catchy name "The Mad Cow Disease". The public, on TV, night after night watched the sorry spectacle of sick ataxic cows sinking and falling to the ground taken from the video produced to educate farmers and veterinary surgeons about the new disease. The worry it generated is not surprising when it is remembered that, in the decade since its first victims in 1985, BSE has claimed over 160,000 cattle in the United Kingdom.

The public quickly became aware of the disease. It was obvious that there would be public disquiet about a previously unknown and invariably fatal disease, transmitted by contaminated feed with the end-product of that disease potentially arriving on individual dinner-plates. As the story unfolded, public concern was fuelled by intelligent individuals who questioned MAFF's assumptions. They were labelled controversial, shuffled, roasted, scorned, hated and made redundant. MAFF kept and jealously guarded its monopoly and the last word as to how and by whom research should be conducted. Using every pretext, including even a shortage of infected material for research (in spite of ultimately having upwards of 160,000 kilos of such brain and untold gallons of urine), they frustrated the efforts of those outside their selected circle to contribute their efforts to a scientific solution.

The slow way the agent spread within the organs of infected animals, and the route of transmission in determining susceptibility were all known and published. Scrapie was not considered to be a subject of great importance in 1988, and research was running down. In April 1988, the Government appointed a working party under the chairmanship of Sir Richard Southwood; later this committee was converted into the Spongiform Encephalopathy Advisory Committee (SEAC) under the chairmanship of Dr David Tyrrell. Those who were put in power, read other researchers results and interpreted them in their own way. Despite understanding that scrapie and BSE were similar diseases caused by similar agents and despite the limited number of studies they concluded that there was ample evidence that scrapie was not related to CJD, and therefore BSE did not present any risk to humans. Although they got it wrong, SEAC members still consider themselves expert and in the best position to advise the Government and media.

BSE is not believed to be a contagious disease. MAFF, therefore, saw no justification for restricting the movement of other animals in the herd. What MAFF failed to consider was vertical transmission as commonly observed in scrapie sheep and, in consequence, they allowed free breeding of progeny of BSE cattle. Until 7 August 1988, it was permissible to move restricted animals under licence to a slaughterhouse. After slaughter, for human consumption or otherwise, the head was removed and taken again under license to a laboratory so that the brain could be removed, fixed, and subjected to pathological examination to confirm the clinical diagnosis.

Rather curiously, the first report of SE in a cat had a greater effect on beef consumption in Great Britain than the epidemic in cattle, presumably reflecting a fear that if one species barrier could be breached, so could others.

Based on independent advice, acquired mostly from MAFF advisors, the Committee, put forward what they considered to be 'fail safe' measures. The initial BSE control measures in the UK were intended only to protect animal health. The Southwood working party believed that, even if no preventative measures were taken, the possibility of BSE affecting humans was 'remote'. They acknowledged the possibility of human susceptibility the the BSE agent, they still allowed BSE cattle showing clinical symptoms, (classified as "restricted animals" under license) to enter slaughterhouses. Their meat went to butchers for human consumption. According to SEAC, the risk is likely to have been very small, but one cannot not say it did not exist. With hindsight, the SEAC members admit that despite the effectiveness of present control measures, it is clear that humans ingested infectivity before the disease was recognised. But they fail to confess that at the peak of the BSE epidemic, for a long time, meat from BSE cattle went into the human food chain with MAFFs' approval and SEAC members knowledge. They also failed to recognise that meat would be eaten by hundreds of thousands of people and the higher the number, higher the risk. They were concerned that "Although there may be benefits in avoiding delays, such a policy also carries the risk of overreaction to an isolated finding seen out of context" (Tyrrell and Taylor, 1996). The working party also recommended that an earlier survey of the occurrence of CJD in England and Wales should be reactivated nationally. This was done by providing a small unit in Edinburgh with resources and expertise to ascertain and investigate all clinically possible cases and carry out the necessary postmortem and epidemiological studies. But after 10 years in the epidemic, Tyrrell and Taylor (1996) consider "A policy of scientific openness, combined with independent advice from the SEAC, has helped to provide a more balanced assessment of the situation and of the measures taken to protect human and animal health, in the long term this has probably been more effective than publicity stunts, however well intentioned." In reality, cows over the age of 30 months now, cannot be used for animal or human food. They do not admit there is no word of sorry from any of them but one can get the feel what they write. Some of them do however, with "hindsight" say "It seems unlikely that any-one could have foretold the interest, controversy and concern of BSE in cattle in Great Britain would cause (Wilesmith, 1996) while Tyrrell and

Taylor want to consider what others thought of history lessons "Hegel is supposed to have said that 'people and governments never have learnt anything from history,' history should be read to learn and understand while those who ignore history, are destined to repeat mistakes. Were these mistakes or blunders, only history will determine.'

Discovery of Bovine spongiform encephalopathy

In 1985, a farmer near Ashford, in Kent, noticed that one of his cows was exhibiting changing behaviour, pathetically kicking. This cow became gradually anxious, developing incoordination of gait with an unexplained nervousness. A vet, Colin Whitaker, was called out on 25 April 1985, to examine the cow on the farm. Over a period of six weeks a number of tests were carried out, while the cow's condition continued to deteriorate. At this stage, Mr Whitaker suspected a brain abscess or tumour and did not think any more about the case until he was called back in January and again in February 1986 to the same farm to see a second, a third, and a fourth cow exhibiting similar strange symptoms. These three additional cases made him question his original clinical diagnosis. Histopathological examination, undertaken at the Central Veterinary Laboratory of these and six other similar cases from other farms in 1986, revealed extensive spongiform changes in the brain and spinal cord very similar to those described in scrapie and Creutzfeldt-Jakob disease (CJD). Even at this very early stage, after histopathological examination of the brains, MAFF realised that the neuro-degenerative damage observed in these cows did not fit into any other known hereditary degenerative disease patterns of pathology except those seen in the spongiform encephalopathies (SEs). They did not, however, see much cause for concern and delayed informing the Ministers for further seven months. MAFF has the monopoly and the last word as to how and by whom the research should be conducted.

In 1959, Hadlow had revealed the significance of vacuolation, both in humans and animals, in a letter to the Lancet, entitled "Scrapie and kuru". The most important observation in the new disease of cattle was the strikingly similar histopathological lesions with widespread vacuolation of the central nervous system (CNS), without the involvement of any other organs, a pathological "hall mark" of SEs. Since, in the cattle brains, the degenerative vacuolar changes were of the spongiform nature, the scientific name, bovine spongiform encephalopathy (BSE) was considered appropriate. In this way a new bovine neurological disease was discovered. The disorder was identified as a new disease among Friesian/Holstein breed of cattle in England. The first 10 cases of BSE were reported from four herds in southern England confirming the world's first case of BSE (Wells et al, 1987).

It was a lucky coincidence that, within a short time, more than one case of BSE had occurred in the same herd and that each time the same vet attended and that as a result, this new cattle disorder was further investigated. According to some veterinary surgeons, however, earlier cases had also occurred, the validity of which can neither be verified nor dismissed. Previously, a single, isolated suspected case of BSE was reported from USA (Marsh et al, 1985). Similar cases had not been recorded from any other part of the world.

The medical and scientific world was informed of the new disease in a lecture given at the British Neuropathological Society (London) on 14 January 1988, in a paper entitled "Neuronal vacuolation and spongiosis; a novel encephalopathy of adult cattle" by Drs. Wells et al. At the meeting, it was stated that a wasting disease, slowly progressive and ultimately fatal for adult cattle, had been observed in a number of herds in England.

In October of the same year, the results of BSE transmission studies confirmed that, like scrapie, the new disease in cattle was transmissible to mice. Both by histopathology and transmission studies, BSE was brought into line with other known SEs. Transmission experiments involving both parenteral and intracerebral infections show the diversity of animal species that can be infected with the scrapie agent, either directly or indirectly. It appears that almost every mammalian species can be affected by the scrapie agent to produce SEs, and, clinically, the disease appears in a wide range of host species, while the host genetic make-up may influence the length of the incubation period. Characteristic of the disease is the length of the incubation period which appears to bear a relationship to average life expectancy of the species.

These spongiform diseases, human or animal, can be initiated by experimental inoculation of the diseased tissue into many other animal species, resulting in similar predictable clinical and pathological outcomes. All SEs result from equivalent pathological processes involving a transmissible slow replicating agent that eventually destroys the CNS. Therefore, it would appear that the separation of transmissible SEs into animal (veterinary) and human (medical) categories is fundamentally artificial and scientifically serves little purpose.

It is clear from a very large number of transmission studies that the agent of the SEs can cross species to produce the clinical disease. It remained, however, to be seen whether the agent(s) of all SEs, human or animal, are closely related viruses, or different strains of a single virus which has been modified during passage through different hosts. The BSE virus like all other SEs agents, has unusual biological properties, such as resistance to heat, irradiation with ultraviolet light and exceptional physiochemical stability.

In 1988 what shocked the scientific community and public alike, was that this strange slow virus disease had somehow jumped the species barrier from sheep to cattle. This discovery called into question the adequacy of our diagnostic criteria and gave rise to the fear that affected cows might enter the human food chain, and cause bovine-to-human transmission of disease. The epidemic of BSE in the 1980s and further appearance of SEs in cats and other important zoo animals, fired the smouldering unresolved debate about the nature and origin of animal and human slow virus diseases. BSE appeared in epidemic form in Britain quickly and produced widespread public concern and economic loss to farmers and the meat industry. The main questions was: "Why and how did a disease, particularly one so insidious as scrapie or like it, suddenly and simultaneously erupt all over Great Britain involving a very large number of cattle on a large number of farms, instead of emerging erratically in a few small pockets?"

Since the emergence of BSE, numerous experimental results have shown that the BSE agent is a novel pathogen naturally transmitted in food from one species to another and jumping species barriers. The relationship between experimentally induced infection through intracerebral inoculation (i.c.) and the potential for infection of a host through oral ingestion requires clarification. It is also necessary to review the evidence of possible oral transmission of Scrapie and BSE to man.

At the early stage in 1987-1988, while this information was available to only a few, its recognition - in November, 1986 - sparked a major internal investigation by MAFF. Scientists in the veterinary profession had been monitoring farms to gather detailed information about the new cattle disease, BSE. Working at the frontiers of a new disease is never easy, and the previous knowledge of other SE experts was considerable and should have been more appreciated. Strangely, those who had been been working with Scrapie, CJD and kuru were never selected for representation on the scientific committees! Right from the start of this crisis the Government has not approached BSE as a matter of science, but as a matter of policy, viewing research as some kind of convenience store where you can pick and choose from the hypotheses that suit you.

So a whole host of obvious experiments have never been done, simply because the results may have been inconvenient. MAFF did not get all the scientists who had practical working experience with SEs together at a 'think tank', but relied on their own experts. There were not many of them. The Government's Chief Veterinary Officer, Mr Keith Meldrum, said "I will remember it till my dying day. I was just down the corridor when the guys from the Central Veterinary Laboratory came in. Quite a hubbub... they were talking about scrapie (in sheep). I understood scrapie. But they were also talking about things I had never heard of, Creutzfeldt-Jakob disease, and kuru" (Peter Martin, 16 March 1994, Mail on Sunday).

By the spring of 1988, MAFF's scientists had collected extensive histories of the first 200 BSE cases in an attempt to establish the cause of the new cattle disease outbreak. Until late March 1991, all the infected animals appeared to be index cases and pointed to a common source. The only promising common factor that emerged pointed to cattle feed containing MBM as the source of infection - the foodstuff which was contaminated with scrapie-infected sheep waste. The first case of vertical transmission - a cow had died of BSE and its calf, which had not been fed on the protein food, developed BSE - was confirmed in April 1991.

Although MAFF scientists had no direct proof, they agreed on one point; that the epidemic in cattle was caused by the recycling of sub-clinically infected sheep tissues in the MBM. Narang in 1990, however, pointed out that the epidemic was not caused by simply feeding cattle with sheep MBM, but was due to recycling of cattle remains added into sheep tissues in the preparation of MBM. The incubation period was reduced due to the serial passage of the BSE agent from cow to cow.

During this period, humans have been eating parts of these sub-clinically infected cattle tissues, including the brain and spinal cord. Incubation periods would be very long as there is no cannibalism involved directly. More likely, there are large quantities of meat stored in freezers from cows killed during late 1980s and early 1990s, which is slowly becoming part of the human food chain. However, indirect contamination in humans occurs when we use human blood in transfusions, and organ transplants. Cows are herbivores. They were deliberately turned into carnivores and most importantly into cannibals. It is believed that contamination during cannibalistic ritual was the sole source of transmission of kuru from man to man, possibly originating initially from a spontaneous case of CJD (Gajdusek, 1976). BSE is a disease caused by a failure in the management of animal wastes and failure to heed scientific reports. It is surprising that before sheep remains were used in MBM no scientist was consulted as to the potential consequences!

Following the initial recorded clinical case of BSE in 1985, a few more cases were observed in adult cattle the following year in Kent, Somerset and Cornwall, confirming the existence of the new disease of cattle on other farms. Once BSE was identified and named, more and more cases became apparent. According to a report in Veterinary Record, 30 April 1988, 2% of the cattle in a dairy herd in Devon and Cornwall were effected. In the early years, the geographic difference in the spread was very marked. The disease was prevalent in the south-west of England, while other areas had comparatively few cases. Large differences in the incidence of BSE were also observed between herds. Some herds were severely infected, others had not had a single case. These findings gave the impression of a marked difference in the incidence rate of BSE in the south of the country versus the north. This variation of BSE in different parts of the country was thought to be related to geographical differences in the market share of the cattle foodstuff, compounding dissimilarities between companies and the rate at which the MBM was used within a herd. Confirmed cases were also being notified from the outlying islands of Jersey, Guernsey, Isle of Man and Northern Ireland. Some cases have been reported from the Republic of Ireland. The peak monthly incidence in the UK in 1993 represents one case per hundred adult cattle.

For a long time, MAFF kept the actual nature of the disease a secret even within the profession. In July 1987, when Mr Whitaker, the vet who had the initiative to investigate the disease further, was asked to present the first paper on BSE in a meeting of the British Cattle Veterinary Association, MAFF forbade him to use the phrase, "a scrapie-like disease", as he was told that this could harm cattle exports. It was not until June 1987, seven months after the first case of BSE was diagnosed, that MAFF informed the Agriculture Minister of the outbreak. It was another 11 months into the epidemic before MAFF announced in the short communication section of Veterinary Record that a new cattle disease had been identified. To many of the general public, the new mysterious cattle disease BSE became known by the unfortunate name 'mad cow' disease. Even after this, a further ten months elapsed before the Government moved to have the threat formally assessed.

Emergence of SE in other species

Within a few years of the emergence of BSE, we have witnessed the natural transmission of the BSE agent from one species to another by contaminated food. Species barriers have been breached and a number of other animal species infected including 70 domestic cats (Wyatt et al, 1991). It is important to note that cats are very susceptible to the scrapie agent. At one time it was considered that cats might act as an intermediate host for CJD, and therefore, in MRC Newcastle (UK), during the period of 1974-1976, the brains of 20 cats with possible underlying neurological disease were histopathologically examined. These brains did not reveal vacuolar lesions as seen in other SEs (Narang, 1990).

Spongiform encephalopathy has been diagnosed in captive wild animals, mostly in the British Isles (Kirkwood et al, 1992; 1994). A total of 28 cases in 10 species at or from seven zoological collections in the British Isles have been reported (Kirkwood et al, 1992; Kirkwood and Cunningham, 1994; BSE in Great Great Britain, A Progress report May 1996). The infected animals included members of the subfamily bovinae: 1 nyala *Tragelaphus angasi*, 6 eland *Tragelaphus oryx*; 6 greater kudu *Tragelaphus strepsiceros;* members of subfamily hippotraginae: 1 gemsbok *Oryx gazella;* 1 Arabian oryx *Oryx leucoryx;* 1 scimitar-horned oryx *Oryx dammah*; 2 Ankole cows: 4 cheetah *Acinonyx jubatus*, (one of these cheetah was in Australia - litter mates born in Great Britain); 2 ocelot *Felis pardalis*; 1 tiger and 3 puma *Felis concolor*. All the kudu cases occurred in a small herd kept by the Zoological Society of London. Given the temporal and geographic coincidence of some of these zoo-animal cases, there is the possibility that these could have been caused by the same strain of the BSE agent.

Three cases of SEs with unknown infectious agent have been reported in ostriches *Struthio camellus* in two zoos in North West Germany (Schoon et al, 1991). These birds showed protracted central nervous symptoms with ataxia, disturbances of balance and uncoordinated feeding behaviour. The scientists considered that the appearance and pattern of distribution of the lesions observed by histopathological examination were similar to those seen in other SEs in mammals. The diet of these birds had included poultry meat meal, some of which came from cattle emergency slaughter cases.

However, according to some researchers, this cluster of cases is explained by increased vigilance following the BSE epidemic. Greater awareness could have led to the diagnosis of SEs in these species or groups in which disease may have been present but previously undetected. It is therefore important to remember the diagnosis of the scrapie-like SE in the Nyala predated the diagnosis of BSE in cattle (Jeffrey et al, 1988) and this may be due to a shorter incubation period in the Nyala. The temporal and geographic coincidence with the BSE epidemic and the pattern of incidence of the disease in these zoo-animals suggests that the disease has entered the herd through feed containing ruminant-derived protein contaminated with the BSE agent being used for feeding these animals.

BSE in Hens

A farmer in Kent in November, 1996 noticed that one of his 20 free range hens the oldest, aged about 30 months, was having difficulty entering its den and appeared frightened and tended to lose its balance when excited. Having previously experienced BSE cattle on his farm, he took particular notice of the bird and continued to observe it over the following weeks. It lost weight, its balance deteriorated and characteristic tremors developed which were closely associated with the muscles required for standing (Fig 15). In its attempts to maintain its balance it would claw the ground more than usual and the ataxia progressively developed in the wings and legs, later taking a typical form of paralysis with a clumsy involuntary jerky motion. Violent tremors of the entire body, particularly the legs, similar to those seen in BSE, became common sparked off by the slightest provocation. Three other farmers from the UK are known to have reported having hens with similar symptoms.

Two hens were killed and histological examination of their brains revealed neuronal death and shrinkage with minimal vacuolation (Fig 16). The neuronal loss was most obvious in the Purkinje cells of the cerebellum, but degenerated neurons were also observed in regions of hippocampus. No sign of local inflammation was present. However, PrP immunostaining of the brain sections revealed PrP-sc positive plaques (Fig 16). This must be regarded as very strong evidence demonstrating that the hens had been incubating spongiform encephalopathy.

Vacuoles in neurons certainly have diagnostic significance and have become the well-entrenched diagnostic symbol of scrapie. Over the years the holes in the neurons continued to get all the attention while everything else either went unrecognised or was plainly ignored. Spongiform change in natural scrapie, apart from being variable, is never as severe as it is in experimental scrapie. The absence of vacuoles is also not a unique feature of SE, and even in the natural disease they may be sparse and hard to find (Fraser, 1976; Hadlow et al, 1982). Its pathologic essence has been troublesome for many years. In the earliest account of neuropathologic changes in naturally affected sheep Besnoit et al (1898) described more numerous variable chromatolytic neurons while Zlotnik (1958) described them as shrunken, angular, deeply basophilic neurons.

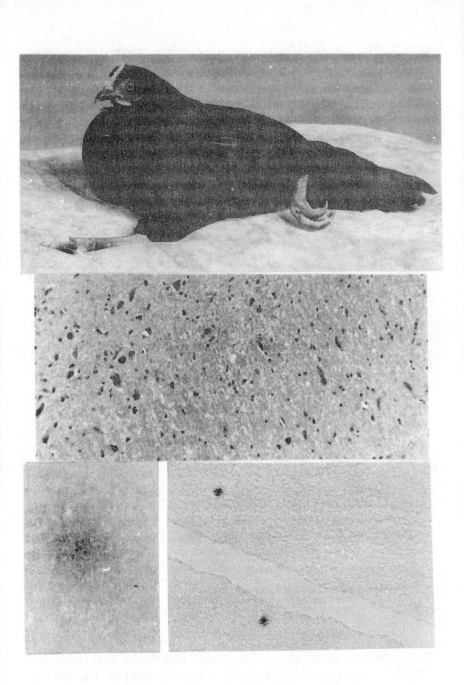

Fig 15. Hen suffering from spongiform encephalopathy. Fig 16. (A) Section of the cerebellar cortex from a case of hen showing mild vacuolation and shrunken neurons X 150 (B) showing PrP immunostained positive plaques.

A distinct features of the BSE agent is its ability to infect other species. During subsequent experimental passages, the BSE agents adapt to the new host: the incubation period shortens when passaged in the same species. During the replication of the agent, native protein is converted to produce abnormal isoform PrP-sc. Lasmezas et al, (1996) in the first passage from cattle to mice demonstrated transmission of the BSE agent to mice in the absence of detectable PrP-sc and vacuoles.

MAFF have carried out their own transmission experiments with hens. In these experiments some of the chickens exposed to the BSE agent showed neurological symptoms, but MAFF have not so far published details of the symptoms seen in chickens. Examination of brains from these chickens did not show the typical pathology seen in other SEs.

Age of Individual Cattle at the time of Clinical Disease

From the initial recognition of BSE, the clinical signs recorded show that, previously, the cattle were in good bodily condition and in most cases with high milk yield (Wilesmith et al, 1992; Hörnlimann et al, 1994). The ages of infected cattle ranged from two years to fifteen years. However, at the beginning of the epidemic the majority of cases occurred in the 3 to 6 year old age group. Observations on suspected cases of BSE, over a period of time, have provided a sound basis for clinical diagnosis of the disease with a hopeless prognosis. The clinical symptoms varied in intensity from case to case, from normal to unmanageable behaviour, to simply the animals 'being lost' in their own surroundings. However, many animals appear anxious and nervous at the initial stage. After a long incubation period, the clinical symptoms of BSE begin to appear, then in a relatively short period, the disease progresses more rapidly. According to the accounts given by farmers, one of the earliest symptoms is loss of seniority in the herd. The infected cows gradually fall back from their peck position during feeding and milking routines and eventually end up at the very bottom of the social order. These symptoms may last months, and infected cows may also be bad tempered.

These signs progress and worsen over a period of time, ranging from one to six months, leading to death. The clinical symptoms begin with anxiety, nervousness, apprehensive behaviour, and aggression (Wilesmith et al, 1988; Wells et al, 1987; Austin, 1994). The signs may progress to frenzy with aggression. The clinical symptoms in the first recorded case in a cow date back to April 1985 (Wells, et al, 1987). A healthy cow in a good body condition progressively became apprehensive. Her legs became emaciated and sprawled out. She developed a mild lack of coordination in her gait. It has been recorded that the mental state of these cows be-comes progressively altered and normal handling provokes kicking. In the initial stage, like kuru and CJD patients, most of the affected cattle appear mentally alert, though anxious and nervous. Some cows may paw the ground or continually lick their nostrils. Licking of the nostrils can be one

137

of the earliest signs in the affected cattle. They show difficulty in rising from the normal lying posture and an increased reaction to sound, and may repeatedly grind their teeth. Attempts to examine them, particularly around the head, are often vigorously resented.

Most of the infected animals, at some stage, take a wide base posture and the abdomen is drawn up. A swaying gait with both fore and hind legs on one side moving together and postural abnormalities associated with high stepping of the feet is evident. The gait abnormalities may be observed at pasture and especially become exaggerated when the cattle are urged to move at a trot. Another noticeable feature associated with trotting is raising of the tail head. As the sick animals become weak, trembling is noticeable. Occasionally there is a reluctance to lie down and animals lick objects while scratching their head with a hind foot. In some sick animals it has been noticed that they fail to negotiate normal obstacles such as milking bail stands, steps or slippery slopes, and they are apprehensive of going through doors.

In many cases any excitement may result in posterior ataxia, often with dropping of the pelvis, kicking and a general nervousness. Fore-leg ataxia is not usually reported. There is evidence that clinical signs may accelerate due to separation or transportation stress. The stress of transportation often exacerbated the disease and caused cases to be reported during surveillance at the market, or at the slaughterhouse. According to some news reports, from June 1988 until the end of that year only 40 out of 63 suspect cases reported from the markets and slaughterhouses were confirmed. None of these cases was from herds in which BSE had previously been recognised so there was no evidence that early signs had been suspected, and that evasion was deliberate, the report states.

The animals splay their hind legs and thus have difficulty in turning, particularly on concrete. Often they are observed stumbling or even falling. As the clinical signs progress, there is reduced milk yield in the absence of mastitis. The fall in the milk yield varies considerably; in some cows a reduction of 5 to 10 litres per day over a two to eight week period to a dramatic drop of 10 to 20 litres per day in one to two weeks. It has been recorded that some animals became very difficult to milk in the parlour due to sudden unprovoked episodes. Milking clusters could not be applied unless a kick bar was first used. The fall in the milk yield may be an early indicator of BSE.

In the majority of cases the duration of illness from onset of the clinical disease was up to six months. Weakness and weight loss were marked. The loss of body weight occurs despite an apparently normal appetite, except in the terminal stages. The degree of weight loss varies from slight (less than 30 kg) to severe (between 70 to 100 kg). The condition of the animals progressively deteriorates and they become unmanageable, either necessitating slaughter or dying within two weeks to six months from the onset of symptoms. There have been a few recorded BSE cases where the illness has lasted up to 14 months. Since the advent of compulsory notification and slaughter, few animals go the full

138

course of the disease. The average time between notification and slaughter has been eight days, with over 80% slaughtered within three weeks. The major difference between Switzerland and the UK were the clinical signs at the onset of disease; a higher relative frequency of altered mental status, as well as reduced milk yield and a loss of weight was noted in Swiss cows (Hörnlimann and Guidon, 1994).

Initial apprehensive behaviour in the BSE infected cattle suggested hypomagnesaemia or nervous ketosis, but the differentiating feature of the disease was that illness was of short duration, similar to that seen in downer cow syndrome. However, some workers in the field of scrapie believe "downer" disorder to be the same as BSE and downer cow to be the silent host for transmissible mink encephalopathy (TME) mink which developed encephalopathy had consumed food which contained raw meat from dead, sick, or paralysed downer cows as part of their ration. This was supported by Marsh et al (1988): TME on a farm in Wisconsin occurred where the mink were fed with downer cattle meat, without sheep remains being included in their feed.

Comparison of clinical symptoms with other SEs

The most obvious difference between the clinical signs of BSE and scrapie is that, in BSE, itching (pruritus) is not an obvious sign. Clinically, BSE syndrome resembles kuru in humans. Both BSE and kuru have been caused by eating large quantities of infected material and should be considered an unnatural infection. Both in BSE and kuru the tremors are characteristic in that they appear to be closely associated with those muscle groups required for standing. In attempting to maintain their balance when standing, cows and humans claw the ground more than usual and stamp their feet as though angry. The tongue is protruded and in the late stage of the illness quick, shock-like jerking movements of the tongue are noted. The ataxia progressively become severe in the trunk, head, arms and legs, later taking a typical from of paralysis, with a clumsy involuntary motion in the patients. The symptoms are less evident during rest or completely disappear during sleep. Any slight provocation or sudden shift of one portion of the body's posture often produces violent tremor of the entire body of kuru patients or the cow shows marked emotional hilarity as if "mad".

In the zoo animals the clinical signs vary from one species to another. However, there is a close resemblance to BSE. Kudu are considered to be more susceptible to the disease than ordinary domestic cattle. The incubation period appears shorter, 19 to 39 months compared with the usual 4 to 6 years for the cattle. The symptoms include general ataxia, or hind-limb ataxia, abnormal head posture, excessive lip-licking and nose-twitching and difficulty in maintaining balance. Some animals have fine muscle tremors of head and neck and some loss of weight. The course of the clinical disease in greater kudu is also much shorter (BSE in Great Britain, Progress report, May 1996).

139

BSE a notifiable disease

After very heated controversial debates, BSE was declared a statutory notifiable disease by MAFF in Great Britain on 21 June 1988 and likewise in Northern Ireland, from 29 November 1988, thereby enabling a comprehensive assessment of its true incidence to be made. By that time, the number of recorded cases had risen to 511. Clearly, the advice was that the earlier the notifiable disease order was made, the quicker the problem would be brought under control.

This appeared to be probably the most detailed monitoring covering an epidemic of an animal disease ever planned. The order was to trace the individual animals, not the herds. However, there was no restriction placed on the movement of cattle from one herd to another, so that the farmers would not suffer the inconvenience of herd movement restrictions. At that time, it was understood there would not be any compensation for the BSE slaughtered animals. As expected, the European Community expressed intense concern and interest in the BSE problem and on 28 July 1989 placed restrictions on the import of cattle born before 18 July, 1988. At this stage MAFF introduced the feed ban on the use of MBM. The disease also became compulsorily notifiable within the EEC from 1 April 1990.

Diagnostic criteria

In the early stages of the incubation period, infected animals show no clinical symptoms and some of the asymptomatic cases may not develop the clinical disease during their lifetime. In these pre-clinical cases, while there are no pathological changes to be seen in the brain, the animals could still be a potential source of the infection for other animals and humans. A reliable diagnostic test is required to confirm infection during the clinical and preclinical stages of the disease.

Electroencephalogram (EEG)

Electroencephalogram (EEG) studies (for detail see CJD section) have been used to identify CJD cases clinically. From a very large previous EEG study of CJD cases, it became apparent that about 50% of the cases showed periodic bursts of slow-wave activity, and a characteristic pattern of high-voltage spikes at a frequency of one to two cycles per second which is specific to CJD. Attempts were made to diagnosis BSE with the aid of EEG. However, the characteristic electroencephalographic regular high amplitude spiking discharge pattern was observed in only a very few cases. Thus it appeared that the electroencephalogram could not be satisfactorily used in the diagnosis or confirmation of BSE.

Post-mortem histopathological studies

In the first instance the diagnosis of BSE is made by a MAFF vet based on clinical symptoms. This visual diagnosis in some animals showing clinical signs of the disease may be difficult. There is no laboratory method for the antemortem confirmation of the disease. Each and every animal suspected of having BSE by the vet is killed and their brains are sent for histological examination. As with all other known SEs of animals or man, post-mortem examination of BSE cases reveals no gross surface lesions of any of the internal organs. The present methods available for confirming a clinical diagnosis are light microscopic neurohistopathological examination of brain sections and detection of scrapie-associated fibril and nemavirus by EM. These methods are presumed to provide accurate diagnosis.

Microscopic examination

The current diagnosis of BSE is based on the demonstration of vacuoles in the brain in the form of spongiform changes by microscopic neuropathological examination. Vacuolation is often accompanied by astrocytic reaction (astrocytes are one of three types of brain cells which become hyperactive) (Wells et al, 1987; Wilesmith et al, 1989). Examination of the BSE brain lesions reveals, as with other SEs, no indication of infiltration of macrophages, (an inflammatory response) which is a hallmark of a viral or bacterial infection. Therefore, a common bacterial and viral agent was ruled out. Several non-specific forms of nerve cell degeneration may occur, although vacuolar changes in the grey matter are regarded as the most characteristic. In the slow virus infection, neuronal loss and vacuolation

is an ongoing pathological process, while distinctive appearances of spongiform changes are an accumulative end product when the clinical symptoms are very obvious. Several neuropathological studies have been performed in Great Britain since 1987 on clinically suspected BSE cattle (Wells et al, 1987; 1989; 1990; 1992; 1994; Jeffrey et al, 1992; McGill et al, 1993). Like other SEs hypertrophy (swelling) of the astrocytes 'spider' cells was common throughout the brain, while diffused mild spongiosus degenerative involvement, went beyond the cerebellum.

Histopathological changes, such as vacuolation of neurones, are confined to the central nervous system, giving the distinctive appearance of spongiform changes within the grey matter. SEs typically have a systematic and bilateral symmetrical distribution of vacuoles. In cattle, such vacuolation is confined to the red nucleus (Wells and McGill, 1991). The apparent invariability of the distribution pattern of vacuolar lesions in BSE prompted a study which validated that, with a high degree of confidence, the diagnosis could be confirmed from a single cross section of medulla oblongata (Wells et al, 1989). This confidence in earlier study justified their belief of the order of 99.6% of BSE cases diagnosed (Well et al, 1992). The distribution of the vacuoles observed in some cases, may be uneven due to the unusual host genotype or type of strain of the scrapie agent involved resulting in atypical or minimal histopathology. The apparent invariability of the distribution pattern of the lesions has been reported in a small number of BSE cases. Often, to confirm diagnosis, it has been necessary to examine more than one section (Wells and McGill, 1990). In one series of 657 clinically suspect BSE cases, minimal lesions were reported in 3%, whereas an unequivocal diagnosis was obtained in 86% (Wells et al, 1989).

In 14% of cattle, although they were not histopathologically confirmed but had been clinically identified as suspect cases of BSE, they were either clinically misdiagnosed or were false negative by the laboratory results. These misdiagnosed cases might have minimal vacuolar changes leading to inconclusive diagnosis in clinically suspect cases. It is also important to emphasise that many BSE suspect cattle are killed for economic and ethical reasons as soon as first symptoms are recognised. It is most likely that these animals, if not killed at the very beginning of the clinical symptoms might have lived for 3 to 6 months from the on-set of the clinical symptoms. As normally the vacuolation is a continuous gradual pathological process, it is possible, however, that the process accelerates, reaching a peak at the time the clinical symptoms appear, and could advance drastically in 3 to 6 months period. Therefore, the number of vacuoles vary in their prominence between individual cases and, if the animal is killed too early, the histopathological diagnosis will be negative for BSE.

Vacuolar changes in the spinal cord in BSE were found to be most severe in the dorsal horn and intermediate grey matter (Wells et al, 1994). Moderate changes in the solitary tract nucleus and severe lesions in the spinal tract nucleus have also been described (Wells et al, 1987; 1989; 1990; 1992). The degenerative changes in the basal ganglia were more striking in the cerebellum. These observations are considered important pathological distinguishable changes which are not recognised in healthy cattle. The vacuolation and degenerative pathological changes seen in BSE cattle do not indicate a diagnosis unlike those associated with any previously recognised disease of cattle.

Clinically suspect cases of BSE, throughout the epidemic, have been identified from the original description of clinical signs and confirmed later by histopathological examination (Wilesmith et al, 1988). In earlier studies a close correlation was found in statistics when comparing clinical field diagnosis with histopathological examination of brain tissues in the laboratory. This close correlation in statistics up to February 1990 indicated that in over 11,000 clinically suspect cases, the diagnosis was confirmed in 88.8% (Mathews, 1990). The proportion of suspect cases of BSE in which the histopathology does not reveal the lesions of BSE are variable and show a seasonal peak each spring (Wells et al, 1990). Annually, in these studies in animals born after the feed ban, an increasing number of clinically diagnosed BSE cases were found to have no significant lesions or vacuolation of the substantia nigra (bilateral focal spongiosis) (Jeffrey, 1992; McGill et al, 1993).

Histopathological differences between the BSE cattle born before and after the feed ban

The ban on contaminated food from July 1988 should have stopped the passage of infection through cattle feed. Up until March 1995, however, over 17,000 BSE cases of cattle born after the ruminant feed ban was imposed, were histologically confirmed in the UK. However, this original figure represents less than half of the 35,000 suspected cases reported by vets (Narang, 1995). In the remaining 17,000 cases, the characteristic histopathological SEs lesions were not observed in the brain, and no alternative diagnosis was made for this large number of cattle. In clinically diagnosed BSE cases born after the feed ban (BAB), histological studies have revealed an increasing number of between 39 to 57% of brains with no significant lesions or vacuolation (Jeffrey et al, 1994). In Scotland, the number of cases with no significant lesions in cattle, BAB has gradually increased from 26% in 1988-1989 to 41%. However, the negative rate had increased to 82% in Scotland in BSE suspects born after MBM ban between July 1988 and December 1991 (Jeffrey et al, 1994). Variable reports from various centres give different statistics, as might be the case when pressures of work enter the diagnostic process. According to MAFF, the over-all confirmation rate has been 78%, while there is no separate rate of detection given for animals born after the feed ban. The number of BSE cases in cattle born after the feed ban climbed to 27,177 by May 1996.

Cattle showing the typical BSE symptoms, but with abnormal histopathological presentations, and where no alternative diagnosis can be confirmed, obviously raise a number of grave concerns. Some of these cases might be atypical BSE with minimal or absent vacuolation. MAFF accounted for some of these early cases of BSE by the "Bin end" theory, meaning old-style foodstuff had been hanging about on farms or that the feed compounders had taken a while longer than anticipated to reformulate their products. But the "Bin end" theory, by itself, cannot explain the number of new cases born after the feed ban. A more likely explanation would be that either the use of contaminated feed was still continuing, or else there was horizontal or vertical transmission, or a combination of both. A major concern in the present BSE epidemic is that the increasing numbers in the group BAB having no significant lesions suggests that all cases of BSE may not be due to the contaminated feed.

MAFF, for some reason, continued to classify all cases of BSE in cattle born after the ban as horizontally-acquired infection. The source was considered to be the feed which had hung about on farms or that the food compounders had taken longer than anticipated to reformulate their product. However, farmers order their feed stock for no more than six weeks in advance and, since calves were not fed with meat and bone meal (MBM) till they were four to six weeks old, there should not have been no MBM on most of these farms. Moreover, a large proportion of BSE confirmed calves were born in 1989, 1990 and 1991. Although all this information was available, MAFF still took the view that there was no

143

evidence of excretion of the BSE agent from cattle, such as via the placenta, or from affected animals calving.

Since a significant number of cattle BAB of BSE suspect cases revealed no characteristic vacuolar pathology, it was vital that a second line of tests be used to determine the nature of the disorder. If the histological tests failed to detect vacuoles in cattle with classical BSE symptoms, brain tissues should have been used to provide materials for inoculation into a new host to resolve if vacuoles were missed or if another strain of BSE was involved. It is strange that none of the brains with negative pathology were used for transmission studies to exclude the possibility that the cows were not incubating BSE. It is important to point out that the incubation period of SEs is related to the titre in the inoculum and the route of inoculation; the transmission from one species to another also has a variable influence on pathogenesis. The ban on feeding animals with contaminated MBM would stop large quantities of the agent going into their food rations, thereby stopping one of major method of transmission. This high negative rate in animals born after the ban raises the possibility that the cows might have been infected with small amounts of the BSE agent or that infection might have passed by a different route. Some of these cases of BSE therefore, might represent atypical BSE with minimal or absent vacuolation, or mean that they had been killed at a very early stage of the clinical disease. It is potentially possible that a sub-population of BSE cases exist in which characteristic vacuolar pathology is absent and that these cases remain undetected. This new pattern of low grade vacuolation may also reflect the possible emergence of a new strain of BSE in animals which have characteristic clinical symptoms,and been diagnosed as suspect cases of BSE. It has been suggested that atypical BSE with no visible vacuolation observable by light microscopy examination, or vacuolation undetected and expressed solely in the spinal cord, might occur (Jeffrey et al, 1994) and therefore be missed.

The original mode of infection through cattle should have stopped with the ban on contaminated food in July 1988. However, since then, till May 1996 over 29,000 confirmed BSE cases have occurred in cattle born after the feed ban (BABs). Usually, the number of BSE cases varies according to season,and is highest during the winter. However, there is a different pattern in BABs: the peak is during the summer months (Narang, 1997). Surprisingly, MAFF did not find the occurrence of cases in animals born after 18 July 1988 alarming. The main reason according to them for BABs was that the use of contaminated feeding for cattle was still going on at this time, with several months supply of unused foodstuffs on farms being used up. Although it is commonly accepted that the disease in cattle had been transmitted by feed containing the infectious agent from Scrapie and BSE cattle brains, there must be a different mode of transmission to account for those cases born after July 1988 if the MBM feed-ban was effective.

144

Identifying preclinical cases of BSE

BSE, like other SEs, has a very long asymptomatic incubation period and a protracted clinical course reckoned in months or even years. Diagnostic methods should have been developed for identifying asymptomatic animals and preventing them becoming part of the food chain. As yet in 1997, MAFF have no way of identifying asymptomatic infected animals during the long incubation period. Over 60% of BSE cases now being confirmed, are cattle born after July 1988 when the ruminant feed ban was imposed in the UK. Beef cattle are normally slaughtered before 18 months of age while the minimum incubation period of BSE is over 18 months. Thus, although incubating the disease, cattle reared for beef would not develop clinical signs, and therefore, are not reported as confirmed cases. The number killed while incubating the disease and going into the human food chain, remains unknown. In early 1996 MAFF, agreed to kill and incinerate all cattle over 30 months of age; no meat from any of these animals was to be allowed into the human food chain or used for any other purpose.

Specific PrP antibodies have been used to demonstrate PrP plaques in SEs (Bendheim et al, 1984). The analysis of several different bovine brain areas has confirmed the specificity of PrP but the sensitivity of detection was low (46.5%) (Scott et al, 1990) therefore the test has not been used for routine BSE diagnosis in the UK. Recently in a configuration and topographic immunochemical study, distribution of PrP in the CNS in a BSE revealed the density of the tissue immunostaining did not match consistently the severity of vacuolar changes (Wells et al, 1994). This type of correlation was not seen in another study where calves were experimentally inoculated with sheep scrapie brain tissue and although the calves developed clinical BSE, their brain sections were negative for vacuolation but positive immunohistochemically for PrP (Robinson et al, 1994).

In clinically diagnosed cases with negative histology and where no alternative diagnosis has been established, particularly in cattle BAB, a number of serious worries exist. These include whether all cases of BSE and atypical-BSE were caused by contaminated feed, or are some the result of maternal or horizontal transmission? Other strains of the scrapie agents with a different distribution of lesions may cause these atypical cases. This feature has been observed in experimental transmission of scrapie to cattle where inoculated calves developed clinical symptoms, yet none of the brains had SE vacuoles, although these brains were immuno-positive to protease-resistant protein (PrP) (Robinson et al, 1994). This new pattern of low grade vacuolation either indicates the emergence of a new strain of BSE or the possibility that the infection has occurred by a different route.

Demonstration of Nemavirus by electron microscopy

The pathological findings by EM in BSE-affected cows resembled those seen in natural and experimental scrapie and CJD-infected animals. Numerous membrane-bound intracellular vacuoles are present, some containing abundant membrane residues. Occasionally some of the processes contain a network of branched intercalating cisterns and tubules with entrapped mitochondria. The results of EM studies have revealed the ultrastructural differences between Alzheimer's disease (AD) and CJD. In AD, neurofibrillary paired helical filaments are observed which are not seen in CJD (Narang, 1990, 1992). These particles have been termed nemavirus (NVP) (Narang, 1990, 1992, 1994) and are not seen in AD. NVP, similar to those seen in natural and experimental scrapie of sheep and CJD, have also been observed in BSE brains (Liberski, 1990, Narang, 1994) and have been independently confirmed by others in scrapie-infected hamsters, CJD, BSE and natural infected scrapie sheep (Liberski, 1990; Liberski et al, 1988; Gibson et al, 1989). These particles are described in detail in a separate section.

The definitive diagnosis of these progressive SEs can be made by showing the presence of NVP and SAF preparation and examination by EM. A simple grid - touch negative-staining method by EM has been developed to demonstrate both NVP and SAF (Narang 1994; 1995; Narang et al, 1987; 1988).

Blind touch technique

In this blind study eighteen hamsters were divided into groups of nine. Group one hamsters were infected with the scrapie agent and group two hamsters were not infected and acted as controls. One hamster from each group was killed on the rota as follows: 3, 5, 7, 10, 14, 18, 21, 24 and 28 days. Examination of grids prepared from both left and right side of the brain revealed NVP and SAF in the right side of scrapie-infected hamster brains from 10 days post-inoculation and both the NVP and SAF were observed from 18 days post-inoculation in both sides of the brain. No NVP/SAF were seen in normal control hamsters. This touch method has been successfully applied to the diagnosis of human CJD (Narang et al, 1990; Narang, 1992). Three BSE brains and three normal cow brains were examined from five different areas by the negative touch method for both NVP and SAF. From each area, five grids were prepared and examined. NVP and SAF were revealed in all BSE cases. Some of the grids prepared were negative, suggesting a patchy distribution. It would therefore be helpful to have grid samples prepared from different regions of the brain.

In another blind trial, ten cow brains were examined by the touch technique, as previously described (Narang et al, 1987; 1988), while conventional SAF preparations for EM and histological examination were carried out independently by MAFF. Examination of the grids revealed both typical nemavirus particles and SAF in three of the five suspected BSE cases. There were no false positive results. Two of the specimens (± results) were tested by only one, not both, of the participating laboratories due to an administrative error, and therefore the false negative result in two cases may be due to a mixup of specimens. The simple touch method can provide a rapid means of diagnosis of BSE with very

146

little handling and risk of exposure. In another study 27 cow brains from apparently healthy cattle over four years old were collected, from a local abattoir, for examination by the "touch technique". Out of 27 brains examined 8 were positive for SAF by the EM. This is about a 29% positive rate in cattle of over 4 years being processed for the human food chain.

Over the years, an ever-increasing number of cows slaughtered for showing BSE clinical symptoms are proving histopathologically "BSE negative" at post mortem, thus throwing a serious doubt on the validity of the histopathological test. To determine the role of maternal transmission of BSE along with horizontal transmission, and to differentiate one from the other, it is important to have the right figures. There are three types of cattle in this analysis:

1 Cattle not infected
2 Infected cattle incubating the disease but showing no clinical symptoms
3 Cattle showing typical clinical BSE

The brains of all suspect cases in cattle reported by farmers are sent for examination and MAFF diagnosis which confirms those found neurohistopathologically positive. Of course, MAFF has classified a very large number of cattle as at risk from July 1996 and under the current rule, animals over 30 months old will not be allowed to enter the human food chain. This is presumably due to the fact that they may have been fed with the contaminated feed and infected. Subsequently, it has been revealed that a large number of animals, BAB have developed the clinical disease which may be due to vertical transmission. Sub-clinical BSE cases can be highly infective. A large proportion of cattle born from mothers-infected but without clinical symptoms, may well be cases of maternal transmission.

Epidemiological study

Evidence from experimental studies has revealed that BSE appears to be a new mutant strain of scrapie in cattle, caused initially by the supplements in MBM. These feed rations were made from sheep by incorporating cattle offal clinically or subclinically infected with BSE. During recycling it appears that cattle selected a particular strain which may have existed in the epidemic after the initial exposure with sheep scrapie (Wilesmith et al, 1991).

Information on cases of BSE has been obtained where suspect clinical incidents were reported by veterinary surgeons to MAFF. A farmer suspecting BSE reports to a MAFF vet on a standard questionnaire used to obtain relevant epidemiological data on every suspect case of BSE. This includes the details relating to cases; dates of birth, if known; breed; sex; the herd of origin of the animal, if purchased; the date of clinical onset; the stage of pregnancy at onset; pedigree of the animals when known; the identities of offspring, retained and intended for retention, if pregnant in the adult herd, and siblings with the same dam. Before 1989 most of this information was not recorded, as there was no legal requirement. In the same year the disease was made compulsorily notifiable in EUC.

A number of reviews have been carried out of the descriptive epidemiological studies during the course of the epidemic and these substantiate the original hypothesis of a food-borne source of the infection (Wilesmith et al, 1991; 1992). The original epidemiological studies, and the retrospective clinical evidence collected, strongly suggest that BSE appeared as a new disease and that the disease did not exist in Great Britain before 1984. The prevalent hypothesis on the origin of the epidemic is food-borne infection, associated with an increase in the absolute numbers of scrapie-infected sheep carcases entering the food rendering chain combined with changes in rendering technology, which led to the clinical infection of cattle. The majority of animals became infected as calves through the contaminated food (Wilesmith et al, 1988).

MAFF originally estimated that the BSE epidemic would peter out at 20,000 cases. In fact BSE has claimed more than eight times that amount. MAFF had heavily relied on predictions, well aware that these could be very wrong or remote from reality. Claims were also made that cattle would be the 'dead end' host for BSE- that it would die out in cattle by 1992. By May 14 1988, some 455 confirmed cases had been reported from 376 farms. At the onset, the disease was reported from all parts of England, though the north east of England, central and southern Wales and northern Scotland appeared relatively free. Throughout 1988 and 1992, the number of cases was increasing every week. There were 110 confirmed cases of BSE in the week ending 29 January 1989 and 159 cases in the week ending 5 February 1989. From then on, the number went up and up.

In the earlier studies of 1991 and during the follow-up, statistics showed that all infected animals were considered unmistakable index cases. This was considered typical of an extended common source of infection, while at the time there was no suggestion or evidence of cattle-to-cattle transmission. Epidemiological evidence collected by MAFF scientists excluded BSE being an inherited disease. Since BSE cases had occurred on farms with no sheep, it appeared unlikely that the transmission of the scrapie agent resulted from a direct contact between sheep and cattle or through the contaminated scrapie sheep fields. No epidemiological studies have demonstrated transmission of the disease through a direct or indirect link between sheep and cattle in the field.

Wilesmith et al, (1988) provided further evidence that BSE was not introduced into Great Britain by imported cattle or disseminated via semen, by analysis of the record of purchases of animals and the investigation of the pedigrees of the sires used, particularly in closed herds. It may never be possible to know for certain how BSE started in cattle, but some of these theories can be tested experimentally.

The incidence of infected cows within a dairy herd appeared to increase in proportion to the herd size. During the 12 months from April 1987 to March 1988, the percentage of confirmed cases varied from herd to herd. It ranged from 0.20% to 11.11% of the adult animals with a mean of 1.52% . In the period from November 1986, from the time when disease was first recognised as a separate dis-

148

order, to 31 December 1988 there were 2,160 confirmed cases on 1,667 farms (Southwood Report, 1989).

Epidemic BSE

In the earlier study, a marked geographical variation was reported on the incidence of BSE from South to North. Relatively few cases were reported in Scotland, although the number of BSE cases diagnosed in Scotland increased gradually. The little we do know about BSE provides evidence that that opportunity to turn a profit on the vast stock of otherwise unusable and unwanted carcases scraps without the due consideration to all the implications led the renderers and compounders to mass produce and promote high protein food rations at a low price to the farmers. This, together with the alterations in the rendering process plus shortsightedness and incompetence, at the very least contributed to the emergence and spread of the disease.

Why has this disease only appeared in the 1980s? First it was considered that the feed renderers had altered their methods in order to cut costs. Instead of high-heat batch production, manufacturers had switched to continuous processing at lower temperatures. Initially, the cause of the epidemic was attributed to the relaxation of rules governing the heat treatment of animal MBM preparations at rendering plants and the fact that use of solvents was discontinued. With the benefit of hindsight, it is believed that this new different low temperature method, without solvents, possibly failed to destroy the scrapie agent.

The scale of the BSE epidemic in Britain increased very considerably during 1988 and 1989 when a greater proportion of cattle became infected with a shorter incubation period (Wilesmith et al, 199; 1994). At this stage, however, officials did not fully realise that the recycling of infected and sub-clinically infected cattle tissues in the preparation of meat and bone meal was an important factor. There was a spectacular increase in the disease in the UK during 1988 and 1989. The total number of cases in June 1988 was 687; in December 1988, 2160; in June 1989, 5375 and in November, 1989 the total reached 8100 (Bradley et al, 1991). The number of suspected cases reported in 1994 was between 400 to 500 cases per week and 200 to 300 cases per week were being reported during 1996. These are significantly fewer cases than at the same time in 1992 (600 to 900 cases per week) and 1993 (800 to 1,000 cases per week). Large differences in the incidence of BSE have also been observed between herds. The peak monthly incidence of BSE in the U K in 1993 represents 1 per hundred adult cattle (similar to that seen in the kuru epidemic in the Fore Tribe in the 1950s). Between November 1986 and 11 March 1994, 121,898 cases of BSE were confirmed on 29, 680 farms and BSE cases continued to rise every year until March 1995 when they reached a total of over 140,000. Up to May 1996, 160,540 cases of BSE were confirmed on 33,455 farms. Since the feed ban, the general picture is one of a continuing decline in the number of cases. According to MAFF, less than 300 suspect cases were being reported each week at the beginning of 1996, compared to 1,000 at the peak of the epidemic in early 1993. 35.7% of herds with adult breeding cattle experienced at least one case of BSE. The incidence was much higher in dairy herds, 59.4%, but only 15.3% in beef suckler herds. From the adult cattle population of approximately 4.5 million, the current annual incidence of confirmed cases of the disease is 0.75%. A reduction in the number of new cases has been reported in animals 3 years old and under, while there has been a continuing rise in incidence in five year old animals.

Origin of BSE on farms

Winter et al in 1989, described 14 cases of BSE in a self-contained herd of 500 cows kept at two separate locations two miles apart. There was some winter grazing by sheep from neighbouring farms on the fields, while the cows were housed in kennel buildings. They examined farm records which showed that there had been only minor alterations to the herd management within the previous 5 years. The records revealed some movement of cows between the two dairies, but no new cows had been introduced into the herd during the previous 10 years. The herd had a concentrated autumn calving pattern, with calving occurring in a 10 week period from mid-August to the end of October.

Feeding of calves on the farm

Newborn calves on the above mentioned farms were left with their dams for the first 24 hours of their lives and thereafter individually penned and fed 4 to 5 litres of soured colostrum. When two weeks of age, proprietary calf pencils (dried pellet concentrate food) were introduced and the calves were accustomed to food other than mother's milk when 4 weeks old. Grass silage and calf pellets were fed post-weaning until they were turned out in mid-April the following year. No milk replacer was used to feed these calves. In Britain, calves in dairy herds receive some 70kg of concentrate of MBM in their three months of life. It has been recorded that only 12 kg of animal protein of ruminant origin had been incorporated into the proprietary concentrate compound foodstuff which was fed to the calves from two weeks old to six months old and this feeding practice continued throughout their life.

Since the animal protein was fed to calves when they were between two weeks and six months old, it is probable that these calves received a contaminated dose soon after they were born. Two Jersey cows born on the same farm in England in 1983 and then taken in 1985 to the Sultanate of Oman as part of a consignment of 14 pregnant heifers subsequently developed clinical symptoms in January 1989 when they were about five years old. These animals were killed 5 weeks later and BSE was confirmed by brain pathology (Carolan et al, 1990). After the ingestion of the infective agent by feeding, the incubation period before clinical signs are evident would appear to be between 4-5 years to be judged from the recorded history.

150

Contamination of farm land with the BSE agent

One of the major MAFF misapprehensions is that only cows with full-blown BSE can contaminate farmland with their dung and urine. This is not true. Any animal eating contaminated rations will be excreting undigested disease agent from day one. The cow does not even have to be diseased itself to be recycling the BSE agent on to farmland - where it will remain, threateningly, for several years. The agent has been shown to be present in stomach parasites.

BSE a major cause of death among the British cattle

Ever since the determined drive for increased food output during the second World War, cattle have been fed with cheap meat protein -- chiefly abattoir waste, which included sheep' brains processed into meal - to maximise production of beef and milk. In the last decade meat and bone meal was widely exported.

Handling of BSE cases in the field

The number of cases throughout the country presented a health hazard for those in first-hand contact with the infected animals. Naturally veterinary surgeons, laboratory workers and farm workers themselves were worried at the risk and faced a very difficult and distressing situation. There is great concern about BSE and the risks of handling known, or suspected cases by vets and farmers. MAFF helped in framing recommendations for guidance of those who were handling known or suspected cases of BSE. Although these rules were prepared with the help of the British Veterinary Association, there was one major difference between its advice and MAFF's recommendation relating to calving suspected cases of BSE.

MAFF's advice gave detailed guidance on the precautions to be taken while dealing with calving, cleansing and caesarean section. The British Veterinary Association paper says 'Because of the unpredictable behaviour of cows affected with BSE and likely danger to operatives handling suspect cases, assisted calving or caesarean section should not be contemplated under any circumstances.' However, it was left to the individual veterinarian's judgment to decide what should be done in the best interests of the animal and client.

Preparation of meat and bone meal (MBM)

In 1988 a survey of rendering plants revealed some 46 operating plants processing some 1.3 million tonnes of raw material (Wilesmith et al, 1991). Not all plants maintained detailed records of the type of material processed. However, estimates collected during this period from 39 plants revealed that the raw material comprised 15.9% fat trimmings, 30.5% bones, 33.4% offal, 8.9% carcases and 11.5% other mixed material. Although not all plant owners were able to provide detailed statistics, the species composition of this material was estimated to be 44.8% bovine, 15.3% ovine, 20.9% porcine and 19.0% of mixed species

151

origin, including poultry. With the exception of whole carcases, collected as dead animals from farms, all of these raw materials were derived from animal waste material from abattoirs, deboning plants and butchers. There was no evidence from the utilisable responses that either the type or species composition of the material had changed during this period.

The raw material was passed through mechanical devices to break it down to an appropriate particle size before entering the rendering vessel. Of the 46 plants, 33 operated batch rendering systems in which 0.5 to 15 tonnes of raw material was heated as a single batch in a steam jacketed vessel. There was considerable variation in the processes used in the rendering plants, but all had the same aim of using heat to remove water and liberate fat. During the process the material was agitated by steam heated paddles. Once most of the water content of the material had been driven off as steam, the temperature increased to the desired operating temperature.

Why did this disease only appear in the 1980s? Firstly, it was considered that the feed renderers had altered their methods, to cut costs. Secondly, cows, herbivorous animals were deliberately turned into carnivores; most importantly into cannibals. It has been known that the cannibalistic ritual was the sole source of transmission of kuru from man-to-man (Gajdusek, 1977). With this knowledge available, it is difficult to understand why no expert consultation was undertaken before MAFF allowed the use of MBM. No one seems to take the responsibility. The UK rendering industry handles and processes 1.75 million tonnes of slaughterhouse animal waste annually. From 1985 to 1989, there was an increase in the exportation of the MBM concentrate from the UK to European countries before it decreased in 1990 (Hörnlimann and Guidon,1994). The primary destination of 62,336 tonnes of British MBM concentrate exported during this period was France (54%), Benelux (30%), Republic of Ireland (13%), Germany (2%) and other countries (1%). These amounts can be misleading, Switzerland imported, on average, 12,664 tonnes of MBM, but only 12 tonnes of it were exported directly from the UK (Hörnlimann et al,1994).

It was impossible to know which, if any, commercial rendering processes could continue to be used. It was only in 1994, the preliminary results of a collaborative study on the effect of different rendering protocols on BSE infectivity showed that at least two systems used in Great Britain were ineffective, but the limited sensitivity of the study means that it is still impossible to identify "safe" systems. However, it has been a well established fact since 1990, that often small amount of scrapie infectivity survives at 360° C (Brown et al, 1990) MAFF spent a lot of money and years finding that rendering processes are not effective. They could have just read Dr Brown's paper and saved the money and effort.

There were no set European rules regarding the process temperature for MBM preparations. In the UK, renderers operate under direct control of MAFF and all plants are inspected four times a year. Since the 1988 Salmonella scare, a dail sample for testing was required by law. The methods for processing and time and temperature currently used are typically at 130° C for 18 minutes in UK. That is similar to the practice in other countries.

Prior to the 1970s, in most of the plants, the material was processed in the conventional batch cooker - a horizontal steam jacketed vessel with an agitator placed in the machine - and steam applied. At the end of the run, fat and solids were crudely separated and fat collected was further refined and known as tallow, sold for various uses, which is used in the cosmetic industry for the preparation of soap and other cream base products. The solids went through a solvent extraction process, similar to a dry cleaning operation, where fat was leached out and collected by a distillation process and solvent driven out by blowing inert gas or steam.

At the end of the 1970s and the beginning of the 1980s, most renderers moved away from the solvent extraction procedure, and replaced it with a mechanical continuous process with high pressure which left 10-12% fat in the solids compared to 5%. One of the theories considered by MAFF was that, with the introduction of continuous rendering, and abandonment of solvent extraction of oils by the UK industry over the period 1980-1982, the scrapie-like agent responsible for BSE were no longer destroyed and the agent found its way into dairy and beef cattle rations. From the early epidemiological evidence it appeared that Scotland had low incidence of BSE. This was credited to the continued use of the solvent process in the local plant. It was considered that this new different low temperature method without solvent failed to destroy the agent of scrapie. According to figures, on the 18 May 1990, the incidence of BSE in Scotland was reported to be 9.9%, Wales 9.5% and North-West England also 9.5%. As more information was made available, it became difficult to conclude that the change of processing was the only reason for the cause of the BSE outbreak. It was also thought that there had been a increase in the use of MBM. In the House of Commons Agricultural Select Committee in response to question "So that a lot more animal protein is being fed to cows and they are producing a lot more milk?", Dr Cooke replied "It depends on your definition of 'a lot'. The total increase from say 1960 to 1980 would have been at maximum, of about a 50% increase in the amount of compound feed per cow" (Dr Cooke, UK Agri Supply Trade Association Ltd. Page 134).

Based on the incubation period the hypothesis put forward is that exposure to infected material commenced around 1981-82 and that the majority of cattle became infected during calfhood. The age 5 and over of infected cattle does not mean that the incubation period is long. Some of the the older cattle may have been exposed later in life. It was suggested that the cattle were infected with the scrapie agent but because of the long incubation period the disease did not become apparent until 1985 or later. Cattle continued to be exposed to infection until the MBM addition to feed was stopped in July 1988. Individual cows might develop the clinical disease with varying incubation periods, since different animals may respond differently to exposure depending on the amount of contaminated food consumed, and the age of the animal when infected. From the laboratory experiments with scrapie, it is also clear that the health of animals and, in particular, the teeth and any ulcers in the mouth may also play a role in the intake of the infection and the incubation period. To explain the observed pattern of sporadic and family related incidence, some authors believe that after exposure to the SE agent, different hosts with different genotype react differently. The breed of cattle may influence the response to the infection by reducing or increasing the incubation period.

A ban on the feeding of ruminant protein to ruminant was considered the single most effective means to prevent the feed-borne transmission of the SEs agents. To prevent further transmission of the infective agent by this route, a ban on the use of ruminant-derived protein in ruminant foodstuff was introduced in July 1988. Continued epidemiological studies have not revealed any evidence to refute MBM involvement. However, crucial experiments have not been done and contaminated feed has not been fed to the cattle to substantiate the hypothesis, "that MBM in proprietary cattle foodstuffs was the vehicle of infection". It was forecast that the ban on the use of MBM would stop further infection in cattle and that, over the following few years, those remaining cattle that were infected would develop the disease and be killed thereby eradicating the disease. The likelihood of vertical or horizontal transmission between cow and calf was not seriously considered.

The more we try to understand BSE, the more we are forced to the conclusion that greed, poor MAFF controls and incompetence have each played a part in its emergence and spread. The feeding of rendered sheep and cattle offal to herbivorous animals is both unnatural and abhorrent and MAFF has responded too late, with too little and perhaps scored own goals, even after spending millions of pounds in research.

A statutory ban on the inclusion of SBO in pet foods

Cases of naturally occurring spongiform encephalopathy in cats were diagnosed (Wyatt et al, 1990), prompting speculation that BSE had crossed a species barrier. The Pet Food Manufacturers' Association (1990), introduced a voluntary ban on the inclusion of specified offals in pet food. However, at that time the Agriculture Minister Mr John Gummer, MP resisted the ban being made statutory. The House of Commons Agriculture Committee, basing their decision not on scientific grounds but on political judgment, took the opposite view. "With a disease as distressing as BSE, people are entitled to expect that the food they feed their pets should be protected by the same basic legislative safeguards as their own food, particularly in view of the uncertainties surrounding the newly identified encephalopathies. We therefore urge the Government to introduce a statutory ban".

154

Ban on the inclusion of SBO for pigs and chickens

Evidence that BSE resulted from the feeding of cattle with recycled protein containing offal of sheep infected with scrapie, raised the important issue of animal feed for pigs and chickens. In July 1988, the all important "MBM feed ban" came into effect to ensure that sheep and cattle would no longer be fed ruminant derived protein. At that time, based on the uncertainties, a call was made to extend the ban to pig and poultry feed in case the BSE agent 'jumped species'. MAFF, however, argued that pigs are not at risk because they are natural scavengers (and have evolved defences against pathogens) and poultry were not at risk because of the enormous zoological divide between cattle and poultry. MAFF did agree to conduct transmission experiments using pigs, but refused to take any action until the results become available. BSE has been experimentally transmitted to sheep, goats, pigs and mice by injection directly into the brain, into the body and by feeding. A ban on inclusion of cattle brains and offal from ruminants, specified bovine offal (SBO) in pig feed was ultimately introduced in 1991. Given the many uncertainties surrounding BSE that MAFF erred on the side of caution, is not surprising. Before the BSE epidemic, the possibility of scrapie jumping species must also have seemed very remote; experience, however, had proved the contrary.

Although MAFF introduced a ban on inclusion of cattle SBO in 1991 in the production of MBM, nevertheless, MBM still continued to be used for feeding pigs, poultry and fish until 29 March 1996, when the mammalian protein ban was extended to feed for all farmed animals, horses and fish and the British Government made it illegal to hoard MBM on farms. It is important to record here, that apart from feeding the farm animals, fish farmers also used this meat and bone meal and it is most likely that water from fish pools ran into river water, thus contaminating water supplies. It only took six years for MAFF to realise that its use for any animals was wrong and potentially dangerous.

On 5 February 1996, in compliance with Euro Commission Decision 95/27, the British Government commenced random sampling in feed mills to check that mammalian protein was not being included in mammalian feed. In an earlier finding by 24 May 1995, 1551 samples had been tested and 12 samples were found positive for such protein. Further legislation which took effect on 19 April 1996, also prohibited the use of mammalian MBM meal as fertiliser and its use on agricultural land, although its use in private gardens, and within greenhouses and glass or plastic structures, is still permissible.

From transmission experiments, MAFF and the Government knew by October 1988 that brains and spinal cord of BSE cattle contained high concentrations of the infective agent. In June 1990 the author gave evidence to the House of Commons Agricultural Select Committee, stating that the BSE agent seems more virulent than that found in scrapie sheep and its a short incubation period gave it a greater chance to develop. It has been established that without exception clinical disease develops in a range of mammals fed with the BSE brain tissues. The chances of disease are very low when scrapie-infected sheep are fed to the same animals.

Ban on the use of brain and offal in human foodstuff

Various measures were taken to prevent the epidemic of BSE in cattle presenting a risk to human health in Great Britain. The Government's first step was based upon an independent working group under the chairmanship of Prof Richard Southwood to advise on all aspects of BSE. Members selected for this committee had had no working experience of SE disorders, and MAFF officials were responsible for supplying it with information and interpretation. Three assumed basic factors predetermined MAFF thinking: 1) there will be no more than 20,000 cases; 2) BSE will be a dead-end disease and 3) like scrapie in sheep the risk to humans does not exist.

MAFF's position was unsupportable, based as it was merely on assumptions that subclinical animals do not contain enough of the disease agent to infect humans. Obviously, people will continue to eat meat from those affected cattle but MAFF wishes us to believe that it is safe to eat meat from cattle which are not yet showing symptoms although affected. To quote Mr Ray Bradley (House of Commons Agri. Select Committee, Report, 1990, page 72), who still advises the Government "Furthermore, the scientific evidence demonstrates conclusively, from studies of naturally infected scrapie sheep, that muscle, the meat, the beef, is not infected or has no detectable infectivity even in clinical cases, never mind subclinical cases. So I am very happy about even the clinical cases going through and the meat being eaten, although we do not want it." He also said "The perception at the moment of the public is that there is still an increasing occurrence of the clinical BSE. While this is happening, I'm very confident indeed that the infectivity is falling". This being how the advisers were thinking, explains why the measures taken were minimal. They were more interested in protecting the meat industry than human health.

In April 1988, the Government decided it was necessary to have an external review and the Minister of Agriculture and Secretary of State for Health jointly appointed a small working party of scientific experts under the chairmanship of Sir Richard Southwood to consider the situation and report on it. This committee was later reconverted into the Spongiform Encephalopathy Advisory Committee (SEAC) under the chairmanship of Dr. David Tyrrell, which met every four months and more often if necessary, to review the development of the epidemic and the results of research as they became available. The government's intention was to base its response to the epidemic on independent scientific advice, and to be open about what was being done and why. Previous work of Ministry scientists had not been published sufficiently freely and SEAC declared that it was their policy that there should be no delay in implementing changes recommended as a result of any new findings and in making public such findings. I personally was told by Dr N. F. Lightfoot in February 1989, that I must submit all my results to him at least six months in advance before submitting for publication. Because of this my publications were delayed for months.

As recommended by the Southwood Committee, cattle showing clinical BSE symptoms were to be destroyed and carcases cremated. However, at the same time, MAFF was aware that not all cattle affected with BSE display the clinical symptoms, and those preclinical cases were still going into the national diet, as if they were healthy cattle. Dr Grant, in a memorandum to the House of Commons Agri. Committee, pointed out "Cattle which are destroyed because they suffer from BSE are those visibly affected -- the tip of the iceberg. Their apparently healthy colleagues, some incubating the disease, and with infective brains, go into our food chain". The brains themselves, along with bits of spinal cord tissue go into so called "mechanically recovered meat." Very high amounts of the agent ranging from one to ten million doses per gm cf brain and spinal cord tissue, were being used in a variety of meat pies, pates, lasagne, soups, and stock cubes during the early years of the epidemic. Not until November 1989, under the Bovine Spongiform Encephalopathy (No 2) Order 1988 the brain, spinal cord, spleen, thymus, tonsils and intestines from all cattle healthy or otherwise were banned from human consumption.

Further details of the SEAC Interim Report in 1992 noted that all high priority studies had been started and that the Committee was content with the progress of implementing earlier recommendations for research. The report also commented that the Committee believes "that all the necessary safeguards are in place to minimise further spread of spongiform encephalopathies in animals and to prevent any risk of transmission to humans". These statements were made to convince the public that all risk factors were being removed from the food chain (BSE in Great Britain, A progress Report March 1994). What SEAC members did not realise was the speed of development in the natural experiment on farms. In 1986 there were six cases of BSE: in 1996 BSE claimed 160,000 cattle. In 1996 there were 10 cases of "new strain" CJD, how many will the "new strain" claim by 2006? Right from the start of this crisis the Government has not approached BSE as a matter of science, but as political policy, viewing research as some kind of convenience store where you can pick and choose the hypotheses that suit.

The measures to protect animal health were strengthened in August 1995 (The Specified Bovine Offal Order 1995) and again in March 1996 by extending the controls on specified bovine offal to require the entire head of all cattle over six months, except for the tongue (provided it can be removed without contamination), to be treated as specified bovine offal. As from 19 April 1996, meat and bone meal was banned in agricultural fertiliser. The Government announced a recall scheme to allow farmers to send back unused meat and bone meal or feed containing it free to charge. Further, legislation has been introduced which would ban the possession and storage of the material on farms, at feed merchants or in feed mills from 1 August 1996. These measures taken have been too late, but it is better to be late than never. The use of brain from animals under the age of six months does pose a great risk for humans, but is still being allowed into the human food chain. If there is vertical transmission at six months of calf life, it is already 15 months into the incubation period. The brain might contain 10,000 to 100,000 doses per gm of brain tissue. (see sheep experiments in the scrapie section). Further, the brains and offal were being removed so as not to enter the food chain from cattle over six months old. However, slaughtermen sawing down the length of potentially infected spinal cords might be spraying nerve tissue everywhere, and could thus contaminate any clean meat on the carcases.

Mechanically Recovered Meat (MRM)

To ensure complete compliance with the regulations covering SBO materials, the State Veterinary Service (SVS) visited premises handling specified bovine material (SBM) unannounced during September and October 1995 and found that in a few instances, pieces of spinal cord had been left attached to carcases after dressing, although all were removed before the carcases left the premises. SEAC considered this potentially dangerous and grounds for great concern. By November 1995, they had detected several instances where potentially infected SBO material could have become mixed with other animal waste and entered the animal feed chain for feeding only to poultry or pigs. SEAC considered this a serious threat to animal health. SEAC considered it only a theoretical risk, but for humans it was a practical reality. The most likely way in which this could have happened would have been if the vertebrae had been used for the production of mechanically recovered meat (MRM). SEAC had considered MRM earlier in 1995 and had concluded that "provided in the slaughtering process the removal of the spinal cord was done properly, the MRM process was safe". The Committee considered these findings at its meeting on 23 November, and noted that controls on SBOs had been further tightened but felt that unless and until it was clear that the removal of SBO, particularly spinal cord, was being done properly in all cases it would be prudent, as a precaution, to suspend the use of vertebrae from cattle aged over six months in the production of MRM.

It was concluded, however, that it would be impractical to distinguish between vertebral columns from older and younger cattle, and that any ban would have to be comprehensive. The Minister therefore announced on 28 November, that the ban would be introduced as quickly as possible. Legislation to ban the use of bovine vertebral column in the production of MRM came into effect on 15 December 1995. It is strange that SEAC and the British Government suggest that humans might have been infected before 1989 because SBO was not being removed, while failing to recognise that a fair amount of SBO was still going into human and animal food chain in 1995 and could be responsible for infecting many more thousands of humans.

The House of Commons Agriculture Committee in 1990 recognised that

158

there are a number of ways in which the BSE agent might theoretically have passed to humans, or might be passed to humans:

(i) "through the injection, for medical purposes, of material derived from bovine sources from an affected animal;

(ii) in specified offals from the infected animals consumed prior to November 1989 (when the sale of such offals for human consumption was banned);

(iii) in specified offals from an affected animal consumed subsequently to November 1989 (through their inadvertent inclusion in mechanically recovered meat);

(iv) in beef or products from an affected animal".

My own view is that the Government should have been advised by scientists with working and practical experience of the SE diseases, rather than intelligent guessers, however expert and eminent they might be in other specialities. One can only wonder and ask, how many more new measures should have been introduced at the beginning of 1988 to control BSE and protect public health. Those experts who sat on committees spent over £50 million on research and now concede with "hindsight" that things should have been done differently. They are still in office - with no direction of work - just another speculation. Hindsight is a luxury they can afford, but who, if anyone is going to apologise to the families of the victims or compensate them for their tragedy? The official line has changed from the "there is no risk" to "there is only a little risk" to "there might well be a risk" with new measures being introduced in steps.

The sudden public announcement by Mr Stephen Dorrell Minister of Health, on 20 March 1996, that there might be a link between BSE and CJD, has further generated anxiety about the disease and in particular the possibility of its transmission from cattle to humans in the form of Creutzfeldt-Jakob disease. There was so much publicity in the media, that this new disease BSE, within a short time became universally known to adults and children alike as "mad cow disease". Fears that BSE may be transmitted to humans, were founded on a number of suppositions. Although this chance may be very remote, there is no absolute guarantee that humans were safe from the risk of handling or eating any contaminated food. Public opinion forced the House of Commons Agriculture Committee to set up an official enquiry into BSE. The report and Proceedings of the Committee, together with Minutes of the Evidence and Appendices were published on 10 July, 1990.

Transmission of scrapie to cattle

To determine the susceptibility of scrapie transfer from sheep and goats to cattle, Dr Gibbs and others (1990) inoculated 8 to 11 month old cattle by simultaneous intracerebral, intraperitoneal, intravenous and oral dosing of brain homogenates from scrapie sheep. After an incubation period 27 to 48 months, three out of ten developed typical clinical signs of BSE and later histological examination of brains confirmed the disease. The incubation periods are inversely proportional to the amounts of infectivity present in the inoculum.

Host range of the scrapie and BSE agent

Transmission of BSE experimentally to mice and to sheep both to "positive" (susceptible) and "negative" (resistant) lines, strongly suggest that BSE is not preferentially controlled by certain PrP genotypes. The pattern of lesions seen in BSE is consistent with individual models of experimental scrapie. In these, mice of a single PrP genotype were infected with a single strain of agent by one route of injection (Wells et al, 1994). The genetic hypothesis could not explain the outbreak with a simple spontaneous mutation occurring either in the cattle, or in the scrapie agent. The evidence strongly suggests that the strain of the scrapie agent has a major influence and maybe there are other reasons apart from a simple association between PrP genotype.

Transmission of BSE to cattle

Dawson et al (1990), divided 4 to 5 month old calves including one Jersey X Limousin into four groups of four from Holstein/Friesian and Jersey herds. The animals were inoculated with 10% saline brain homogenate prepared from four cases of BSE. For control purposes, an additional group of four calves were inoculated with saline only. In the group of calves inoculated with BSE symptoms identical with the clinical disease developed between 37 to 78 weeks post-inoculation. The clinical symptoms observed in all cattle in group 1 to 4 were similar. Therefore it was apparent from this study that the source of the four inocula - each prepared from a separate case of BSE and from breeds of cows (Holstein/Friesian and Jersey, Jersey x Limousin) had no significant influence on the experimental outcome. However, it is strange that two of the control calves, those inoculated with saline only, also developed BSE, approximately five years after the initiation of the experiment. The difference in the incubation period between the calves inoculated with the BSE tissues and normal saline is very significant. Development of the clinical disease with a very long incubation period in the control cows would suggest that the cases were not due to inoculum contaminated with the BSE agent, but represent vertical or horizontal transmission. The incubation period of 37 to 78 weeks for cow to cow infection is much shorter than the incubation period of 108 to 208 weeks from sheep to cow; demonstrating that the scrapie agent for cows has been selected with less than half the incubation period.

Transmission of BSE to sheep and goats

BSE was readily transmitted to both sheep and goats both by intracerebral (i.c) and the oral route (Fraser et al, 1994). In a wide range of sheep breeds a single sheep gene called Sip with alleles, sA and pA, was considered to exert precise control over the timing of appearance of symptoms and incidence of natural scrapie. Based on their response to the scrapie agent challenge, Cheviot sheep at the Neuropathogenesis Unit (Edinburgh, UK), were divided into "positive" and "negative" lines (Foster et al, 1988). Both susceptible and resistant lines of sheep developed BSE after inoculation by i.c and oral routes without significant or clear difference in the progress of infection or incubation periods between the routes or lines. These studies demonstrate that allelic complexity in sheep PrP gene failed to identify any genotype resistance to BSE. Transmission experiments in mink involving both i. c. and oral routes also revealed a greater affinity to the agent of a bovine origin compared to the scrapie sheep (Robinson, 1994). Direct transmission to mice from BSE infected tissues gave the same incubation period as those observed in experimentally passaged BSE sheep, goat and pig (Foster et al, 1988).

Transmission to pigs

Dawson et al (1990), reported experimental transmission of BSE into one of ten challenged pigs with approximately 17 months incubation period, but there is no record as to the other nine pigs. In another experiment, all inoculated pigs developed neurological signs between 32 and 37 months postinoculation. The SE was confirmed by histological examination of the brains.

Transmission of BSE to monkeys

In 1993 Baker et al, inoculated two young common marmosets by the i.c. and intraperitoneal (i.p.) routes with crude brain homogenate prepared from a BSE case. Two other marmosets were similarly injected with brain homogenate from sheep with natural scrapie. One of the marmosets inoculated with scrapie was reported to have an "odd vacant" expression after 38.2 months and the same day was found to be severely incoordinated. In the second marmoset inoculated with scrapie, the onset was insidious and the animal was reported to have slight incoordination of movements from 42 months post inoculation.

Researchers noticed that one of the marmosets inoculated with BSE started fighting with its cage mate 30 months after inoculation and thereafter each animal was caged alone. However, neurological signs appeared 46.5 months post inoculation. The animal became shy when approached. There were extensive salivation and swallowing problems. The animal was seen to sleep during the day. The clinical signs progressed to include a truncal ataxia with a broad-based gait and high-stepping of the hind limbs. The second marmoset inoculated with BSE showed apprehension 47 months after the injection. There was salivation and the animal started to deteriorate and appeared to have difficulty in grooming. A mild ataxia was also observed and by 49.5 months post-injection it developed oral dyskinesia (impairment of the power of voluntary movement, resulting in incomplete movements) and had some difficulty in swallowing and was killed.

Histopathological examination of the brains of animals inoculated with BSE tissues showed significant microscopic changes with bilateral symmetrical vacuolar changes of grey matter and with widespread astrocytosis (Baker et al,

1993). The predominant type of vacuolar change were seen in the basal nuclei and diencephalon of all animals. There was tendency for the lesions to be less severe in the brain stem and, in cerebellum, changes were mild with scattered vacuoles throughout. The changes in the cortex were much more severe in the scrapie-injected animals than in BSE-injected animals. These histopathological changes were similar to those seen in BSE cases.

The experimental details of the above study were published in April 1993 (Baker et al, 1993). However, four months earlier, in December 1992, the Medical Research Council announced the results of its four-year scrapie and BSE experiments. In effect, the news was given out even before the experiment was completed. This appears to have been done simply to assure the public that the two monkeys which had been injected with scrapie material had both died, but the other two, injected with BSE, were still alive and well. Given the closeness of monkeys to man, the result was extremely important and reassuring and, therefore, with the encouragement of MAFF was given considerable media exposure. The Meat Trade Journal was understandably delighted and led with the headlines, "Beef given clean bill of health". About four months later, however, during the summer of 1993, the BSE-inoculated monkeys, too, both succumbed to spongiform encephalopathy. Many of the transmission experiments done in the past have been terminated because the animals did not become ill within the same time period in the two groups of animals, therefore MAFF took the opportunity to publicise the results of an incomplete study, misleading the public. It is important to stress that with long incubation periods, negative results in the short term can be meaningless.

Transmission of BSE to mice

Like scrapie in sheep, BSE has been experimentally transmitted to mice, both by intracerebral inoculation and feeding infected tissues (Fraser et al, 1988; 1994; White, 1994). Further, comparative transmission studies using infected brain tissues from scrapie sheep and cases of BSE revealed that inoculated mice developed a clinical disease similar to both scrapie and BSE. The mice recipients of the BSE agent develop the clinical disease at a higher efficiency and more rapidly than mice given scrapie sheep tissues (Fraser et al, 1988; 1994; White et al, 1994). There are many pure breeds of mice. Once these breeds of mice are inoculated with the same infected tissue, reproducible differences in the incubation periods between different breeds of mice of different genotypes are found. Of the various breeds of mice, RIII mice have the shortest incubation periods (Fraser et al, 1994). Transmission patterns of the BSE agent compared to the scrapie agent are different and very interesting. BSE cases transmitted easily to 100% of the inoculated or fed mice compared with scrapie sheep, where less than 75% develop the disease with very long incubation periods. In a number of studies a combination of strain of the agent and host genes have been shown to exert a major influence on the incubation period of experimental scrapie (Dickinson et

162

al, 1968; Bruce et al, 1987).

There are very obvious apparent genetic variations in different breeds of mice. In mice and sheep the gene which is considered to exert some control over the timing of appearance of symptoms of scrapie has been termed *Sinc* (mice) and *Sip* (sheep) respectively. The *Sip* has two alleles termed sA and pA in sheep and in mice the *Sinc* gene has two alleles termed s7 and p7. A *Sinc* gene based on two alleles s7 and p7 can have three possible combinations of homozygote and heterogygote (Bruce et al, 1991). Using different breeds of mice, by serial passage into the same breeds of mice under specified conditions, over 20 strains of scrapie have been characterised. These distinct strains of the scrapie agent have been identified on the basis of their peculiar relative incubation periods and neuropathological properties in relation to distribution of the lesions within the brain (Bruce & Dickinson, 1987). When scrapie strains are serially passaged in mice under specific conditions, the responses are predictable depending on the amount of dose, route of inoculation and breed of mice used.

The BSE agent strain-typing was carried out by inoculating mice of different *Sinc* genotypes from seven unrelated BSE cases. The brain specimens from cows were collected at different times from separate geographical locations and compared with transmission tests set up using three brains collected from natural scrapie sheep during the same period (Bruce et al, 1994). The pattern of incubation periods in mice corresponded closely for each of the seven transmissions of BSE but was different from previous transmission studies undertaken with sheep and goat scrapie. These results strongly suggest that the same major strain of the agent was present in each BSE case.

Comparative mean incubation periods in mice in the *Sinc* p7 gene allele was about 300 days shorter with BSE than was the case with sheep scrapie (Bruce et al, 1994). There were large reproducible incubation period differences between mice of different *Sinc* genotypes, but also, unexpectedly, between mouse strains of the same *Sinc* genotype i.e, the incubation period in RIII mice (*Sinc* s7), 328±3 days was about 100 days shorter than that in C57BL mice (*Sinc* s7), 438±7 days. Further, in the F1 cross between C57BL and VM mice (*Sinc* p7), the incubation period was over 700 days - well beyond the incubation period in the two parental mouse strains (Bruce et al, 1994). The comparative results with transmission attempts set up with three brains collected from natural sheep during the same period revealed that the incubation period in RIII mice was 381±11 days , C57BL mice 404±5 while in the F1 cross between C57BL and VM, the incubation period was 611±8 days (Bruce et al, 1994). Further, the two strains of BSE isolated by serial passage in mice of different *Sinc* genotypes, also differed from other mouse-passaged strains previously characterised (Bruce et al, 1994). In comparison, the three transmission attempts from natural sheep scrapie showed no such uniformity, but had long incubation periods and in some cases even failed to produce either clinical disease or any pathology.

163

Sip gene in sheep plays no role in susceptibility to BSE

These comparative transmission studies demonstrated that the *Sinc gene* may not have any influence on the incubation period and not be the sole factor in controlling the incubation period. The distribution of the degenerative lesions - "spongiform changes" - and regional intensity of vacuoles appears to be controlled by a number of factors of which the strain of scrapie agent is the most important. The sustained uniformity of the lesion profile observed in BSE throughout the epidemic to date (Foster et al, 1994 ; Bruce et al, 1994), strongly suggests selection of a single major strain of the BSE agent. These results suggested that, by the time the disease was first recognised, recycling had already selected a single strain of the agent. All these findings demonstrate that host variations, whether in the host PrP gene or other genes, are not a major factor in the susceptibility to BSE. Further, these inoculation studies show that almost every mammalian species can be affected by the BSE agent to produce SEs. If similar conditions were applied to humans, man would be at a greater risk of being infected than previously thought. Great care must be observed and every effort made to eradicate BSE from herds to prevent BSE becoming endemic and self-sustaining like scrapie in sheep. At the same time, every effort must also be made to eradicate scrapie, otherwise the infective agent may well spring forth again to threaten us in the future.

Transmission studies carried out using brain tissue from cats, greater kudu and nyala with SEs also revealed similar reproducible incubation periods and lesion distribution in the recipient mice to those seen with BSE. After experimental transmission of BSE into pigs, goats and sheep, all of which developed clinical disease, the brain homogenates were used to inoculate different breeds of mice and compared with the direct source from BSE (Foster et al, 1994). All mice developed clinical disease with reproducible incubation periods, as in direct transmission from BSE cases. Furthermore, transmissions carried out using tissues from experimentally inoculated sheep- goats and pigs with BSE into mice, have also given results corresponding to direct transmissions of BSE from cattle. There are very strong arguments that a single major stable strain has been responsible for SEs in domestic cats and other zoo animals.

Furthermore, these transmission studies from one species to another also revealed that the BSE agent remains unchanged when passaged through a range of species and that "donor" species has little specific influence on the disease characteristics in mice. This is a unique property in the cattle-selected strain of the BSE agent which has not been previously identified in any other scrapie strain. The BSE agent appears to be a new strain of a scrapie agent, probably originating from sheep. According to some investigators this may be due to mutation following the heat-treatment process of MBM, whereby a heat resistant strain survived the system or developed due to chemical changes, before being included in the supplement feed of cattle. Until we are more certain, every possibility must be considered and experimented.

A selection of mammals used in transmission studies all develop the clinical disease when injected by i.c. and i.p. routes, showing the diversity of species that can be infected with scrapie and BSE. However, it has been demonstrated using mink, sheep and goats, and on mouse-to-mouse passage, that the incubation periods in i.p. are consistently longer compared to i.c. In contrast, when BSE is transmitted to mice, sheep and mink there is very little difference in incubation period between the i.c. and oral routes. Moreover, previous studies have revealed that scrapie strain passage between hamster, rats and mice show the species barrier resulting in a reduced efficiency of infection where only a proportion of animals inoculated develop the clinical disease on interspecies transmission. A reduction of incubation period between first and subsequent passage is observed in a new species. This has been considered by some as resulting from a selection of strain of agent which replicates more quickly in the new host species (Kimberlin et al, 1989). However, it is most likely that the strain has adapted itself to the new host.

Comparative transmission experiments have revealed that the BSE agent has 100% efficiency and also differences in the incubation period between first and subsequent passage in a new species are not as marked as in scrapie sheep. This would suggest that a more stable single strain has been naturally selected in cattle. This major strain appears to have further infected several other ruminant and non-ruminant species and remains stable in its properties.

The mouse model has been considered to be very sensitive for transmission of the SE agent. Also, infectivity can be detected in infected cattle brain at similar titres to those found in scrapie-sheep brain (Fraser et al, 1994). In the past, presence of the scrapie agent in organs other than brains from scrapie sheep was demonstrated using sheep and goats but not mice: therefore, further research is required to evaluate the sensitivity of the mouse model for other tissues from BSE cattle. Cattle were experimentally infected by feeding with BSE brain tissue, as is the case in natural BSE, and infectivity was detected in the distal ileum six months after the challenge while the clinical disease developed at 35 to 37 months after the challenge. The results using the mouse model suggest that the BSE agent is less widely distributed in cattle with BSE than is the scrapie agent in sheep with scrapie. These negative transmission results have been used to provide reassurance about the safety of meat, milk and semen and certain offals which are commonly eaten.

These comparisons of the BSE agent with scrapie in sheep are artificial as they have not been made by comparing like with like, but by using very different host animals. In the case of BSE, they tried to transmit the disease into mice, while with scrapie it was from sheep to sheep or goats (Pattison et al, 1962). It is a well established fact that in scrapie sheep and mice, organs outside the central nervous system such as the 1,000 to 100,000 fold less infective dose present in kidney, spleen liver and lymph glands than in the brain. It follows that BSE cattle will have similar differences in titres. Mice can be inocula-

165

ted with about 0.002 ml homogenate tissues, or fed with such small quantities that they may not develop the clinical disease in their life span but nonetheless may "carry" the sub-clinical infection. If on first passage the clinical disease did not develop, the pool brains of subclinical animals were passaged into a new host. There appear to be no such studies available for BSE. However, the reduced dose of infectivity in tissues other than brain can be raised by increasing the inoculum from 1 mg to 10 gram and more, but this is only possible in larger animals, like goats and mink. With the importance to man of such a disease, the question has to be asked: "Does red meat, kidney, spleen liver, lymph glands and milk from infected cattle contain the BSE agent?" Additionally in the circumstances and because of the importance for bioassay, goats and mink should have been used, since both animal species are highly susceptible to the BSE agent.

Selection process of the BSE strain

Since in the UK rendering process, both sheep and cattle remains were included concomitantly in the preparation of the MBM, it is difficult in epidemiological studies of BSE in the UK to distinguish between the two alternative hypotheses, namely 1) Bovine origin. An unrecognised reservoir of infection existed in UK cattle before the outbreak of BSE; 2) Ovine origin, that is the agent, at some stage, jumped species from scrapie infected sheep remains to cattle.

MBM has also been prepared by rendering in other countries and therefore, it is important to know whether, in those countries, cattle offal together with their heads and brains were used in the rendering process as in the UK. It is difficult to determine when cattle remains were first included in the rendering process. During visits in the early 1970s to local abattoirs in Newcastle UK, the author personally saw the heads of cattle along with sheep heads in the waste skips destined for rendering. The major effect of cattle head recycling would have commenced much earlier than 1985 and would have continued until the statutory ban on the feeding of ruminant derived protein to ruminants was introduced in July 1988.

Host genetic variation is not a factor in the occurrence of BSE
Role of PrP gene

It has been widely considered that the normal host PrP gene plays a major role in determining the susceptibility to and incubation period of scrapie (Hunter et al, 1994). There are striking differences in the normal mammalian PrP gene sequence and a great deal of allelic complexity in both PrP coding regions. Differences in the incubation periods have been found in both natural and experimental scrapie in sheep and experimental scrapie in mice (Hunter et al, 1994; Laplanche et al, 1993; Ryan et al, 1993). Two polymorphisms in the bovine PrP gene coding region have been recognised in a study of approximately 400 cattle. In both BSE infected and healthy cattle no difference in BSE incidence was found between the two groups in frequencies of these variant PrP alleles (Pattison et al, 1972). The same does not seem to be true of the bovine agent.

BSE has emerged simultaneously in widely differing geographical areas throughout the UK since 1985, on an epidemic scale, although it has been noted that, in a small proportion of early BSE cases, there was a family relationship between infected individuals both within and between herds. Based on these observations, a number of researchers in the field have suggested that the disease undoubtedly has some genetic component. However, there is no supporting evidence that the occurrence of BSE varies in different breeds of cattle (Wilesmith et al, 1993). Data collected has revealed that BSE occurred in one of each of nine sets of female twins of which seven were confirmed (Wilesmith et al, 1988).

At the same time, epidemiological studies show a substantial amount of familial aggregation of the disease with 99% of BSE cases having infected first or second degree relatives, strongly suggesting genetic effects (Curnow, et al, 1994). The important point to stress here is that all cattle within a herd were consuming the same contaminated MBM in their feed. The problem is separating the effects of vertical and "first" infection hypothesis in a common shared environment, particularly where MBM was part of the daily diet. The aggregation of cases observed could be due to shared environments or to the highly structured nature of pedigree herds. Curnow, et al (1994), in one study identified 501 BSE cases and extensively examined their records which revealed that 239 were from different sires. A logistic regression analysis of data on 30 pedigree herds failed to link a possible sire effect. These results provided little difference in disease incidence among the progeny of 302 different sires, which included sires of different sire groups (Curnow et al, 1994). These researchers in their study found that herd effects varied from 3% to 28% which are statistically significant, but sire effects failed to reach the 5% significant level. The incidence within breed groups did not differ significantly by a simple chi-square test: 15.5% for Holstein, 11.9 % for Friesian x Holstein and 12.1% for Friesian (Curnow et al, 1994).

These results suggest that, in cattle, there were no host genetic factors which contributed to the susceptibility to the BSE agent responsible for the epidemic proportion of the BSE outbreak. The number of sires involved, and the absence of any common breed, militated against an autosomal genetic mode of inheritance as a cause of BSE and demonstrates that it is not a familial disease. Specific analysis of these cases, in one of the herds, further eliminated the possibility of BSE being exclusively determined by simple Law of Mendelian inheritance (Wilesmith et al, 1988). However, these researches ignored, or did not investigate, the possibility of horizontal or vertical transmission. There is a need for further careful studies, particularly of infected animals born after the feed ban, and these studies must include the possibility of maternal transmission.

To understand the genetic familial type hypothesis, one must compare kuru studies, since kuru was common among the relatives and close families. Gajdusek recorded many cases of old women and their daughters living in the same hamlet areas who were ill with kuru at the same time, although, at the time, Dr. Gajdusek concluded that the epidemiological pattern strongly appeared to suggest some genetic determinant of the disease. Even in this early kuru study, geneticists saw many problems in the simple genetic constructions for kuru. For some time, it was believed kuru was an inherited disorder. Since then it has been established both the mother and child were infected by simple coincidence. Gajdusek eventually concluded that kuru was associated with extensive cannibalism, a prevailing practice in the region. He dismissed the genetic idea, even though he was led to believe that some individual sufferers of kuru had not engaged in ritual cannibalistic consumption of their diseased relatives. The story is not much different in the current BSE epidemic.

Origin of BSE

In front of our eyes and with all the preventive techniques provided by advanced modern day science, BSE exploded simultaneously in widely separated areas of the UK. The most important feature has been the spectacular increase in incidence from the second half of 1989. This appears to have been related to the change in the incubation periods, which dropped to an average of two to three years. This gradual change and reduction in the incubation period suggests adaptation of an infection from another species.

So the genetic hypothesis, although seriously considered, could not explain the outbreak with a simple spontaneous mutation occurring in cattle with the scrapie agent. We now know that within the herd families of cattle were extensively fed with the same contaminated food rations of MBM. The BSE epidemic has been linked to an increase in the overall numbers of scrapie-infected sheep also entering the animal food chain by way of renderers (Wilesmith et al, 1991). The majority of animals became infected in calfhood through their food (Wilesmith et al, 1988). It is possible that some cows had more to eat than others, some were younger, others older, when they were fed with the MBM. Obviously some cows would develop the taste gradually, while others had more than a fair share from the start. In some cows, the dry pellet may have embedded in the gums and produced the effect of direct inoculation. All these factors would influence the incubation time.

More likely - as cattle are ruminants - the time of year strongly affects the behaviour of their digestive system - in winter (in British climates) they are consuming hay (dried grasses) and from spring they are grazing fresh grass. The bacterial content of the stomachs, therefore, changes in number and, possibly, in balance of various flora. Some conditions may help in the absorption of the agent into the host body.

Evidence from various investigations indicates the commercial concentrates as a major responsible factor, either as finished rations such as pelleted calf feed and dairy cow cake, or protein supplements which have been used in home mixed rations and were fed, at some time or other, to all BSE cows for which accurate records were available. Two animal derived products - MBM and some tallow - had been incorporated into these cattle foodstuff rations (Wilesmith et al, 1988). The distribution of MBM in cattle rations appeared to have been limited to farms within a relatively small radius of the processing factories compared with tallow (MMC, 1985).

In terms of animal waste in abattoirs which is unfit for human consumption, about 15% of all rendered material is ovine compared to about 45% of bovine origin, a ratio of 1:3 (Costelloe, 1994). The investigation of the origin of the meat and bone meal added to the different ruminant concentrated feeds fed to BSE-affected herds was extremely complicated and time-consuming. Since, in the UK rendering process, both sheep and cattle remains were included, it is difficult in epidemiological studies of BSE in the UK to distinguish between the two alternative hypotheses, the bovine and the ovine. Since the majority of cattle are killed before they are 10 years old, although infected with the scrapie agent from sheep, they have not had time to develop the clinical disease in their life span.

Mr Reed, in a statement to the Commons Agriculture Select Committee said: "On the face of it that might not have been a very serious handicap on the compounding industry using MBM, but in practice I think it has turned out to be a little more serious than any one of us thought, because it has proved impracticable to separate one type of material coming from one species from another". The high protein feed which contained the scrapie agent was prepared from both sheep and cattle. As the recycling of cattle to feed cattle continued in the 1980s, it may have been, at first, second or higher passage levels. As a result of the passage or passages from cow to cow (the true term for this should be cannibalism) the incubation period has been reduced from first passage to second, to a level where the clinical disease became apparent in the life span of the average cow. This phenomenon of reduction in the incubation period has also been observed in experimental scrapie animals. The epidemiological evidence collected so far suggests that exposure of cattle to the scrapie agent continued at a constant rate until July, 1988, when the inclusion of ruminant derived protein in the cattle rations was stopped. Based on these conclusions, Wilesmith et al (1988; 1989) predicted that the incidence of BSE would continue to rise until 1992, provided there was no further horizontal or vertical infection.

Bovine hypothesis

The theoretical possibility exists that there was an unrecognised reservoir of infection in UK cattle long before the outbreak of the BSE epidemic. The occasional death of a cow for an unexplained reason would not prompt farmers to meet the cost of having the deaths investigated. Although it is possible that a small number of isolated cases might have been misdiagnosed, as appears to have happened with the very first case, many more might also have been missed if all early cases had not appeared on the same farm and the same vet had not attended them all and realised that something was greatly amiss.

Unlike sheep, herdmen are in daily contact with their dairy cows and come to know them intimately. They would quickly spot even the earliest signs of anything developing even though the full clinical symptoms, which only show at later stages of infection, would not be apparent. It would be difficult for the farmer or herdsman in daily attendance to miss the pretty obvious clinical symptoms such as apprehensive behaviour, walking abnormalities, kicking, reduction in the milk yield and the eventual fatal outcome within six months. Sick animals would have been noticed during herd management. Although unnamed, the clinical signs of infected cows, would be recorded in herd histories and would provide indicators of the disorder. The clinical symptoms are so odd it would be hard to forget the death of such a cow. Thus, if BSE clinically had occurred even in moderate numbers, farmers and veterinary practitioners would have remembered it. There is no doubt, with the increasing number of cases, that the balloon had burst. The disease is not only important for the farmers and vets, but also to the general public. The question remains: Why did BSE cases start appearing from April 1985?

A disease known as "staggers" existed in cattle for many years in the UK, USA and France which could be confused with other disabling cattle diseases - such as Ketosis and hypo-magnesium deficiency - both of which cause the animals to be ill or to have various terminal symptoms. Long-distance transporting/shipping and travel excitement was often thought to cause the symptoms to appear. With several possible diseases of similar clinical description (and few would question the diagnosis by the vets), many BSE cases could quite easily have been wrongly attributed. Mr R G Eddy, from the Veterinary Centre Somerset, believes in retrospect that he had seen a number of cases with an annual incidence of one per 20,000 to 30,000 cows. These cases had probably been diagnosed as brain tumour or, for want of a more accurate diagnosis, chronic hypomagnesaemia. On veterinary advice, those animals which did not recover would have been slaughtered. Some veterinary practitioners agreed with him; others considered they had not previously seen the disorder in their practice. What is important to know is the ages of these suspected cases reported by Eddy (1992).

Since sheep remains had been included for many years in the preparation of MBM, a species cross-over may have kept the incubation periods well beyond the age of the average cow. However, a very few old cows may well have developed clinical symptoms and, diagnosed as having brain tumour or chronic hypomagnesaemia, been slaughtered and processed back into some type of food.

For the bovine hypothesis to be upheld, the disease must have previously existed widely throughout the country but with a very low incidence. Previously,

170

a single isolated suspected case of BSE was reported from the USA (Marsh et al, 1988) and support for this hypothesis comes from outbreaks of transmissible mink encephalopathy (TME) on some ranches in the USA. TME is considered to be a food-borne disease of mink and most often, outbreaks were related to use of scrapie-infected sheep in mink feed (Hanson et al, 1971). They always blamed sick or paralysed "downer" cows for TME outbreaks, as mink which developed TME had consumed food containing raw meat from dead cows, as part of their ration (Marsh et al, 1991). Linking scrapie sheep with outbreaks presented problems since experimental efforts to reproduce TME by intracerebral inoculation of sheep scrapie into mink had only marginal success and oral transmission experiments were not successful (Marsh et al, 1979). It has been suggested that cattle acted as the silent host (Marsh et al, 1991). Based on the TME outbreaks, using several assumptions, it was calculated that in Wisconsin, among adult cattle, the incidence of BSE could have been one in 900,000 per year (Robinson, 1994).

More recently, the susceptibility of mink to agents of bovine and ovine origin was tested by inoculating and feeding a homogenate made from infected 10% (w/v) BSE brain tissues (Robinson, 1994). In this study, all the mink, both inoculated or fed with brain tissue from BSE, developed the clinical disease with incubation periods of 12 months and 14 months respectively. However, only 15% of the mink inoculated with scrapie sheep brain developed the clinical disease, while those fed remained healthy. The results of this study indicated that mink, like the "negative line" of sheep, are relatively more susceptible to the BSE agent than to the scrapie agent through both i.c. and oral transmission (Robinson, 1994).

Ovine hypothesis

Sheep to cow infection would represent a species crossover. At the first passage of transmission from sheep to cow, the clinical disease would have a long incubation period. Further infection would establish only in a small proportion of cattle, and a small number of sporadic cases of BSE might have occurred before 1985 with a very low incidence of the order of 1 per 100,000 adult animals per year. At some stage, cattle and sheep remains were mixed together (although at the time of killing, the infected cattle appeared clinically healthy). This became a very common practice and was used at many abattoirs in England to clear away unwanted meat at the end of each day.

In the early 1970s, I noticed cattle heads, along with sheep heads, being put in the waste skip. No one saw any danger in this practice of mixing the remains of one species with those of another and using the mixture to feed back to the same species. While a cow infected with the scrapie agent directly from sheep may not have developed the clinical disease within its lifespan, the use of subclinical infected cattle in the preparation of MBM created a situation similar to that of serial passage of the agent. Transmission of the agent from cow to cow helped in the selection of a unique virulent strain of BSE, with a reduced incubation period, to a level where the clinical disease became apparent in the life span of an average cow.

To test the feasibility of the "scrapie sheep" hypothesis, it must first be shown whether or not cattle can be infected by the scrapie agent from sheep. Previously, susceptibility of cattle to scrapie from sheep and goats had been demonstrated by simultaneous i.c., i.p., intravenous (i.v.) and oral dosing of brain homogenates from scrapie sheep (Gibbs et al, 1990). Three out of ten cows developed typical clinical signs of BSE, and later histological examination of brains confirmed the disease. The experimental transmission of scrapie to cattle has been independently confirmed (Robinson, 1994) but it is important to point out that in the second study, none of the calves revealed the histopathological changes seen in natural BSE cases. However, these brains were positive for immunohistochemistry for PrP (Robinson, 1994). The transmissibility of scrapie to cattle by parenteral exposure shows the susceptible nature of the scrapie sheep.

These results, because of negative pathology, do not directly address the issue because the study was carried out with an "American strain" of the scrapie agent, and that may not be representative of the scrapie sheep strain in the UK. Scrapie of sheep is one of the most common SEs to be found throughout Europe, America and Asia. Important questions about the interspecies transmission of these diseases are now very relevant.

The negative histopathological results in significant numbers of clinically suspected cases, BAB, suggest that they are indeed BSE cases which might have been either infected with scrapie or with a different mutant strain of the agent. The clinically diagnosed BSE brains that were found negative by histopathological examination were not tested by transmission studies to rule out the possibility of a different strain of scrapie.

Although at least 20 stable strains of the scrapie agent have been identified, numerous studies have revealed that the BSE agent is a novel major strain and is naturally transmitted with food from one species to another.

However, based on clinical signs, as stated before, there are two readily recognisable clinical varieties of scrapie, Type I, the 'itchy' variety and type II, the 'trotting' variety. Throughout the world, the itchy type is by far the most common. In the Type 2, the 'trotting' type of scrapie, the animals tremble while standing and exhibit a peculiar action of the forelegs while running, the so-called 'cuddie trot'. When a sheep so affected is unexpectedly chased, or excited, it collapses to the ground in a faint exhausted condition and is unable to rise. In this trotting variety itchiness may be apparent, there is seldom any loss of wool.

Clinically, this 'trotting' variety resembles symptoms seen in BSE and kuru. It is the same major symptom as that of 'new strain' CJD . In short, Type Two trotting is the disease agent most likely to have infected cattle and humans. It would appear that BSE has been derived from the recycling of the 'trotting' variety and not the common 'itchy' variety of scrapie. Yet, despite this, most of the experiments being done to demonstrate the origin of BSE are being carried out using the 'itchy' variety. In most experiments, it appears that if cattle are experimentally inoculated with 'Type One', they will develop a clinical disease, but there will be no equivalent BSE-typical lesions in the brain. Yet no experiments have been done by MAFF to determine whether or not Type Two is the real source of BSE.

Additionally, evidence to support BSE being a new strain comes from other animal transmission studies. Four calves were each inoculated with a different strain of TME. All calves showed the clinical signs around 15 months post-inoculation (Robinson, 1994). Histopathological examination of their brains revealed both the astrocytic response and vacuolar degeneration to be much more extensive than the negative SE pathology seen in calves inoculated with the scrapie sheep (Robinson, 1994). The extensive vacuolar lesions in the TME inoculated calves, the new host species, suggests that a new strain or source of infection has occurred. It is strange that no further investigation is being carried out to rule out this possibility.

Other factors involved in the origin of BSE

A number of factors have been identified which, when combined, explain the origin of BSE. To maximise production of beef, calves and milk after the second World War, cattle were fed cheap high protein- chiefly abattoir waste including sheep's brains - processed into meal. The total use of MBM increased between 1960 and 1980 to a maximum of about 50% compound feed per cow (Cooke, 1990). In the last decade, MBM has also been exported and therefore a lot more animal protein was being fed to cows which were in turn producing more milk. It has been suggested that there has been a more gradual increase in the number of sheep flocks infected with scrapie. These two changes were considered to account for an increased and wider distribution of the source of infection. Morgan (1988) suggested that the increased exposure to the scrapie agent led to the species barrier being crossed. However, to this day, contaminated ruminant derived protein feed, MBM, theoretically responsible for the infection, has not been used experimentally in the laboratory animals to produce the disease. It is hard to understand why this vital experiment has not been done.

BSE in cattle born after the feed ban (BAB)

In July 1988 the feed ban on the use of ruminant-derived protein in ruminant foodstuff was introduced however, the occurrence of cases in animals born after 18 July 1988, did not surprise MAFF officials. MAFF had originally suggested, that the number of cases would decline after a ban on the inclusion of "animal protein" in the livestock feed, and the disease would die out by 1992, presumably when all the cattle born before the feed ban had died. Over the years,

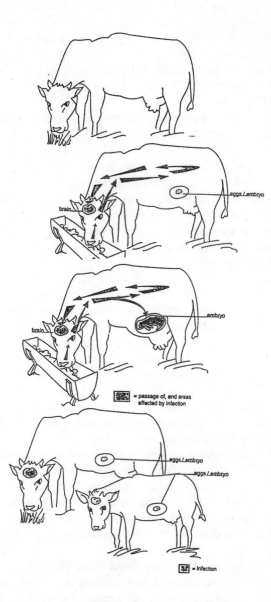

Fig 17. Four natural sources of infection of cattle: 1 natural infected pasture; 2 and 3. contaminated feed infecting both mother and foetus. 4 Vertical transmission

an ever-increasing number of cows BABs showing BSE clinical symptoms were found histopathologically "BSE negative". Based on the assessment of a case-control study, MAFF continued to classify all cases of BSE in cattle born after the ban as horizontally-acquired infection. Farmers, however, order their feed stock for no more than six weeks in advance and since calves were not fed with MBM until they were four to six weeks old, there should have been no MBM on most farms.

The ban on contaminated food which should have stopped this mode of infection through cattle began in July 1988. However, as at May 1996, there have been over 29,000 confirmed cases of BSE in cattle born after the feed ban (BABs). In herds where supplementary feed had been given, the number of cases varies according to season and is highest during the winter. In BABs however, there is a different pattern and the peak is during the summer months. It is commonly accepted that the disease in cattle originated and was transmitted in feed containing the infectious agent from scrapie and BSE cattle. It seems, therefore, that there must be a different mode of infection in BABs. Moreover, a large proportion of BSE confirmed calves were born in 1989, 1990 and 1991. Although all this information was available, MAFF still took the view that there was no evidence of the infection being spread among cattle from the presence of such natural tissues as placenta and ever present excrements.

It is very difficult to explain how over 29, 000 confirmed cases of BSE in calves were born after the ban on the 'Bin end' theory, or by 'old-style foodstuff hanging about on farms'. Of course MAFF has classified a very large number of cattle as at risk. This is presumably due to the fact that they were fed with the contaminated feed. Further, MAFF did realised that sub-clinical BSE cases could be highly infective. A considerable number of cattle born from cattle-infected without clinical symptoms might well be cases of maternal transmission.

There are two other possible explanations for these large number of BSE cases in cattle BAB.

1) It is known from experiments that, when pregnant mice are inoculated with the scrapie agent, mother and litter develop the clinical disease. Since cows have been fed from calfhood with MBM containing the BSE agent and this feeding continued throughout their life, it is therefore possible that the foetuses were being infected from the feed the cows were eating while pregnant (Fig 17).

2) Although MBM which could in fact contain the BSE agent was not being directly fed to cattle, until April 1996 it was being used to feed poultry, pig and fish. Initially MAFF argued that poultry were not at risk, because of the enormous zoological divide between cattle and poultry. Because of long incubation periods the BSE agent may or may not get established in the bird's brain. It is a fact that the BSE agent can survive very harsh conditions. It is most likely, therefore, that once the bird is eating MBM, the BSE agent will be present in concentrated form in bird droppings. These bird droppings from poultry farms are mixed into some feed compounding for cattle feed. Poultry manure is also

175

used on organic farms where cows graze. This has been an unknown indirect route of recycling of infection of cattle with the BSE agent producing the disease on some organic farms.

Enzymes in foodstuff

It appears that, in the early cases, the affected animals had received proprietary foodstuffs. Renderers take the remains of animals from the butchery trade, process the material into tallow or lard and the residue becomes MBM. Tallow and MBM are supplied to feed compounders for use as ingredients in livestock feed. The function of the feed compounders is totally different from that of renderers of animal wastes. The role of the feed compounders is to blend together raw materials to provide livestock with balanced rations that will give the necessary proteins and energy, either as finished rations, such as pellets for calf feed and dairy cow cake, or as protein supplements to be combined in home mixed rations. Some compounders use enzymes which are added in the processing of the feed stuff to improve the overall digestibility and to release valuable feed nutrients from the raw materials. The raw materials used include: home grown cereals, cereal by-products from the food industry, oil cake fat as well as animal proteins. However, there is no reason to hold any one compounder of proprietary food particularly responsible.

To improve milk production some feed suppliers supplemented the dairy feed at a rate of 30 g per cattle per day with enzymes (Kemin Industries Des Moines Iowa, USA, EZ/K/34), for example Alpha-maylase, beta-glucanase, cellulase complex (including pentosanase, xylanase, pectinase and cellobiase), hemicellulase, protease, lipase anise flavour and carriers. These enzymes have been used extensively, although their side effects, if any, on human, or animal health in general remains unknown! The quantities of enzymes used would certainly break up the food during digestion, but would also release the scrapie agent from its protected hard protein shell. They could also change the ruminants' bacterial flora and cause physical changes to the stomach walls and the absorption rate throughout the digestive tract. Enzymes might simply alter the structure and damage the intestinal wall and so create a route for the agent (Narang, 1996). This process of damage of intestinal wall would help in entry adaptation of the agent from one species to another. Once the infection has been established in a new host species, the practice of cannibalism would then produce the epidemic disease without any need for enzymes.

The possible harmful effects of enzymes on animal health are unknown. While investigating BSE with one farmer, I found that, enzymes could be very harmful to human health and the risk requires further full investigation.

A pig farmer, who has kept about 800 pigs for over 15 years, has three children 7 to 10 years of age. The family had always enjoyed good health. He was in the Ministry Pig Health Scheme and an Approved source of breeding stock in the UK. He suddenly started having problems on his farm. In April 1988, he had

176

chest pains during the night and was found to have a blood clot on his lung. He recovered after the blood clot was removed. However, chest spasms continued in 1989-90-91.

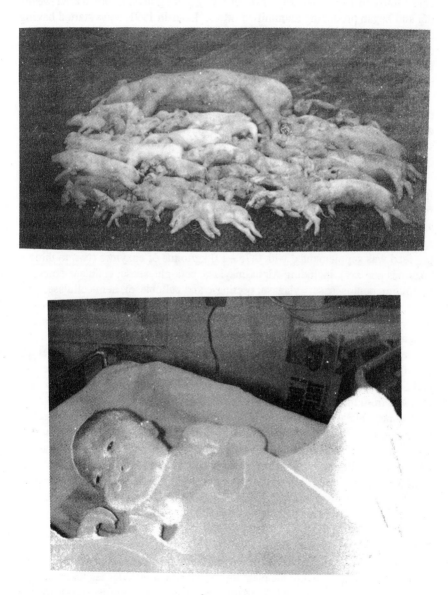

Fig 18 A group of deformed piglets. Fig 19 The deformed baby.

177

In the spring of 1989, his sows went out of condition and he was advised by a nutritionist that they required extra minerals. Later that year, piglets were born with their skin like raw meat and within three to four weeks developed red blotches. Early in 1990, the farmer had difficulty getting them to breed after weaning and began producing mummified litters. Later in 1991, sows started having deformed litters. The perinatal mortality among these pigs was very high. The detailed deformities varied widely (Fig 18). The degree and combination of defects continued for three generations when all the stock was killed for humanitarian reasons.

In spring 1991, the farmer's wife became pregnant but continued working on the farm feeding the pigs. The pig food comes in a powder form which is very dusty and often the feed ducts were blocked and had to be cleaned. At 29 weeks a scan revealed that the baby was not viable, and it was born deformed at the end of October 1991, dying within 1 hour of birth (Fig 19).

Looking back in the records, it appears that, from 1987-88, the pig feed came from a different supplier to that previously used. The pigs were fed with pig feed, two to three kg per head, per day and were provided with straw for eating and bedding. After discussions with the food compounders, it was found that enzymes had been added to the feed. Checking on such products revealed that the pig feed was supplemented with 0.75 - 1.0 kg/tonne of enzymes (two to three g enzymes per day), including Alpha-maylase, beta-glucanase, cellulase complex (including pentosanase, xylanase, pectinase and cellobiase), hemicellulase, protease, lipase anise flavour and carriers. Some of these enzymes are also used extensively in Biological washing powders where their side effects on human or animal health remains as yet unknown.

Defects and disabilities in thalidomide children are well documented (Smithells, 1973). Recently, thalidomide deformity has been reported in the second generation. However, the defects seen in pigs and the baby reported here, are different from those seen in thalidomide children.

The possible accidental co-incidence of deformed piglets in the pig herd and the tragic history of the farmer's wife, where there was no previous history (within a short time) should arouse awareness of possible effects of enzymes on developing embryos of all species. The occurrence of similar deformities, both in piglets and the baby, suggests a common environmental source. It is important therefore, that new animal experiments be conducted and coordinated to look at this accidental unique challenging opportunity.

Spongiosis due to toxins

It was considered that the extensive widespread neuronal degeneration might be due to the toxic effect of the plant locoweed, which includes leguminus plants of the genus *Astragalus* and *Oxytropis* and causes chronic locoisum in live stock, including cattle, horses and sheep. The disorder is characterised by motor and sensory nerve damage resulting in peculiarities of gait, impairment of vision

178

and extreme excitement, sometimes with confusion. However, clinical signs of BSE are unlike those observed in locoweed poisoning in the USA. Locoweed does not grow in England. Moreover, epidemiological studies of BSE cases revealed no evidence of any toxic agent being involved in the aetiology of the cattle disease (Wells et al, 1988).

The organophosphate link

Mark Purdey (1992), a farmer in Somerset, England considered that in Britain the epidemic was centred on areas which had been designated by MAFF as 'warble fly eradication zones' some three years earlier. Farmers in these zones were legally obliged to treat their cattle with one of three pour-on quasi-systemic "phenyl-phosphorothionate" organophosphorus insecticides known as Phosmet, Famphur and Fenthion (O'Keefe et al, 1983). On large production unit farms, these prophylactic organophosphorus substances are regularly applied to the whole herd. In support of his hypothesis, Purdey was able to chart the history of a cow that died of BSE. The cow had been treated with organophosphorus during its life three years prior to the onset of the disease (Purdey, 1994). Further, he gave an example of a farmer who had one of his three farms included in a warble fly zone in 1985. The replacement cattle which were moved onto the two farms outside the zone remained BSE free while a high incidence of the replacements moved onto the farm within the zone developed BSE a few years later.

However, he also found farms where cattle had been treated with organophosphorus but had no cases of BSE. He considered that it might be a coincidence that those farmers who avoided the use of organophosphorus substances had no incidence of BSE in the cattle they reared. However, outside the warble fly zones, organophosphorus substances have also been applied, although perhaps not extensively. There is no reliable link between the number of BSE cases and the use of organophosphorus substances. The spread of BSE cases throughout the whole of England and Ireland discounted the theory that organophosphorus substances were responsible for BSE. Organophosphorus substances are chemical neurotoxins while the BSE agent is a replicating agent.

It is however, possible that neurotoxins do play an indirect role in reducing the incubation period, since some of these substances damage the nerve cells and might well make them more prone to infection and thereby reduce the period of incubation. This phenomenon is well illustrated by the example of Down's syndrome mice. The scrapie infection susceptibility study in chimeras and control group mice revealed that the onset of symptoms of scrapie in the chimeras mice was brought forward by 17 days compared to the control. The probability is that, in the chimeras mice, the neurons are developmentally immature relative to control, thereby shortening the incubation period.

Although it is known that there are a number of neurotoxic substances which selectively destroy neurons and damage the central nervous system, one important difference between viral encephalopathies and neurotoxic substances is that,

179

after inoculation or feeding a new host with these two substances, neurotoxins do not replicate and increase in amount or produce a similar predictable disease, while viruses replicate and increase in number.

From the known properties of the BSE and scrapie agents, it is unlikely that organophosphorus insecticides are the cause or that they play any significant role in the pathogenesis of the disease. BSE is a transmissible disease. The tissues from a BSE cow brain when inoculated into a variety of hosts which have not, in any way, been treated with organophosphorus compounds, always develop a similar predictable clinical disease. Furthermore, the amount of the BSE agent increases throughout t' ' incubation period. Further, with the SE agent there are a number of predictable differing strains of the scrapie agent which support the hypothesis that the scrapie agent, like other living organisms, contains a nucleic acid genome which replicates and produces the clinical disease.

Hexachlorohane (Hexachlorophene) toxicity

Hexachlorohane is a bactericide and anthelmintic (an agent which is destructive to worms), and was marketed as a disinfectant and used in cosmetic antiseptic soap, talcum powder and in toothpaste. In animals it has a limited use as an extremely efficient skin antiseptic, particularly as an under-wash. Its toxicity in cattle was reported in calves over a period of three years (Jack, 1988). The calves had become intoxicated by drinking milk from buckets which had, at times, been contaminated with under wash containing 9.6 w/v hexachlorohane. Essentially, clinical signs were muscular tremor and nervous degeneration (Jack, 1988). Examination of the brains from these calves revealed no histopathological abnormalities and no cases resembling those seen in calves were recorded in adult cattle.

Prospect for BSE vaccine

A phenomenon analogous to "interference" has been demonstrated by the inoculation of mice, first with a long incubation strain (600 days+) of the scrapie agent followed by inoculation a few weeks later with a short incubation strain (150 days) of the scrapie agent into the same mice. Inoculation first with the 'long' strain inhibits replication of the 'shorter' strain, but inoculation first with the 'short' strain inhibits replication of the "long" strain. In experimental serial propagation, the scrapie strains breed true with a precise copying process, to ensure stability of strains of the agent within a fixed host (Bruce et al, 1987; Dickinson et al, 1979).

Experiments where cattle and mink were fed with 'type I' scrapie sheep brain tissues revealed that these animals did not develop the clinical disease (Robinson, 1994). Since these animals stayed healthy, the phenomenon of 'interference' should be explored. The pre- challenged mink and cattle should be inoculated with the BSE agent to determine the blocking mechanism and potential for a vaccine. Development of such a vaccine would stop horizontal transmission of

SE in cattle and help to eradicate BSE.

Treatment, remission and recovery of BSE cases

There are only a few experimental studies published where cattle have been treated for BSE symptoms. In experimental tests animals at all stages of the illness, particularly those in the early phases, were put on a variety of therapeutic regimens. None of the drugs employed was able to influence the course of the disease. Purdey (1994) treated one of his BSE cows after this cow calved in January 1991. The cow went down with a severe relapse of milk fever, due to complex biochemical disturbances and the symptoms were ascribed to chronic magnesium deficiency. The cow was twice injected with calcium borogluconate and magnesium sulphate before regaining health. During the following spring, the cow gradually developed the classic initial symptoms of BSE, including apprehension and an uncoordinated gait with loss of milk yield. The cow, in June of the same year was injected with two bottles of magnesium sulphate. This caused a dramatic remission of the majority of neurological symptoms approximately 30 hours after the treatment. However, after a short remission, the symptoms of BSE worsened in the cow which also suffered weight loss. Diagnosis of BSE was confirmed in this cow by histopathological examination of the brain.

Many other farmers who suspected BSE, treated their cows for chronic magnesium deficiency in the first instance. In some of these cases, they noticed a similar short-term alleviation of the initial symptoms as observed by Purdey. Eventually these cows developed full blown BSE, and were diagnosed as BSE positive after slaughter. MAFF also carried out similar trials with magnesium treatment. The treated cows showed only a temporary remission cf BSE symptoms. It is important to stress that true chronic magnesium deficiency cases would recover. It is possible for a temporary remission of clinical symptoms in BSE cases to occur, but the underlying degenerative process of the CNS continues unhindered.

Eradication of BSE from the herd

Statutory action to control a disease which ffects only animals, must generally be justified on economic grounds. However, where public health is at risk, the arguments are very different and economic arguments are far from the sole consideration. Having decided to attempt control by statutory means, MAFF had to formulate an appropriate programme to control and eradicate the disease. BSE being a 'new disease', with no precedents to follow, other than the link with scrapie the need to study and understand scrapie became all the more crucial. The measures taken to control BSE failed to take account of what was known about scrapie in sheep. There were no recommendations discouraging farmers from breeding from offspring of infected cows. MAFF reaffirmed that such universal advice should not be given because such a measure would not provide an effective way of controlling an outbreak. The epidemiological advice was unequivocal: however frequently maternal transmission were to occur, BSE would still die out because it would be impossible, under British farming conditions, for each BSE case to produce one female offspring surviving long enough to develop the disease. Therefore, MAFF hoped that the disease would be self-limiting.

Wilesmith (1991) states that to sustain natural BSE in the cattle population through vertical transmission, each infected individual animal would have to pass on the disease to at least one other individual animal, that is 1:1. Most cattle which eventually develop the disease do so at approximately four to five years of age, by which time a cow would have produced a maximum of four calves. Given the current pattern of breeding and herd replacement in the UK, only one in four (25%) calves produced by an individual cow, will enter the adult herd, because bull calves and beef breeds would be slaughtered at 18 months to two years of age before the clinical disease would develop in them. Therefore, according to Wilesmith, each BSE cow will produce, on average less than one female calf to reach adulthood, and herself produce offspring. Also, if BSE is maternally transmissible, it may not achieve an incidence of 100%, which in turn would reduce still further the likelihood of an infected cow passing the disease on to successive generations; culling would remove 75% of cattle, and therefore, with it BSE would be eradicated.

These are assumptions; that the one calf which would reach adulthood will not be an infected one. Often terms are used like 'there may be slight vertical transmission'. An infection cannot be 'slight', either the calf is infected or not infected. What if the calf which is infected was not the one culled and those culled were not infected? It is important to stress that farmers have observed that, where the mother cow has died of BSE, her calf also developed BSE. From their accounts, it is an established fact that vertical transmission does exist: therefore by breeding from BSE infected cattle the UK herd will never be free of BSE. The first recorded case of vertical transmission where a cow died of BSE, and its calf also developed BSE, was confirmed in April 1991.

In one of MAFF's own experiments of transmission studies, Dowson et al (1994), inoculated 16 calves with the BSE agent and four with saline solution. Two out of these four control calves which had not been inoculated with the BSE agent, also developed BSE. These investigators suggested, BSE cases in control calves were due to cross contamination. The detailed results published however, revealed that the incubation periods were longer in the control group of calves, and suggested maternal transmission was the route of infection. Results of the other two control calves are still not published. Breeding and herd replacement patterns, combined with the age at which BSE develops, strongly suggest that it is unlikely that BSE will eradicate itself and disappear from the national cattle population.

Comparison of congenital mechanism in BSE and scrapie

Although transmission of the disease from parent to offspring, namely vertical transmission, has been talked about in scrapie, it is known that calves born of BSE mothers develop BSE. In the broad sense, vertical transmission includes utero exposure. Maternal transmission has been used in many studies to mean vertical transmission including both prenatal and neonatal infection (Dickinson et al, 1974). Many of the previous attempts to detect the scrapie agent in foetuses of infected sheep failed. The scrapie agent however, has been detected several times in the placenta from infected sheep and also often in various parts of the ewe's reproductive tract (Foote et al, 1993). What role, if any, the placenta and reproductive parts of infected females play during gestation, is not known. The infected organ however, could provide a frequent source of extraneural infection in the herd. The involvement of the mammary glands, colostrum, and milk in maternal transmission also needs urgent evaluation.

Evidence indicating a hereditary or congenital mechanism in the spread of scrapie among sheep, has been well documented throughout the literature. If cows which have not been fed with MBM, developed BSE, it would strongly demonstrate involvement of vertical transmission of BSE in the same way as seen in scrapie sheep. From July 1988, the reduced risk of infection from feed following the introduction of the ruminant feed ban, made it possible to investigate the occurrence of other potential modes of transmission of the disease in cattle. After the feed ban of MBM, it is possible that on some farms, this contaminated feed would remain for six to eight weeks, thereby allowing the suspicion of horizontal transmission to exist. It is also possible, cows have continued to infect the land with the BSE agent, and so also facilitate horizontal transmission. The possible role of maternal transmission from a cow to its own calf continues to be studied by both field and experimental investigations.

To address the vital questions of vertical transmission, MAFF began an experiment in 1990. They housed 630 cattle in relative isolation on four farms since 1990. Calves were divided into 2 groups: Group I (315) were the progeny of cattle known to have died from BSE. The other half (315) were taken from the same farms at the same time but their parent cows were then healthy. The purpose of the study was to demonstrate one way or another the existence of vertical transmission. A moment's reflection however, reveals the lack of a proper control in these experiment. Who can say whether the allegedly healthy parent cows subsequently went on to develop BSE? Neither MAFF nor anyone else knows what happened to the parent cows. From its very start, the experiment was fatally flawed, and the whole purpose of the study defeated.

Moreover, MAFF is now claiming both groups to have been fed ruminant protein the source of which may perhaps have been contaminated. If this is true, it is very strange that these experimental cows on MAFF's own farms were being fed with MBM. So even if the proposed control had been provided, the experiment would still have been valueless. Millions of pounds of research money has been wasted by these elementary mistakes of MAFF scientists. That experiment was due to end in 1997. During this experiment, MAFF mislaid 32 cows from each group which they are unable to account for. Results so far reported showed that 42 of the 273 cows in group 1 have developed BSE and 14 in group 2. With no record of the parent cows in group 2, it is impossible to assess whether the 14 cases of BSE in that group represent horizontal transmission or maternal/vertical transmission, and with the experiment still for some years having to run, and many more clinical BSE cases may well develop. Diagnostic lesions have been found in the brains of four others. The group these animals belong to is unknown, but they were killed when seven years old without clinical BSE being suspected. Therefore, results so far available as to maternal/vertical transmission are unreliable and probably underestimates.

The evidence supporting vertical transmission is further supported by the point made here: The epidemiological data on clinical onset by age, taking account of: (1); the long incubation period of BSE, (2); feeding with contaminated meat and bone meal, (3); the degrees to which animals develop clinical disease, (4); the fact that not all animals will get infected with the first dose, which itself may also vary. So the true incubation period can only be guessed. Maternal/vertical transmission may alter the incubation periods and a low dose of infection would considerably extend them. Currently, the fact that 60% of BSE cases being confirmed are in cattle born after the feed ban., must be sound evidence to support maternal/vertical transmission.

Within two years of the beginning of the BSE epidemic, the incubation period suddenly decreased from five to six years to between two to three years. This reduction is thought due to direct feeding of MBM prepared from BSE infected cows. In BAB cattle, the incubation period appears to have returned to five and six years. This changing pattern reflects the fact that calves born after the MBM feed ban have been exposed either to a smaller dose of the infected BSE agent or by a different route. The slaughter of about 75% of calves destined for beef at ages between 18 and 24 months, will have prevented their showing clinical symptoms and so in MAFF statistic returns being reported free of BSE. The remaining 25% of animals would be used for breeding replacement (Wilesmith, 1991).

MAFF considered that if there was vertical transmission, the killing of three quarters of animals would eliminate BSE but no one knows what percentage of cattle are infected by vertical transmission. It may be that those not infected will be killed leaving open the big question: Will British herds ever be free of the BSE agent? BSE may well occur with variable degrees from year to year, appearing on some farms, then disappearing and reappearing, in the same way as scrapie has done in sheep. BSE would become a permanent feature of British cattle and it will be impossible to eradicate the disease. A ban on breeding from affected offspring would have been the only way to halt the spread of the disease by vertical transmission. The policy should have been to breed only from ani-

184

mals in herds where no BSE case had ever been confirmed and the herds were never fed with MBM. Our new stock should be rebuilt from these BSE free herds.

MAFF had every reason to believe that BSE to follow the same path as scrapie. In spite of knowing from the experience of generations of shepherds that the only way to eradicate scrapie from a flock was to speedily remove infected sheep and prevent their breeding, MAFF apparently favouring short-term commercial considerations over long-term concerns, ignored the warning signs. They allowed the free movement of cattle from infected herds onto BSE-free farms, seeing no risk or reason to ban this mode of spreading the disease: they saw no reason to remove the offspring of infected beasts from the herd and no reason to prevent them from breeding. Infected blood-lines were allowed to continue. They regarded talk of any transmission in the blood-lines (maternal transmission) as mere speculation and went blindly ahead ignoring the evidence that the offspring of infected animals nearly always develop the disease. They disregarded the lessons of history and the warnings of many experienced scientists. The cost of these mistakes was to be horrendously high, leading to the culling of thousands of beasts -- infected and uninfected alike. The maternal transmission they regarded as speculation proved to be fact; horizontal transmission also contributed to the spread of the infection. Unfortunately, breeding from infected animals - admittedly only those showing no clinical symptoms - still continues, and the increasing number of generations stemming back to an infected animal, confuses the identification of future generations of potentially-infected animals and in four or five years eradication of the disease has already become impossible. What MAFF did not take into account was that farmers, who were breeding from BSE affected cattle, were in fact running a natural experiment all the time in the field and running well ahead of MAFF's own experiment. The most recent change in policy adopted by MAFF claims that simple culling of animals over 30 moths will eliminate BSE. European Union officials, however, insist on far wider and more extensive culling policies. The British taxpayer will be required to meet much of the cost of cattle culled whether infected or not and on top have to pay millions for their incineration.

Mr Kevin Taylor, Britain's assistant chief veterinary officer, concluded that scientists had only limited understanding of the two infection routes of BSE. Maybe he was thinking of MAFF, whose own scientists do have limited understanding, when he said of vertical transmission: "Evidence that they occur, but infrequently," (Independent, November 1994). He went on with the assurance that neither maternal nor horizontal transmission gave cause for much concern. While vertical transmission has been confirmed, the culling of cows before the clinical disease develops limits the apparent number of BSE cases. The true effect of vertical transmission can only be assessed when cows are allowed to live beyond the age of five years. Although, when he made the statement, he must have realised that the animals culled would go for human consumption, he makes no announcement about this anomaly and the sequelae for both animal and human health.

The obvious danger of this policy is that BSE is firmly established in British cattle and may persist for years with great economic loss from time to time. The House of Commons Agricultural Committee in 1990 considered the slaughter of all calves of cows with BSE; this was based on the presupposition that BSE is a maternally transmissible disease from mother to calf, a possibility which had not been confirmed at the time. In the Committee's view: "If vertical transmission were proved to take place, the policy implications would be substantial. The slaughter of the offspring of BSE-infected cattle or ban on breeding from these offspring might be warranted on precautionary grounds." But again economics came in its way, " Britain's substantial export trade in cattle, semen and embryos would be badly hit."... "MAFF must be prepared, however, to implement them if maternal transmission is confirmed". Right in front of their own eyes, it has been confirmed to be the reality.

Without experimental confirmation, for MAFF, vertical transmission does exist. MAFF believed that BSE would die out within one generation but they apparently saw little reason to initiate such experiments as a matter of urgency. MAFF believed that even if BSE were maternally transmissible from mother to calf, it would see itself off by breeding and culling, in spite of knowing that scrapie in sheep does not disappear by culling alone. But, for practical purposes, most of the measures taken are too late. It certainly appears that eight years have been lost. MAFF has been wasting valuable time, and still is, while all the time the agent has been gaining strength and the cost of eradicating the disease could be well over 100 to 1,000 times as much as might have been. The only reasonable policy at the very start would have been to cull the progeny of BSE cows and ban their use for breeding purposes. There is no doubt that some prudent live-stock farmers did avoid breeding from infected lines - a policy developed from their own experience and supported possibly by their veterinary surgeons. This, however, would only be a drop in the ocean. Voluntary action could never be enough to eradicate the problem.

BSE in other countries

The outbreak of the BSE epidemic in UK cattle has carried with it major implications for the risk of the disease spreading to other countries. The first notified case to occur outside mainland Britain was in 1988, in Northern Ireland, where over 1,700 cases have since occurred. Epidemiological studies suggest that BSE in Northern Ireland did not originate from indigenous scrapie but from MBM imported from Britain (Denny et al, 1992). Outside the UK, BSE has occurred in home bred animals in the Republic of Ireland , France, Portugal and Switzerland. In other countries all the cases which have occurred have been among animals born in the UK. The most likely explanation for this is the export of asymptomatic infected cattle or the use of infected feedstuff.

186

BSE in The Republic of Ireland

The first case of BSE in the Republic of Ireland was confirmed in January 1989, in a four year old Friesian cow from a dairy herd of 25 cows in County Cavan. Until the end of August 1993 there were a total of 74 confirmed cases of BSE of which ten were imported from the United Kingdom (Costelloe, 1994), and the remaining 64, with the possible exception of 4, would have received feed containing MBM. By the end of 1995 there were 112 and by 1996 this had risen to 124.

In the Republic of Ireland, no case has been recorded in animals born since the introduction of a total ban on the feeding of MBM to ruminants. Costelloe, (1994) suggested that the situation in Ireland is very different from the UK in that there is less scrapie, and the ratio of ovine to bovine material rendered is approximately 1:10. Further, the use of animal meat in feed is about 10 times less in Ireland than in Great Britain. Ireland practices a traditional, highly intensive livestock production system based on grass and silage. The Department of Agriculture and Food as it was then known, introduced compulsory notification of suspected cases of BSE in 1989, with restrictions on movement, the destruction of carcases, payment of compensation and the ban on the use of milk except to feed a cow's own calf (Costelloe, 1994). The progeny of infected dams in 1989 have been purchased, and held at the Department's Veterinary Research Laboratory farm at Abbotstown (Costelloe, 1994). Movement restrictions were placed on the herds in which BSE had occurred (Costelloe, 1994). To compensate for the severe financial and management problems the herd owners were suffering, a scheme of voluntary depopulation of the herds was introduced. Up to September, 1993, 71 herds comprising 9,474 animals have been depopulated at a cost of £6.7 m. The depopulation policy still continues (Costelloe, 1994). The Government in the Republic of Ireland decided to kill all the cattle in a herd following the diagnosis of one BSE case, to remove any chance of vertical transmission. Depopulation of infected herds formed a major difference between the UK and the Republic of Ireland, and the success of the policy strengthens the belief that BSE cases in cattle born after the feed ban in the UK might be due to vertical transmission.

BSE in Switzerland

The first case of BSE in Swiss cattle was recognised in November 1990, four years after the first UK case. The number of cases gradually increased to 40 by the end of July 1993 in a total of 796,000 animals. That number rose to 183 at the end of 1995 and, at 10 May 1996, the BSE cases reached 214. Switzerland has hardly imported any living cattle from Great Britain in the last decade. Most of the Swiss cattle had been fed concentration rations containing MBM (Hörnlimann et al, 1994). (Switzerland has a relatively small sheep population, about 10 sheep per square kilometre vs. 175 in the UK. Further, Swiss sheep are free from scrapie. There was only one confirmed case of scrapie in a sheep in

1991, one in a goat in 1993, and two more in sheep in 1993). Since the major factors contributing to BSE did not exist in the country, the occurrence of the disease in Switzerland was particularly unexpected.

Swiss animal waste renderers always used the wet heat "pressure cooking system" at greater than atmospheric pressure (120°C or 130°C for 30 or 20 minutes respectively). However, 22% of all MBM concentrate foodstuff imported from 1985 to 1990 came from the UK and it was concluded that Swiss cases were the result of the importation and the use of contaminated ingredients in concentrated cattle feeds (Hörnlimann et al, 1994). The majority of cattle at risk were dairy and beef cows, all of which were exposed to MBM concentrate during their calfhood prior to December 1990. The fact that beef cattle are slaughtered before 18 months of age, while the minimum incubation period of BSE is about two years, precludes the development of the clinical disease by feeding cattle, although this does not mean that beef cattle would be free from infection. When the BSE survey was put into effect, out of a total of 215 suspect cattle only 40 (19%) revealed the microscopical lesions of BSE (Hörnlimann et al, 1994). This confirmation in Swiss cases is relatively low compared to comparatively high correlation of about 88% between suspected and confirmed cases in the UK (Matthews, 1990).

BSE in other countries

Historically, there is a description of what may have been a case of scrapie in an ox in an old French writing, and, although the symptoms described were typical of scrapie, it was not accepted, from one case, that the ox was susceptible to the disease. In 1912, Quevedo described a condition like scrapie in horses, sheep and cattle in Argentina. BSE in other countries has been confirmed, six cases in France, one case in Denmark and one case on the Falkland Islands. The six confirmed French BSE cases out of 112 BSE suspect clinical cases were in indigenous cattle (Sayey et al, 1994), while in Denmark, and the Falkland Islands, the affected cattle were imported from the UK.

As at 10 May 1996, the following cases have been confirmed in other countries; Isle of Man, 464; Guernsey, 564; Jersey, 120; Alderney, 2; France, 20; Germany, 4; Portugal, 37; Denmark, 1; the Falkland Islands, 1; and the Sultanate of Oman, 2. Clinical cases of BSE in Oman, France and Denmark were all imported from the UK (Kimberlin, 1994). These cases were confirmed histopathologically by the CVL, England and their history suggested that the cattle were fed the contaminated foodstuffs in calfhood prior to their exported from England.

Possible risk of BSE in United States and Spain

Assessment of the risk of BSE occurring in the USA has been carried out (Marsh, 1990) and, despite intensive surveillance efforts for the past three years, no variant of the disease has been detected in the US cattle population (Robinson, 1994). In the USA, however, 478 flocks of sheep have been diagnosed with scrapie. The lower incidence of scrapie in the smaller number of sheep, and current practice of only feeding small quantities of MBM were the reasons given to believe that the risk of BSE has been lower in the USA than the UK (Marsh, 1990). More recently, before the UK experience of BSE, the tendency to feed non-degradable "by-pass" protein resulted in the use of more MBM, hydrolysed feather meal, fish meal, poultry meal and blood meal in cattle rations. These products were being fed mainly to lactating dairy cows which would indicate that their average age on first exposure would be between two and five years (Marsh, 1990). Since the incubation period for BSE is estimated to be three to eight years, only a small proportion of American cattle would have time to develop BSE before being killed. Whether or not any cattle remains were included with sheep carcases in the preparation of MBM in the USA or other countries as was the case in the British foodstuff is uncertain.

There are two points for selection of the BSE strain: (1) sheep brains from tremblie, a rare type of scrapie, were used in the preparation of MBM; (2) cattle remains have been recycled. Inclusion of cattle remains from the first passage from this rare tremblie type in the sheep remains in MBM will have reduced the incubation periods from over nine and 10 years at first passage, to five to six years at second passage. Exposure of cattle to MBM, prepared from cattle subclinically infected with BSE, will remain a threat in USA for some years to come. In December 1989, American renderers discontinued processing fallen and sick sheep and some States have stopped rendering sheep material (Marsh, 1990).

Great Britain, with some 41 million sheep in 1990, has the highest sheep population in Europe, with Spain coming in second place with 24 million, but, whereas in Britain half the sheep are less than one year old, the majority in Spain are older than one year, and yet scrapie has been found in only 30 Spanish flocks, all in the one province, Aragon. In Spain, 32% of sheep and goat carcases go to the renderers and their processing, apparently governed closely by law, does not commonly involve the use of solvents. Much of the protein content of that processed "feed stuff", however, is obtained from fish meal and most of the finished product is fed to pigs, poultry and trout. This may help explain the comparatively low incidence of scrapie and the complete absence of BSE in Spain.

Scrapie - BSE Connection and Relevance to Man

As is very obvious from the accounts given, over the centuries, cattle and sheep - often scrapie-infected sheep - shared the same grazing fields without any disease being passed to the cattle or to us when we have eaten both. Attempts by farmers to eradicate scrapie, or at any rate, minimise its incidence by selective culling seemed sufficient to tackle a problem seen to be facing farmers alone. That, at least, was the view both the experts and the Government maintained throughout the crisis: "Scrapie has been common throughout the country for at least the last 250 years, and we have been eating mutton without any ill-effects.

189

If it is all right to be eating the scrapie sheep, why should it be any different so far as BSE-beef is concerned?" Initially, neither MAFF nor the Government gave any great priority to research into the origin and nature of the new cattle disease, and seemed more concerned with the economic and financial factors than with the continuing effects on animal husbandry and the potential risk to human health. MAFF and the British Government, in assessing the risk factors, obviously put consideration of crude economics uppermost. The Government and SEAC cannot on the one hand claim that experts are thin on the ground for it takes years to train them, and then on the other hand make those who had inside knowledge, redundant. It does not add up except to say there appears to have been a hidden agenda. Unfortunately, the human risk factors and long term BSE eradication policy, based on science, seem to have got lost en route. The public has been misled on safety while science is being hijacked under the name of Peer Review by those who made the mistakes. Most important of all, experts advising the Government considered BSE research to be a long term project, and relied on one-sided assumptions and not facts for their conclusions. They believed that - BSE the same as the scrapie agent in sheep, and therefore BSE would disappear by itself. Risk assessment research by expert individual scientists is based on the "think tank" or on commercial grounds. The naive pursuit of a zero risk solution to the BSE problem seemed set to continue: think negative and it will go away!

What the Government experts did not consider was that scrapie, which has been known since 1750 or longer, has not disappeared by simple culling. Most of these experts did link scrapie to BSE, but we are left to wonder why they concluded BSE would eradicate itself without culling of progeny of BSE infected cattle? With hindsight, we can see that, once started, a simple inexpensive disease protection system has turned into billions per year for many years to come. Although at the time we might have questioned the need for expensive measures, these would have been low compared with the price we are now paying. With the right policy, the epidemic could have been tackled effectively. We would have not seen the large number of BSE cases, we would have been spared the widespread concern for the safety of the food we eat. The threat of humans contracting the fatal CJD will stay for generations. Our international reputation has been badly dented. Only fully effective useful experiments providing reliable data can produce forecasts and remove the risks. We need a prevention system at what ever the cost. Mathematical modelling, particularly with imperfect data, cannot be expected to produce perfect forecasts. Only effective useful experiments will improve our ability to ask better questions and to make better judgments. What is so strange is that, after such devastation of the farming and associated industries - the same mistaken advisors are still there in place today. Maybe they are to protect themselves.

Taylor of the MAFF dismissed criticism that the Ministry did not act swiftly enough at the beginning. However, he summed it up when he analysed the historical development of the BSE outbreak and the Ministry's reaction at each stage. He acknowledged that MAFF had been forced to make decisions while "standing on shifting sand" and that further control measures might be necessary as circumstances changed and more information was gathered. What is strange is that the sand had shifted before the first measure was taken. The scale of this shift can be seen in the new legislation brought in during March to July 1996. The consequences of failure to provide appropriate advice and cover in areas related to public health need spelling out properly. There can be no stronger case than that. Health of humans and animals should always be paramount. Preventative measures are required before a disaster. Incorrect theories would not solve the problem nor it would it simply fade away with time. Only a proper action and openness will help. Coherent policy should be based on scientific facts. When results are not known and policy is required, integrated means of estimating risks should have been applied. Possible means to eradicate BSE from British cattle and to safeguard human health are important from the start. It is better to pay a higher premium for a disease insurance policy, than to take risks.

In 1990, The Agriculture Committee produced a report which concluded: "Most scientists we examined appeared to believe that there were too many unknowns to say anything about the disease with absolute certainty; on the other hand, no evidence had been forthcoming .... that it did pose a threat to human health. If they shrank from giving cast-iron reassurances, it was mainly for the philosophical reason that nothing in this life is certain."...."research is unlikely to provide early or decisive answers to many of the questions of public concerns". However, the committee realised "This second provision allows for the fact, essential to understanding of BSE, that animals affected with the disease do not manifest clinical signs until it is well advanced: it is therefore likely that sub-clinical affected animals are being sent for slaughter. Calves under six months are excluded from the ban on the grounds that they will not have been fed ruminant protein and are not in anyway likely to harbour the BSE agent in significant quantities - disease has never been diagnosed in an animal under 22 months". This statement is true perhaps, but takes no account of the risk that the animal is still incubating the agent.

From the very large number of cattle born after the feed ban that have developed the disease (in 1996, they represent over 60% of the total BSE cases), it is obvious that the policy advocated by MAFF has failed, had done little to eradicate the disease. Calves brains under six months are still used in the human food chain. These might have a infective titre for mice of 1,000 to 10,000 doses per gram of brain tissue compared to 100, 000 or more doses per gram when clinical symptoms appear. How mistaken the advice given by MAFF had been. If BSE is to be eradicated and human health protected, nothing short of a full reassessment will be enough. The safety of food and not volume of sales must be the sole criterion, no other policy should be allowed. Whinging and accusing others is a pathetic response. Health must take priority over political excuses.

BSE had succeeded in crossing the "species-barrier" from sheep to cattle and other species. The question arises as to whether in turn the agent could transmit to humans. Although BSE is relatively restricted in its geographic distribution compared with the worldwide distribution of scrapie, it is a matter of major worldwide concern and worry. It is one of a few recognised diseases to have crossed the species barrier, from sheep to cattle and a number of other ruminant and non-ruminant species. In crossing a species barrier, the risk is that a particular strain of the agent has been selected and that the agent has mutated in such a way as to alter its virulence and increase the number and type of the species it can attack. If BSE is a selection or mutation with a changed target range, humans, like other ruminant and non-ruminant species, could be at risk. One animal disease known to have crossed into humans is rabies and this is a good example of a virus adapting to another animal species.

All scientists with the exception of Prusiner and colleagues, agree on one point: as a group of diseases, all SEs in human and in animals are essentially the same, caused by a slow virus in different host species. The disease agent is a living thing - the smallest and most lethal - which, after entering a new host, even in very small amounts, will, after a long incubation period, always produce a completely devastating fatal disease. A very large number of experimental transmission studies using different animal species have demonstrated the BSE agent to be more virulent than scrapie.

Few of the veterinary and medical staff who have been deeply involved with Government policy and regulatory matters had any practical research experience with the SE disease conditions. Few of these appointed experts, including the past and present chairmen of SEAC, had seen a human CJD case, a BSE cow or had experimentally inoculated animals with the SE agent. Even seeing a few cases of BSE or CJD, does not make an expert overnight. The important thing is to separate science from expediency and, in this crisis, political and commercial considerations have taken priority over all else. Consumers were left to hope that the risk of BSE transmission to humans would be remote. At its origin in 1985, the number of cases were few and the threat they posed was not appreciated. The disease was given little priority and regarded as unworthy of immediate research. BSE, however, quickly became one of the major causes of death in British dairy cattle and that brought massive publicity in the media. The co-incidental identification of SE in cats and of a new form of CJD in young patients rang even more alarm bells and added to the worry of the public and medical profession alike that the eating of sick animal products might transmit the infection.

BSE, "Mad Cow Disease", and its implications, were of such wide public concern that they began making headlines in daily newspapers from 1988 onwards. This publicity brought all SEs to public attention. Opinion polls published at the height of the controversy about BSE indicated that, not only were many people worried about beef, but statements by MAFF and Government

Ministers setting out the facts, as they saw them, were widely distrusted (Sunday Telegraph,20 May 1990). Consumers and farmers alike throughout Europe were alarmed at the possibility that animals in their countries might also harbour the disease. The economic implications of BSE 'exploding' in Europe would, in the light of the United Kingdom experience, be measured in billions of ECU. The added fear is that the introduction of rigorous controls to prevent the spread of the disease will inhibit the further development of a free market.

The fact that cats were discovered to have developed BSE in May 1990,and that the agent had crossed yet another species, added greatly to public concern. Within days, a number of local education authorities in Lancashire, Derbyshire, Staffordshire, Oxford and Surrey had followed the lead set by Humberside Council in imposing a full or partial ban on the use of British beef for school lunches. To lessen the shock on the public mind, the Government approach received the backing of the Department of Health Chief Medical Officer Sir Donald Acheson who said, "I have no hesitation in saying that beef can be eaten safely by everyone, both adults and children, including patients in hospitals." To cool the situation, at a fair in front of the press, Mr John Gummer MP the; then Agriculture Minister, fed his young daughter a hamburger, to demonstrate - that British beef is safe! With this kind of public reaction, the decision of MAFF not to disclose the findings of BSE in dogs for several years until late 1997, is understandable. The recent discovery of disease in chickens gives rise to yet more alarm.

Transmission experiments of BSE with animals, using non-human primates, sheep, goats, pigs, mice, hamsters and many other species, have been carried out to determine susceptibility to the disease. An important discovery was the natural selection in cattle of a single strain of the agent which produced the disease with a relatively short incubation period and high effectivity of primary transmission to mice and other animals. It is a well established fact as detailed elsewhere in this book that sheep can be divided into two groups - those susceptible to the scrapie agent and those which are resistant. Both groups of sheep, however, were found equally vulnerable to the BSE agent when eaten. This has created a very serious problem on farms where MBM had been fed to sheep prior to the feed ban for all animals. MAFF suggested that sheep did not enjoy the taste of MBM and that it had previously been too expensive to feed to sheep. However, following the feed ban for cattle, the product became cheaply available. The amount of MBM used for feeding sheep cannot be assessed. The number of sheep which will eventually contract the disease partially depends on the regions where MBM has been fed. Since the important discovery that even the type of sheep most resistant to scrapie infection when fed with BSE tissue, do develop the clinical disease could mean that there may well be no scrapie/BSE-free sheep in the years to come. This was the main reason for the Government bringing in new legislation removing the brain and spinal cord from sheep carcases being processed for human consumption.

The risk that humans will develop the disease if inoculated or fed with infected tissues, obviously cannot be determined in laboratory experiments. Such experiments would not be permitted. But is such an experiment really essential? Humans do suffer from the similar natural diseases, CJD and kuru, and these are infectious. Furthermore, this natural experiment is already in progress. A number of people have died with the new strain of CJD. It is hard to see why, if all other animals with very different genetic make-up so far tested are susceptible to BSE, humans alone would enjoy protection from the BSE agent.

The House of Commons Agriculture Committee report of 1990 reflects the concerns that were being expressed by the public. Dr David Tyrrell was asked the question by Mr Richard Alexander (number 280): '"In paragraph 2(3) of your report, Dr Tyrrell, at end of the that paragraph, you say this "Many of the practical measures taken have been based on shrewd judgments of the analogy between BSE and scrapie of sheep" and you go on to suggest that specific studies are now needed. I would first like to ask you whether those specific studies have been done and whether they have shed further light on the similarities or differences as regards BSE and scrapie?"

Dr Tyrrell replied, "Many such studies have begun. We do not know the answers to them yet. Such studies as were just beginning when we were writing our report and which are now beginning to yield results, I think, do in general indicate that this is a very scrapie-like agent, for instance, the fact that it kills mice, ...So yes, we are beginning to find out that it is similar but, of course, there are not a lot of very specific tests which can be done, and there are some things which, from the practical point of view, are important, such as whether the agent can be readily inactivated, and this is not done yet. ...There should be a surrogate for the human brain. The best we have so far is the marmoset. Such studies have been set-up and they indicate that scrapie and BSE both seem to cause, so far as the test has gone, no harm to marmoset at time when, if the marmoset had been injected with Creutzfeldt-Jakob material, it would either be sick or dead. But marmoset is not a perfect model of the human brain. All I am saying is that all these points, as they begin to come up, are gradually giving an overall picture that says yes, it is like scrapie".

For this experiment, four marmoset monkeys were injected, two with scrapie material and another two with BSE. Those injected with scrapie developed the clinical disease some six months earlier than those inoculated with BSE. In the first place, the use of two monkeys in a comparative study provides only a limited significance. In addition, when considering difference in the length of incubation period, it is important to remember that, under identical conditions, variations occur in the incubation periods within the same strain in the same species. The difference in the incubation period between the two monkeys with the same inoculum was about four months, therefore in slow viral infections, four to six months or even longer difference between scrapie and the BSE incubation period cannot be regarded as sufficient to indicate whether or not humans are at risk.

Humans live much longer than 6 months - up to 60 years and over. On the other hand, in comparative transmission studies using infected brain tissues from scrapie sheep and BSE cattle, it is obvious that BSE infection is more readily transmitted than scrapie (Fraser et al, 1994).

The Southwood Committee realised that if it turned out that humans were susceptible to BSE, it might be that people who had consumed certain offals from infected cattle prior to November 1989, would eventually develop similar neuropathological disorders. As the incubation periods are very long and clinical signs might not be apparent, they, therefore recommended that cases of CJD should be monitored with particular care; to see whether any link with BSE could be established (Southwood, 5.3.3). Although it was obvious to real experts how things might develop, untested theory and future forecasts are impossible to make, based on chance or looking into a crystal ball. The risk, no matter how small, is there and the question remains: "Is that risk worth taking?" Vets should have been advising farmers not to breed from infected animals or their progeny, and once any case had been found in a herd, to avoid the breeding members of that herd.

Random testing for BSE not a high priority
The Tyrrell Committee realised that the incubation period is very long and that nevertheless the clinical disease appears suddenly. During its long incubation period of three to five years the agent of BSE replicates to develop 10 to 100 million units of infective doses per gram of brain tissue. Obviously, the agent has increased gradually over that long period. In the natural disease, although infected animals are asymptomatic for many months, how many infective doses may be present in the earlier stages of incubation and how quickly they replicate, cannot be assessed but the probability is that there is a steady increase in the amount of the agent. Other animal experiments so far done, suggest that, after a quarter of the incubating period, the cow will have at least 1,000 doses per gram of brain tissue and therefore, random testing of cattle which have been slaughtered without any clinical symptoms, should be routinely carried out. This would not only monitor the incidence of the disease but enable meat from infected cattle to be removed from the food chain.

To avoid further strains on technical resources, the Tyrrell Committee did not regard testing as meriting a top priority. Not only would random testing have helped remove infected food from the human and animal food chain, it would also have helped to identify diseased farms and the progeny of their cows could have been selectively culled to eradicate BSE. I proposed random post-mortem testing of cattle in 1988. But random BSE testing was then judged to be of low priority, because MAFF considered that a visual examination of animals - before slaughter - was adequate. Had random testing been started in 1990, the true extent of the disease would have been assessable.

Relationship of Narang Disease to BSE

The first case of "New Strain CJD" - for which I have proposed the name, "Narang Disease" (ND) - was identified in 1989. Unlike the traditional strain of the disease, this strain was found to strike down the young, people under the age of 41 . The official view is that people over that age are, for some unexplained reason, immune to ND, and therefore, will not catch BSE infection. Does that imply that persons over this age, can eat BSE infected meat? This is questionable. Many researchers are unable to understand why this agent should be thought to select its target on the basis of age. I, strongly, personally believe, all age groups are at risk. In 1996, ten cases were reported and a further seven added by April, 1997. All proved fatal. No-one can estimate how many are still incubating the disease. The most recent report is that of a young Spaniard, age 27, succumbing to the disease after having lived in the UK for several years. Inadvertently and unintentionally, the British public are taking part in the first natural BSE animal-to-human transmission experiment with the final outcome unpredictable. The gravity of the threat to humans, however, makes the need for solid research into the disease all the more essential, to determine the nature of the agent and so lay the foundation for its treatment and the development of a vaccine.

The clinical symptoms of ND are very similar to those seen in BSE and kuru, but are very different from those seen in the sporadic CJD cases. These similarities together with the unusual histopathological appearance of lesions in the cerebellum common to both in all these ND cases and BSE cases strongly suggested a relationship between the two conditions. The existence of a relationship between the strain of the agent in these cases and BSE - if, in fact, they were related - should have been quickly tested and established by the inoculation of brain tissue from them into different breeds of mice, as was done with cats and various zoo animals. That experiment would have taken some three years, and would have produced undisputed facts.

Back in 1989, I identified four Narang disease cases of CJD in the Northern region of England in two years. The likelihood of a link between them prompted me, in 1989, to begin to test and compare these "atypical" CJD cases with BSE in a series of laboratory experiments. Within 18 months of mice being inoculated, some were beginning to develop symptoms. Unfortunately, in 1990, before the work could be completed, its termination was ordered on the pretext of safety by Dr. Nigel Lightfoot, Director of the PHLS Newcastle, and the test animals destroyed. That frustrated finding a means for the early detection of BSE and CJD cases, and the development of a vaccine to protect both cows and humans. The first essential in any investigation of an infectious disease is the identification and nature of the disease agent, paving the way for a quick, reliable and cheap method to diagnose the condition. In this instance, the urgent need for such an investigation was not recognised and no priority given to it. It was to be some six or seven years before MAFF, in March, 1996 officially acknowledged that: "Yes: humans have been infected with a new variant of the scrapie agent and the most likely source is BSE infected meat".

Only now, almost 10 years later (and after the expenditure of millions of pounds with little benefit to show) are the official scientists being given encouragement -and another 10 million pounds being made available to them in 1997 - to rush ahead and start the research which should already have been completed.

Influence of age of host

The effect of developmental maturity on susceptibility to the scrapie infections by the intraperitoneal route studies have suggested that 50 to 500-fold less dose is required for adults inoculated by the intraperitoneal route than that required by an intracerebral inoculation. The result of these studies suggest that the peritoneal cavity of an adult is a much more favourable environment for the scrapie agent compared with that of the neonate. The incubation period therefore in adults may well be shorter.

The Public Health

Experimental transmission studies from BSE infected muscles have so far not been successful. It does seem clear, however, from the positive scrapie experiments, that there could be a relationship between the incubation period and the titre of infectivity, especially if scrapie and BSE behave similarly to each other. It must be borne in mind that biceps femoris muscle can contain the scrapie agent and eventually, after a long incubation period, produce disease in experimental animals. For conclusive results, experimental animals such as mink should be fed with BSE red meat.

It is important to remember at this stage that animals were no longer allowed to eat "the specified offal" once the Minister of Agriculture had placed a "feed ban" on feeding animals with protein derived from other ruminant animals (July 1988). There was, however, no equivalent legislation for humans. The Government offered the scrapie analogy; humans have nothing to worry about. We have been eating scrapie-infected sheep for 250 years and BSE is much the same as scrapie.

Public pressure mounted until in March 1989, the Minister of Agriculture, Mr MacGregor, was asked in Parliament if he would ban all organs for human consumption that were known to harbour the infectious agent. His parliamentary secretary conveyed his refusal on the grounds that it was "not appropriate". Facing increasing pressure, the Agricultural Minister held out for another eight months until there came another sudden reverse. The "offal ban for humans" was introduced in November 1989. It must be remembered that Mr MacGregor's successor as Minister of Agriculture, John Gummer, MP persuaded his four year-old daughter, Cordelia, to eat a beefburger in front of the assembled British media in May 1990. "Eat this for Daddy" - Mr Gummer gave the assertion in the House of Commons that "Beef can be eaten safely by everyone....There is no

197

evidence that beef is harmful to humans". Whether his daughter appreciated the opportunity to take part in the experiment is not recorded.

Situation or Scenario

The public health implications of BSE are particularly difficult to address. At the beginning there may not have been evidence that BSE was a risk to man, and in the short term there was virtually no way of finding out. But the possibility of the risk to man had to be taken seriously. SEAC did not regard the risk of BSE to humans significant and implied that it was unlikely for humans to become infected. It did recommend, however, as a precaution, that the specified bovine offals ban be introduced to minimise that risk to man. Ray Bradley, one SEAC member who still advises the Government, said "So I am very happy about even the clinical cases going through and the meat being eaten, although we do not want it." People working in the meat industry were assured that BSE constituted no threat to human health. With this type of assurance, the risks involved in the handling of meat and meat products were belittled and, all too often, casual attitudes were adapted to safety measures by many working in the trade. It is almost like playing a game of poker, relying on the power of bluff.

The effect of feeding of cattle with scrapie-contaminated feed is clear. Quite simply the cattle are put at risk. They became infected. Having successfully crossed one species barrier, what if the scenario is the same for man and the agent of BSE can jump one more species? The long incubation period will prevent us knowing the answers for a long time, perhaps many years, as in the case of disease caused by the inoculation of growth hormone prepared from human pituitary glands. This unintentional, unforeseen experiment presumably started somewhere in the early 1980s, or before, when subclinically infected cattle were slaughtered and the organs, which might have contained high titres of the infective agent, were put into human food. Thus it would appear that a large section of the population was exposed to the BSE-infected foodstuff for a period of at least 5 years.

Appointment of Government Committee

In Great Britain on 21 April, 1988, the Secretary of State for Health and the Minister of Agriculture appointed the first Government committee, the Southwood Working Party, under the chairmanship of Sir Richard Southwood, to examine the problem from all possible angles and assess the significance of what had become known as the BSE epidemic. The credibility of the committee was in doubt. Although there were experts qualified in the field of SEs in Britain, none of them was appointed to the Southwood Committee. The committee estimated that 20,000 cattle would die as a result of eating contaminated feed. The developing epidemic quickly showed that Southwood had grossly under-estimated the problem. Until march 1996 MAFF and the Department of Health continued to claim that there was no reason for suggesting that the new cattle disease could be harmful to man - if they thought otherwise they kept their response to themselves.

The Southwood Working Committee, in an interim report, concluded that there was adequate evidence that scrapie posed no risk to humans; in particular, that it was not associated epidemiologically with CJD and other SEs of humans. The initial BSE control measures in Great Britain therefore were designed only to protect animal health, it being assumed that if scrapie posed no risk to human health, neither would BSE. The carcasses and organs of suspect cases, other than the brains, therefore were safe for human consumption. It is clear, however, that the measure did not prevent the consumption of tissues from cattle that were infected and incubating the disease but had not yet developed clinical symptoms being allowed into human food chin. They suggested that even though scrapie could have caused BSE, it could not be assumed that BSE could not affect humans, even by the oral route, and in an interim recommendation received the day after statutory controls were first introduced, advised that although there was no known hazard to human health it would be a sensible precaution to remove suspect cattle from the food chain while the working party considered the evidence.

Following the first meeting on 20 June, 1988, certain interim recommendations for urgent attention were put forward by the Southwood Committee. The first was that as a precautionary measure, at least until more was known about BSE, the carcasses of infected animals should be destroyed and prevented from entering the human food chain. Second, that milk from suspected BSE cattle should be destroyed, "..although the transmission of BSE via milk is unlikely". Third, that BSE be made a notifiable disease. The fourth was that an Expert Consultative Committee on Research should be established to discover the full extent of the threat to animals and the potential threat to man, and to advise on any further research. The Government accepted and implemented all the recommendations. A slaughter policy was introduced on August 8, 1988, the first public health control measure to be implemented with the prime object of safeguarding human health.

The eventual publication of the Southwood Report was in February 1989 but prior to this, a further, three additional interim recommendations were made on 10 November 1988. The first, a ban on the use of ruminant-based protein feed for the cattle, second, that milk from suspected BSE cattle should be destroyed or should be used only for the calves and third, to "keep tabs" on offspring of infected animals.

Some critics say that publication of the Southwood Report was delayed for another seven months partly because information was still coming in and also because MAFF and its ministers did not like what Southwood had to say. There were suggestions that some of these steps should have been taken sooner. Sir Richard Southwood himself said " With hindsight, things could have been done a bit quicker" (Observer, 20 May 1990).

The House of Commons Agriculture Committee, in their report, also conclu-

ded that there were, nevertheless, three instances where too much time elapsed between the need for certain action arising and that action being taken:
(i) the introduction of the specified offals ban;
(ii) the publication of the Tyrrell Report;
(iii) the introduction of full compensation for slaughtered animals.

The first of these delays was blamed on a number of factors. First, the Southwood Committee's Report in February 1989 recommended only that certain offals should be excluded from baby foods (Southwood 5.3). Four months were then spent examining the feasibility of that proposal and deciding that a full offals ban was more practicable. Having reached that decision in principle, however, the Government does seem to have been slow to act. In answering a House of Commons Agriculture Committee question from Mr Jones: "Could you explain why there was a delay of five months from the announcement on the ban of bovine offals entering the human food chain on the 13 June 1989 and its implementation on 13 November 1989?", Mr K Meldrum replied "Yes, I certainly can. It is difficult to take all our minds back to the time, first of all, when the Southwood Committee was set up and, secondly, when they reported in February 1989; but bearing in mind what it said in that report, there was no need at that time for a Minister to propose a ban on these specified offals, because the suggestion in the report was quite specific and concerned offals in baby food".

The Minister at the time, Mr MacGregor MP, decided it was wise to go further than the evidence supported, in fact, to go further than the experts even suggested. However, after the suggestion had been made in June, a consultation period was necessary under the Food Act. During this period, work was carried out in some depth at the Government laboratory in Weybridge on various tissues, to determine in particular how much lymphoid tissue was present in various parts of the intestinal tract. "We were not in a position" said Mr MacGregor "to bring forward final recommendations for consideration, until that work had been completed. I know very well that Sir Donald Acheson and his colleagues in the Department of Health, who were consulted in detail on this, would never have wished to take a decision until we had given them that information, which we did. So it took some time to consult and some time also to carry out the detailed investigation on lymphoid tissue at Weybridge. In that context, therefore, I do not think that the delay was all that material".

Spread of the Disease

It is too soon to be sure whether bovine maternal tissue transmits BSE and, if so, to what extent. Taking the optimistic view, if only limited cattle to cattle horizontal transmission does occur, the incidence of BSE will be reduced and by 1995, those cattle under five years old will not develop BSE.

Looking at the dark side, however, what might occur, as some animal experiments have indicated, is that life could be difficult for the farmer and the public.

Mice born of pregnant females inoculated during the gestation period, but separated from their own dams at delivery, do become infected prenatally or perinatally. All mice except the foster mother (not inoculated) develop the clinically recognisable disease, and die following an incubation period not significantly different from that observed as occurring in their inoculated mothers. If this were to be true of cattle, merely separating calves from sick animals would not alone be sufficient to eliminate BSE from the UK.

The results of the seven year long vertical transmission experiment, flawed as it was, reveal that the more pessimistic view of vertical transmission is more likely correct. Further, if maternal transmission is a fact, then it could be that the number of infective units passed to the offspring would be limited and, therefore, the incidence of the disease would be correspond to that seen in the scrapie sheep. Based on our current knowledge, the incubation period may range between two and seven years or longer. Therefore, after six years or more, we may find that a small percentage of cows have developed the clinical disease, but, even then, no authoritative evidence will be available to preclude the risk that some of the rest at least, are not still incubating the disease. What do we do then? No expert scientist would accept the responsibility. Are we going to start the experiment afresh? Life is too short for that, the damage will be done. If we draw an analogy between BSE and scrapie of sheep, the disease will not burn itself out. Based on British breeding practice where the norm is four calves per mother cow, it is possible that all four calves born are infected. If three are killed prior to the 30 month period, there is no way of knowing which one of them is not infected. If the main goal is eradication, then the policy must be to prevent breeding from infective cattle.

If BSE is regarded as being caused by the same agent as scrapie in sheep, then the next generation of cattle must be safeguarded. It is known from large field experiments that infected sheep may transmit the agent of SE to their progeny, although they themselves are clinically normal. The infection is passed from generation to generation, meaning maternal transmission. If BSE has the same features, one has to appreciate that if controls are not put into place now while family records are still available, the consequences could be graver and eradication of BSE may well become a major problem for future generations. It is also important to stress that virus diseases are not static in their progress, but continually change and adapt to new circumstances.

From their statements it would appear that MAFF always favoured waiting for the results of experiments to become known. Even if these results were a long time in coming they preferred that policy to taking early decisive actions. They left the door unlocked rather than risk going out without a key.

Three of the main points made by the Southwood committee in 1989 are worth particular note. On intensive farming, "Considering BSE and how this new disease has arisen has led us to question the wisdom of some of the intensive practice of modern animal husbandry because they risk exposing man to new zoonoses, that is disease communicated from lower animals to man. On the potential danger of BSE to man: "[It is] most unlikely that BSE will have any implications for human health. Nevertheless, if our assessments of these likelihoods are incorrect, the implications would be extremely serious." Also, "With the very long incubation period of SEs in humans, it may be decades or more before complete reassurance can be given."

However, in a joint announcement of the Southwood Report, the Departments of Agriculture and Health not only failed to mention any of above points, but twisted Southwood's cautious summation into: "The report concludes that the risk of transmission of BSE to humans appears remote and it is therefore most unlikely that BSE will have any implications for human health."

The Southwood Committee, on the basis of available epidemiological evidence, concluded that BSE resulted from the feeding of cattle with ruminant protein containing the offal of sheep infected with scrapie, and that research was in progress to test the validity of this conclusion. This part of the research either was not undertaken or the results have never been published. BSE appears to be a new strain mutation in cattle following their exposure initially to the supplements present in the 'ruminant protein'. In order to arrest further progress of the presumed cause of the disease in cattle, the Minister of Agriculture, John Mac-Gregor, announced, in July 1988, the all important 'feed ban' on animal protein derived from cattle or from other ruminant animals, under the 'Bovine Spongiform Encephalopathy Order' 1988. Sheep and cattle would no longer be fed the brains and offal of their own brethren.

Apart from one sided assumptions and unproven hypotheses which they considered as true facts, the Southwood report identified widespread concern about BSE and the reasons why additional research was essential. For instance, when unexpectedly (because MAFF did not think pigs could develop clinical BSE and therefore had advised the SEAC to allow the use of MBM for feeding pigs and poultry),parenteral injection of BSE caused infection and clinical disease in pigs, they advised that the ban which already forbade the use of specified bovine offal in human food,should be extended to prevent it being fed to pigs and poultry. Furthermore, even after infectivity was found in the distal ileum of calves that had been given BSE by mouth, SEAC still thought that the risk of infection to humans from tissues taken from calves under six months old,was "minuscule or absent". They at this stage advised the Government to be ultracautious and amend the regulations to prevent the use of intestines and thymus from cattle of any age, rather than applying the ban only to these tissues from cattle six months of age and older. The Tyrrell Committee made the most important point: "We like to seek reassurance that the Southwood group was correct in their belief that this disease would not have implications for human health, say, through food, through occupational exposure or through medicinal products that use bovine ingredients." As pointed out in the Tyrrell Committee report "Many of the practical measures taken have been based on shrewd judgments of the analogy between BSE and scrapie of sheep. Specific studies on BSE itself are needed to be established whether the conclusions were sound."

Medicinal Products

The Medicines Control Agency, through the Committee on the Safety of Medicines which is independent of the Government, also had a role in protecting public health. The Agency was aware that if BSE was a hazard to humans, then the most direct and immediate risk would be from products given or used parenterally, such as vaccines, suture materials, and so on. The Agency considered it a potential problem since apparently healthy animals might be infected, and, by analogy with scrapie, there was no sterilisation method that was likely to eliminate infectivity without destroying the product. In addition, any risk from parenteral use would probably be greater than from oral consumption. The Agency therefore issued guidelines and sought information from all manufacturers to find out what bovine materials were being used in their products,and suggested use of bovine materials from irreproachably BSE-free well-supervised herds in a country where neither scrapie nor BSE were present. The industry took up these recommendations very efficiently and within months, intestines for the manufacture of surgical materials were being imported from Australasia .

House of Commons Agriculture Committee Enquiry into BSE

Natural public concern about the safety of their food and the media coverage of "mad cow disease" with banner headlines quickly ensured that everyone in the country knew something about BSE. Uppermost in the minds of most was fear for their own safety and that of their families - fear that beef from infected cattle might infect whoever ate it. To allay this fear, the public urgently required a categorical and unequivocal answer. That was something that MAFF was unable to give and,by appearing to be giving out information only reluctantly, they gave the impression of having something to hide. That did nothing to help restore public confidence. In the hope of doing so, however, the House of Commons; on 16th May, 1990, set upon an inquiry to examine whether or not BSE might affect humans. Their discussion and conclusions have been reported throughout this book. At that time the U.K. was virtually alone in suffering BSE in its herds where some 15,000 cases had been confirmed -- about.1% of all UK cattle.

In answer to a question put to him at that Agricultural Committee Inquiry, Mr. John Gummer, M.P. replied: "I am sure you will understand that, with hindsight, of course we can decide what it is we ought to have started with but, at that time, with only seven cases, it might have been a whole range of things that would have caused this. Weed killers and herbicides also had to be considered and eventually the common factor identified was protein feed derived from scrapie-affected sheep".

203

The Committee also considered what was to be done, in the long term, with the offal of British cattle. They were banned for sale for human consumption, were banned from export to the ECU and, under rules voluntarily accepted by them, pet food manufacturers refused to include them in their preparations. Somehow they, and the infection they might contain, had to be effectively destroyed. There was then no means of achieving this in the tonnage involved and an alternative rendering process capable of killing off the agent was urgently required.

In a debate on May 21st, 1990, Dr. David Clark, Shadow Minister for Agriculture claimed: "The actions of the current Conservative administration were directly responsible for the disease appearing in the UK. The last Labour Government had proposed draft regulations for the rendering industry which would have prevented the spread of the scrapie agent to the cattle population but succeeding Conservative Governments had not proceeded with the legislation."

What has not been made clear is whether or not MAFF had laid down adequate controls for the regulation of the rendering industry and, if so, whether they had taken the necessary advice from experts as to, among other aspects, the safety of sheep heads being included in MBM. Was this overlooked and were the manufacturers free to do as they chose? If so, the price we are now having to pay for that initial mistake is enormous, and similar mistakes must never again be allowed. Science and the scientific assessment of risks of this nature, based on sound experimental evaluation alone must provide the foundations for policy and policy decisions. The cost of such assessments will be a small premium to pay for the benefits insured.

Compensation

To guard against the risk of farmers attempting to cut their losses by selling infecting cattle and hustling them off to market at the very earliest indication of possible affection, Southwood recommended that they be paid at least 75% of the value for infected cattle destroyed. Resisting that advice, the Ministry insisted initially on paying just 50% by way of compensation but, later, realising its error raised this to 100%. Southwood and MAFF were not alone in seeing the need for adequate compensation.

Mr. Francis Anthony, Chairman of the Farm Animals Committee, told British Veterinary Association on 23rd June, 1988 that compensation was necessary and that, without it, farmers might be reluctant to notify all cases. Unlike the Chief Veterinary Officer, Mr. Keith Meldrum, he did not believe that the threat of a fine of up to £2,000 for failure to notify a suspected case would be adequate to ensure absolute compliance with the notification requirements. Notifications, at that time were running at some 60 per month and the Ministry was closely monitoring these returns to guard against any shortcomings.

The number of BSE cases were based on the fact the cattle were exposed from around 1981-1982 until July 1988, when the feeding of ruminant derived protein was forbidden, and the assumption that 300-400 cases a month would develop until 1993. Thereafter, the number of cases would decline and disappear after 1996 with an accumulative total of 17,000 to 20,000 cases. These figures, however, required continued revision and prompted further debate. The number of BSE cases showed no signs of decline while infected cases continued to be detected in the market place. These figures were being revised from month to month. Soon after the publication of Professor Southwood's report, Ministers and in particular, Mr Francis Anthony, started a second debate, by expressing concern on several issues (Vet Rec 15 April 1989). The fact was that the number of BSE cases was increasing beyond predictions of 300 to 400 a month. That there were up to 200 sick animals a week, and still further speculative predictions, that the numbers might level off at 100 a week. It was difficult to know what the degree of under-reporting was? And would the Government introduce 75% compensation? The minister was sure such a move would help farmers. It has been expressed that Mr Donald Thompson, Parliamentary Secretary Agriculture, was worried to hear that 27 out of 40 cases which had been found in the market were positive for BSE.

Implication for the farming industry and economic damage

BSE must be seen in the perspective of a new disease in cattle. The appearance of BSE has presented several implications for both the cattle and the sheep industries. These industries consist of a number of interdependent industries, which include the farmer, the primary producers; the abattoir-owners; the wholesalers butchers; the retailers; the renderers and the compound feed producers. With the slump in demand for beef - it is 25% down on the normal lowest point - all these industries suffer.

Farmers - the real victims of the disorder

The sudden onslaught of the epidemic had grave implications. The abattoir owners, the wholesale butchers and retailers, the renders and the compounders feed producers, were all equally hit. The demand for beef in this country collapsed overnight by some 25% at the lowest point and the traditional overseas market for our beef limited their intake to reflect to the reaction of their customers. The ban was extended throughout the world. The public have been going along with what they know from news media and mostly have been onlookers. The inconsistencies and changes in the policy of MAFF and the Government together with a general lack of authoritative direction has left them cautious of the future. The recent debate over the culling policy of over 127,000 cattle on about 6240 farms, was considered by the Farmers Weekly (6 September 1996) "MAFF's selective cull is economic madness, but without it the ban stays". There was argument based on a high tech computer study by scientist at Oxford University and Central Veterinary Laboratory, that the cull should not go ahead. What farmer,s MAFF and the Government did not realise was that this computer study was only a prediction, more a forecast of what might be expected, and that after all the economic madness of the past and present, the ban might not be lifted until BSE had been completely eradicated from the British herds. Even the decision in 1996 to go ahead with the policy of culling more than 500,000 cattle aged over 30 months in the expectation of having the ban raised,has proved inadequate to restore overseas confidence in the safety of our beef. The ban still stays firmly in place. The cost to the British taxpayer has been billions, the overt gain has been zero.

Effect on rendering industry

Mr Harrison, Vice-Chairman, United Kingdom Renderers Association Ltd., in evidence to the Commons Agricultural Select Committee states that "Certainly for the last 50 years the feeding of animal protein in animals rations has continued throughout the rest of the world. There is nothing unique in the animal protein we produce, and nothing unique in the use to which it is put within our feeding industry." There is a chain from farmers, the primary producers to transporters, the abattoir-owners and workers, wholesalers, the retailers and renderers, the compound feed producers and retailers. The rendering industry has been dramatically affected and has painted a gloomy picture of their present situation. Previously they were buying offal from the primary producers, rendering and selling the by-products as meat and bone meal to compounders for inclusion in animal feed. Since the meat and bone meal has been the source of infection, the compounders trade association has banned the specified offal from feed rations.

The rendering industry has been dramatically affected with very gloomy future prospects. They have no market for the offal and animal waste which is considered of the order of 1.75 million tonnes per year. No one has a use for it. Thus, renderers think they are providing a waste disposal service which they are not obliged to provide and therefore now abattoir-owners should pay for the removal of offal from their premises (Memorandum submitted by the United Kingdom Renders' Association Limited, 1990). Store-rooms had been piling up with unsaleable MBM. The hope is that a use will be found in the near future. In a Commons report, it has been suggested that rather than find a taker, and recycle the material in a dubious way, it would be wise to destroy it. Raw material from the animals could not be land filled as this would create another environmental problem. There was an urgent need to develop a safe disposal method. The cost estimated for the disposal was something between £250 to £400 million per year. Burning alone would be difficult. Tests were supposed to be carried out in Northern Ireland, at a peat fired power station. It was to be mixed with pulverised peat and burned but public opinion objected and prevented everything.

The policies need to reflect the growing unease among practising veterinary surgeons and research workers alike, about the complacent MAFF approach to

206

the BSE problem and above all it needs to establish a credible independent line on this issue.

As I see it, three pressing issues need to be addressed:
1) The present culling policy
2) The proper eradication of BSE from the national herd
3) Will BSE continue to infect humans?

Current policy on eradicating BSE

There is no scientifically based policy for eradicating BSE. The culling policy makes as much sense as claiming that killing a vast number of known, suspected and unknown AIDs patients would eradicate AIDs.

There appears to be no end of BSE in sight. According to MAFF, continuing cases of BSE occurring after the feed ban of 1988, are the consequence of having fed MBM to cattle. If this MBM has, as MAFF says, caused BSE in cattle BABs, the implications are appalling. To put it simply, since 1988, this MBM has been prepared from normal cattle - that is, cattle assumed to be healthy and fit, while meat from these cows went for human consumption. This proves that MAFF's simple visual examination of live cattle did not stop subclinically infected cattle from getting into the food chain.

These findings alone highlight the gross shortcomings of the culling policy. Meat from animals over 30 months old is no longer allowed into the food chain. Culling animals over 30 months old - those most likely to exhibit obvious symptoms if they had BSE - merely means that animals under 30 months old that are incubating the disease but not yet showing symptoms continue to go into the food chain, as before.

The death or compulsory slaughter of more than 166,000 adult cattle over a period of more than seven years, and the policy of culling cattle over 30 months old deemed unfit for human or animal food had a great effect on the farming industry. Tyrrell and Taylor (1996), advisors to the Government from the very beginning of the epidemic, are trying to put on a brave face, suggesting that, probably, the epidemic has not been as great as might have been expected, and that many of the problems have been caused by the international factors to the UK epidemic rather than domestic circumstances. European counties will not accept beef from cattle herds in which any case of BSE had occurred and to meet this selective demand, the British public have had to make do with what was left - beef from herds where BSE has occurred. Relatively few countries have reported cases of BSE, and the disease has occurred at high incidence only in the United Kingdom. Nevertheless, the policy in some countries has been to regard the occurrence of one case of BSE in a herd as sufficient grounds to require the slaughter of the entire herd.

Tyrrell and Taylor (1996) suggest that the UK response to BSE has provided a model of how to deal effectively with a previously unknown disease, basing

207

the immediate response on sound scientific principles and arranging and funding
the research needed to build on that immediate response, while providing detailed
information to scientific authorities throughout the world. Separate but interre-
lated measures have been taken to protect public health against any risk that BSE
may pose, to prevent infection being spread to other animal species, and to eradicate BSE from UK cattle. The costs of doing so -- more than £160 million
(approx $256 million) on compensation and disposal costs alone at the time of
writing have been borne by the government .

Rather than using well developed science to debate these issues, MAFF and
DoH made it their business to express their doubts to the public through the
newspapers, television, often in revelations. Results of half done, incomplete
studies with a highly selective presentation of information and interpretation
were put forward to suit themselves. Such confrontational tactics made excellent
publicity, but did considerable disservice to attempts to implement a rational
control policy firmly based on scientific evidence.

Creutzfeldt-Jakob disease

Creutzfeldt-Jakob disease (CJD) is a fatal neurological disease of man, attributed to a slow virus infection, with an incubation period extending into many years. Neurohistopathological examination of the brains of CJD cases reveals degenerative changes with a varying degree of nerve cell vacuolation. There is still much uncertainty as to what constitutes a vacuole in tissues on the histological slide when viewed through a light microscope as the differences between normal and infected tissues can be minimal and identification of the vacuoles can be extremely difficult. It is therefore essential to use all other available diagnostic procedures to confirm all suspected CJD and related neurological cases. It is because of the strikingly similar histopathological lesions of the central nervous system that CJD has been grouped together with scrapie of sheep and bovine spongiform encephalopathy (BSE), and five other spongiform encephalopathies (SEs).

Typically, CJD presents as a progressive mental deterioration accompanied, or followed by, lesions of the cerebellar or visual signs. A subsequent course usually includes movement abnormalities. In a number of cases, the illness is associated with the cerebellar rather than mental deterioration. The prominent neurological disturbance in most parts of the cerebellar form of CJD appears to be limb and truncal ataxia. The important diagnostic symptoms of CJD are: myoclonus, mental deterioration, and EEG pattern of slow tracing. In about 50% of CJD cases, EEG specific pattern changes are important diagnostic indicators. However, in 25% of sporadic, and in almost all the new variant of CJD cases, the EEG pattern changes appear only in the advanced stage of the illness, when patients are no longer able to stand or walk. This initial difference in clinical symptoms may lead to confusion with hysteria, primary spino-cerebellar degeneration, or tumour of the posterior fossa. In many CJD cases, death occurs within 3 to 6 months, but cases have been recorded with deaths resulting after 10 years. When one or more of these features is absent, particularly in cases with a long clinical duration of illness, the diagnosis of CJD becomes less certain (Brown et al, 1984).

Relationship of CJD with other Neurological Diseases

It is obvious from published studies that the term CJD used by many authors has covered a wide spectrum of clinical symptomatology and neuropathology features which are known to vary from case to case. CJD shares several clinical and pathological features with Alzheimer's disease (AD), another dementing disorder. In the initial clinical stages AD and CJD can be so similar that the two diseases cannot always be distinguished while the patient is alive. A comparison of AD with CJD, at every level, epidemiological, clinical, pathological, and biological, reveals similarities between the two diseases. At every level, however, there are distinct features distinguishing the diseases from each other. This similarity, with differences, does, however, suggest the possibility of an interesting relationship between the two disorders. This has been, to a large extent, caused by CJD patients presenting with dementia as a leading feature, and very often being misdiagnosed as AD. Clinical manifestations, in the majority of cases, both CJD and AD, appear in late middle-aged and elderly individuals. For CJD, the incidence peaks between 55 and 75 years (Brown et al, 1987), whereas for AD, the incidence continues to rise with increasing age (Rocca et al, 1986). There is substantial overlap so that, in an individual patient, age alone is not a criterion for distinguishing between the two diseases. Often, the duration of illness separates CJD cases from AD, but diagnosis can be problematic in cases where the illness extends for two or more years. A variety of clinical and pathological forms of CJD and AD occur. The main distinguishing factor, as in other SEs, is the existence of a transmissible agent in all CJD cases. Another difference between the two diseases is that AD is at least 100 to 1000 times as common as CJD (Brown, 1989).

In recent times, diagnosis of CJD has greatly improved. Historically, CJD was first recognised as a specific disease by psychiatrist Hans Gerhard Creutzfeldt and physician Alfons Jakob in 1921. In 1968, Gajdusek found it to be transmissible, indicating that the disease is caused by an infective agent. Over the years, a very large number of case reports have been published covering different clinical symptoms, and retrospective studies have revealed a miscellany of different diseases. In fact, only two of the six cases published by Creutzfeldt and Jakob themselves would today qualify for the clinical and neuropathological criteria of CJD.

Sufficient clinical blurring exists as to create a situation in which, at least in its earlier stages, each disease (CJD and AD) is a principal diagnostic alternative to the other, and in certain cases, this uncertainty can extend throughout the entire clinical course (Watson, 1979; Brown et al, 1984; Brown, 1989). Huntington's disease (where patients experience ceaseless occurrence of a wide variety of rapid highly complex jerky movements that appear well coordinated but are performed involuntarily) shares some of the clinical and pathological features of CJD. This was reported in a family where several of the first-born affected members of the second generation were diagnosed as suffering from Huntington's disease (Masters et al, 1979). After the diagnosis of CJD had been made in their relatives, a review of histology slides of brain tissue of one of the Huntington's cases, and of the medical notes of the other cases, confirmed the diagnosis of CJD. It has also been shown that occasionally CJD is associated with other underlying diseases, including tumours, brain abscess, AD and stroke, with CJD only subsequently being confirmed by transmission of the disease from these cases into animal hosts (Masters, Harris, Gajdusek et al, 1979).

Three Groups of CJD Cases

Epidemiological studies of the world-wide occurrence of CJD have revealed the existence of three groups: (1) Familial: these cases occur within the same family and represent approximately 5 to 15% of CJD (Masters et al, 1979). (2) Iatrogenic: these constitute a small percentage and are caused by accidental inoculation (through contaminated instruments) and some through the effect of contaminated human growth hormone (hGH). (3) Sporadic: Sporadic CJD, which forms the majority of cases, is rare, but found worldwide. Whatever the initial symptoms of the clinical disease and pathological findings may be, a transmissible infecting agent is common to them all, as is the case with all other SEs.

Modes of Transmission

After more than two decades of intensive epidemiological research, the means by which the usual sporadically occurring disease is acquired remains unknown. There are very few cases of iatrogenic transmission cases of CJD, while there is no evidence to support the idea of the disease spreading from clinically affected persons to healthy contacts. This brings us back to the question: " how do humans "catch" CJD"? It is possible that there is a silent spread of a ubiquitous infectious agent early in life, with the disease developing in "susceptible" persons after a long incubation period?

It has not been possible to distinguish between the three presumed modes of transmission, viz. zoonotic transmission (scrapie or BSE); activation of a latent endogenous virus infection; or person-to-person transmission. In exceptional circumstances, accidental transmission of CJD has occurred from man to man. CJD is predominantly a disease of late middle age, with the onset ranging between 35 and 86 and averaging 60 years; the age at which the disease appears has been taken as a major indicator of the natural CJD cases. Some exceptions have also been reported amongst the more than 3,000 cases worldwide, and nine autopsy-verified cases have been documented in patients under 30 year olds, the youngest being 16. Three of these 'under-aged' CJD patients were the well-known cases of surgical transmission described later in detail (Duffy et al, 1974; Bernoulli, 1977).

The undisputed fact which differentiates CJD from AD and other neurological disorders is, that after intracerebral inoculation with brain tissue from human CJD, animals develop the disease at a level approaching 90% in the most susceptible primate hosts (Brown, 1989). Transmission experiments from CJD have resulted in a demonstration of a low titre of infectivity 1000 units/ml in the patient's blood. The transmission of the disease by inoculation with human blood, from several members of AD families, who were unaffected but presumably at risk, or had early signs of disease, into hamsters, has been reported (Manuelidis et al, 1988). This suggested that the transmission of AD might be more effectively accomplished at the preclinical rather than the clinical stage of the disease. This did not accord with results obtained for CJD or any other transmissible SE.

The occurrence of viremia (presence of virus in blood) in encephalopathy cases, caused by conventional viruses, is well recognised (Johnson & Mim, 1968). However, transient viremia in scrapie has been demonstrated within 48 hours, when serum or whole blood from mice was used for the inoculation (Field, 1967). In experimental animals, blood of CJD patients has been shown to be infectious, both during the incubation period and the clinical phase of CJD (Klein et al, 1993; Manuelidis et al, 1985; Tateishi, 1985; Tamai et al, 1992).

The only mechanism of transmission conclusively demonstrated is iatrogenic; accidental inoculation through contaminated instruments, or tissue in recipients of hGH. This mode of infection was recently highlighted by an outbreak of CJD in recipients of growth hormone prepared from human pituitary glands collected during autopsies. The incubation period in these cases has been demonstrated to be of the order of 15 months but occasionally even 20 to 30 years or more. The incidence of sporadic CJD in people under the age of 40 has been established to be about 1 per 20 million. In the USA, in the under 30s, the first three cases of CJD due to growth hormone occurred within one year (1985). From the world-wide statistical figures of sporadic cases, the chance of three CJD cases occurring in one year in this age group, should be of the order of 1 in 10^{12}. The diagnosis of CJD in these three cases was considered, but rejected on the basis of the patients' ages. Further investigation of these cases produced vital clues in assessing the modes of transmission of the agent of CJD in underage patients, leading the investigators to discover contaminated hGH to be the cause of the disease in these patients.

Similarly, microscopical neuropathological examination of the brains from kuru patients, revealed marked similarities with CJD, but the two disease groups were considered different because of the astonishingly different ages of the patients at the onset of the two disorders.

The successful transmission of kuru and CJD to a non-human host altered radically conventional thinking as to the nature of the origin of SEs (Gajdusek and Gibbs, 1975). CJD, like other SEs, terminates fatally in most cases between three weeks and six months after the first appearance of clinical symptoms. These experiments finally established that kuru, scrapie and CJD shared common neuropathology. All were transmissible with a long incubation period and with a fatal outcome. By definition, CJD is a SE, similar to scrapie in sheep and kuru in humans.

The outbreak of CJD in recipients of growth hormone prepared from human pituitary glands, reminds us that there may be many infected sub-clinical cases of CJD in the general population. This experience has taught us that tissues or tissue extracts from such people cannot be transferred with impunity among humans. An epidemiological survey, with a view to obtaining pathological specimens from other neurological diseases or suspected CJD cases, for confirmation, would give a better insight into the level of risk that is being taken with tissue transplants.

It has been well established that the agent causing SEs is transmissible, replicates and that the titre increases with incubation period. The fundamental question which will solve many of the problems still remains unanswered: What is the biological nature of the agent?

History of CJD

The first case of CJD described by Fischer (1911), in the course of discussion on "status spongiosus", appears to be the earliest recorded instance of the disease in a subacute form. The first detailed account of the disease was given in 1920 by Dr. H. G. Creutzfeldt, in a 22-year old woman with the title of "Peculiar focal disease of the central nervous system". Subsequently, Jakob (1921, 1923) published a comprehensive report of three other middle-aged patients who had died with progressive dementia. He identified this as the central nervous system disease in his publication "Anatomic Findings, Spastic Pseudosclerosis, Disseminated Encephalomyelopathy."

Heidenhain (1928), reported the disease in a paper entitled "Concerning a Peculiar Organic Disease of the Presenium". Hallervorden (1930) gave examples of a similar condition, and he also regarded the disease in his patients as some form of degeneration of the central nervous system. He, however, differentiated his case from CJD, especially based on the histological changes in the cerebral cortex and wrote " Unter diesen Umständen wird es wohl nicht angängig sein, unsere Fälle mit den Jakobschen ohne weiteres auf eine Linie zu stellen" (Under these circumstances it is not practical to put our cases at once on the same line as Jakob). He designated the condition affecting his patients as Presenile Corticostriatal Degeneration : as opposed to Spastic Pseudosclerosis, a name given by Jakob to his reported disease. Furthermore, he regarded the condition as being due to a primary degeneration of the nerve cells. Over the next few years, additional cases were reported by Davison (1932); Jansen and Monrad-Krohn (1939).

Meyer, Leigh and Bagg (1954), under the title "A Rare Presenile Dementia Associated with Cortical Blindness" (Heidenhain's Syndrome), described another example of this disease, asserting that Heidenhain regarded the condition as closely related to the "Creutzfeldt-Jakob syndrome" and also belonging to the "Creutzfeldt-Jakob syndrome," but in order to distinguish it from other varieties of this disease, they suggested that the name "Heidenhain's Syndrome" be used to designate their case and all similar cases. Jakob et al (1950), and Bornstein et al (1955) published further examples of CJD including Heidenhain's cases. They suggested that attempts made by Meyer, Leigh and Bagg (1954), to establish a subvariety of the disease, were unjustified. A detailed study of some more new cases was published under the title "Spastic Pseudosclerosis" (McMenemey et al, 1941).

The first paper entitled "A rapidly progressive presenile dementia of the Jakob type" was published by Jervis (1942). In 1960, Nevin et al, further described

213

eight examples of the condition and discussed further the pathological changes. In these studies, they considered the particular possibility of whether or not CJD was some form of degeneration or vascular dysfunction and whether that was the primary cause. Over the years, this exceptionally rare dementing condition, a form of dementia rare in adult life, originally described by Dr. Creutzfeldt and Dr Jakob, became known as CJD. It will be generally agreed, that clarification of the nature of the disease under discussion can only be achieved by the recording of the clinical and pathological details of all such cases as they come to light.

Clinical Features of CJD

From the time of the original description of CJD in 1921, until the transmissible nature of the disease was discovered (Gajdusek, 1968), many authors considered the spectrum of CJD to include a syndrome of slowly progressive dementia, with lower motor neuron signs, with or without the presence of extrapyramidal signs. CJD has been referred to by various names including cortico-pallido-spinal or cortico-striato-spinal degeneration (Davison, 1932; Wilson et al, 1940). Ultimately, in patients where the transmissibility remained unclear, the disorder became known as the "amyotrophic form" of CJD (Allen et al, 1971; Garcin et al, 1963; Hudson, 1981).

CJD is complex, but similar in some ways to Alzheimer's disease (AD), with dementia in the later years, and an impairment of mental ability and personality changes as the main features. Some CJD patients develop typical clinical features, which, with our current state of knowledge, present problems in clinical diagnosis. In large autopsy surveys of patients dying with dementia, Alzheimer's disease has been recognised 100 times more often than CJD (Jellinger, 1976). Both sexes seem to be equally prone to the disease.

Sporadic CJD appears in patients who have previously enjoyed good health, without obvious precipitating factors. Some of the patients might have suffered previously from other diseases which may or may not be significant. CJD presents a broad variety of clinical manifestations, with a range of clinical syndromes involving dementia during middle and late life. Compared with Alzheimer's disease, CJD follows a more rapid course over a period of four to seven months and is almost invariably accompanied by a variety of neurological abnormalities, especially visual, cerebellar, and extrapyramidal deficits, often in association with myoclonus and other involuntary movements. Dementia in AD is usually slowly progressive over a period of four to seven years and is associated with few, if any, neurological signs, apart from a tendency to rigidity and tremulousness in the terminal stages of the disease. When one or more of these features are absent, particularly in cases where duration of the illness is longer than a year, the clinical diagnosis becomes less certain (Brown et al, 1984). Some of these similarities between AD to CJD cases are associated with old age, particularly dementia in the older patients, due to the ageing process. However, most patients with either Alzheimer's disease or CJD have easily recognisable charac-

214

teristic symptoms. Because of atypical clinical or neuropathological features, the question remains as to whether some diagnosed cases of transmissible disease, which were never submitted to experimental transmission, may have escaped discovery due to misdiagnosis. This feature is well illustrated from the first few cases of human growth hormone recipient cases.

In patients where CJD developed more slowly with a prolonged course of the illness, exceptionally when some of its most characteristic elements such as myoclonus and periodic EEG were absent, the major alternative diagnostic conclusions were of the primary degenerative disorders, i.e. Alzheimer's disease, Huntington's disease, amyotrophic lateral sclerosis (ALS) with dementia, and Parkinson's disease and Pick's disease (on clinical grounds, it is difficult to separate Pick's disease from AD (Brown et al, 1993). Pick's diseased brain contains swollen neurons with Pick's bodies). The mechanisms of Amyotrophic lateral sclerosis (ALS) are unknown, but it affects a subset of nerves and can occur at any time in adulthood, the peak age being about 55. The symptoms in ALS patients progress from minor muscle weakness to slurred speech and weakness in the arms and legs, and finally to complete paralysis. About half of the ALS patients are dead within three to four years of diagnosis. To this list of diagnostic considerations, the literature has added vitamin deficiencies and bilateral subdural hematomas (Brown et al, 1986), drug toxicity associated with bismuth (Buge et al, 1977; Von Bose and Zaudig, 1991), and cyclic antidepressives (Foerstl et al, 1989; Koponen et al, 1990).

In the UK study, neuropathological examination has been critical to the correct diagnosis of CJD especially in the 5% of cases with stroke-like presentation and 10% of cases with a duration of illness of greater than a year. It is possible that the use of even strict diagnostic criteria will miss some of these cases and there is justifiable concern that CJD may be missed in the elderly and even more so with the "new strain" of CJD cases.

Prodromal Symptoms

More than one quarter of patients exhibit nonspecific symptoms that could be considered part of a prodromal period, which began weeks or months before neurological signs. These symptoms usually consist of uncertainty, feelings of anxiety, disturbance in sleeping, changes in eating patterns and weight loss with only minimal mental deterioration. Brown et al (1993), summarised a series of 300 CJD cases, all confirmed by experimental transmition. One third of these patients had experienced some form of mental deterioration at the onset of neurological disease. The symptoms included memory loss, confusion, or uncharacteristic behaviour in the earlier stages described as coincidental to the onset of physical neurological symptoms (Brown et al, 1986). Another third of the patients had an onset of an exclusively physical nature, and the remaining third of patients had a mixture of both mental and physical symptoms.

In some patients, the onset of neurological symptoms might be abrupt, in

215

that they had a stroke, visual symptoms, ataxia and even paralysis, followed by emotional deterioration and eventual dementing with severe loss of analytical capability. Brown et al, (1986) in another large study of CJD cases found that, in about a third of patients, the presenting symptoms were exclusively neurological, mostly of cerebellar or visual origin. The symptoms also include gait disturbance, clumsiness, perception of two images of a single object (diplopia), bizarre colour perception and generalised blindness in half of the visual field (hemianoptic), and a sensation as if the external world is revolving around the patient (vertigo), while headache and sensory symptoms were reported less often. However, the manifestation of any one or more of such symptoms does not necessarily mean the existence of these transmissible diseases in the patient.

Less frequent neurological abnormalities reported among CJD cases are a variety of oculomotor disorders. Visual symptoms most often consisted of diplopia, blurred or distorted vision or hallucinations. Altered colour perception has also been occasionally reported as the presenting symptom (Brown et al, 1993). The single most common oculomotor defect - observed in 5% of cases was paresis of conjugate upward gaze and failure of convergence on the upward gaze (supranuclear palsies), (Parinaud's syndrome) (Brown et al, 1993). In the later stages of the illness, visual symptoms frequently evolve into cortical blindness.

A number of patients suffer from auditory, olfactory, or sense of taste (gustatory) abnormalities of a central origin, such as changes in appetite, thirst, libido or menstruation, or recurrent episodes of high fever (hyperthermia) and perspiration. Apparent imperception and neglect of a limb or of one side of the body pointing to dysfunction, have also been reported.

In the great majority of patients, the onset of the illness has been reported to be rather gradual. Brown et al (1993) measured this period in weeks to months, but found that some of the patients experienced a rapidly progressive or even sudden onset. They noted that this group of patients had not had any prodromal symptoms. The first sign of the illness was often an episode of confusion, vertigo, diplopia, or blurred vision. Less often, a sense of clumsiness, tremor, slight paralysis (paresis), or an abnormal sensation (paresthesia) in one limb were also observed. In patients with the more typical subacute onset, they reported a gradual failure of memory taking the form of an inability to remember names or recent events, losing one's way in familiar surroundings, or general confusion. Behavioural abnormalities were usually a consequence of an agitated or depressed state, that began during the prodromal period. Defects in higher cortical function were most often manifest where the patient has difficulty in finding words, performing simple arithmetic or writing correctly. The patients were rarely aggressive and almost never violent (Brown et al, 1993).

Cerebellar Dysfunction

The most common signs of early cerebellar dysfunction were ataxic gait, vertigo, and an involuntary rapid movement of the eyeball (nystagmus) and truncal and limb ataxia. Severe incoordination and marked rigidity, and abnormal movements with trembling, have often been observed. The clinical disease usually progresses in the majority of cases without interruption to a state of mental deterioration, which often produces hallucinations, and eventually results in death. Brown et al (1989) reports one case, in which the patient reported involuntary movements at the onset of the illness; movement disorders are observed in the majority of patients. Cerebellar and extra-pyramidal signs have also been described. The average duration of the illness observed has been approximately eight months, but the majority of deaths occurs within six months, frequently within two to three months. In patients where there was a slow progress, the illness might last two or more years. In a French study, Brown et al (1986), reports that 90% of the patients died within a year of onset, and 5% died within the following year, with the remaining 5% of the patients having a longer disease duration. Kirschbaum (1968), reported that 46% of cases died with a duration of illness of under six months, 25% up to 12 months, 14% up to 18 months, 10% up to 36 months, and 5% over 36 months. There has been no particular correlation with any other form of disease, or with the age of onset of the disease duration of the illness and symptoms. Brown et al (1986) suggest that patients with exclusively physical neurological presentation tend to have a rapid onset and correspondingly shorter clinical illness, while younger patients appear to have the longest duration of illness.

There are no ready explanations for the differences reported among various studies in regard to sex ratio, familial incidence and age at the onset of the disease. Differences in the frequencies of other clinical features can often be attributed to varying analytical formats, or classification of symptoms. Patients with a long duration of illness have often presented difficult if not impossible problems in the differential diagnosis, where the major alternative is Alzheimer's disease. Several patients have been found, on autopsy, to have had AD, sometimes in association with Parkinson's disease or amyotrophic lateral sclerosis (Brown et al, 1986). They also reported individual cases of bilateral internal capsule haematomas, striatonigral atrophy and diffuse cortical gliosis. It was once considered that without neuropathological examination or experimental transmission of the disease to monkeys, the correct diagnosis cannot be established. During the past 20 years, however, we have been able to refine diagnostic criteria to the point where typical clinical and neuropathological features in the great majority of cases make the definitive verification by transmission experiments an unnecessary exercise.

Odd cases of CJD

Aronyk et al (1984) described a CJD case in a 68 year old female. The patient developed resolute movements, in the absence of paralysis (apraxia), of the left hand and intermittent partial elementary motor seizures in the left upper extremity. Within a few weeks, her mental status had begun to decline, and her left-sided seizures had become almost constant. She became increasingly lethargic and finally stuporous. Her seizures remained primarily left sided, while her head and eyes deviated to the left and rhythmical twitching involved the left side of the face and left arm and leg. Occasional myoclonic jerks of the right arm were observed, while no spontaneous movements other than the seizure activity were recorded. Muscle tone was generally reported to be increased, while cranial nerve examination revealed intact brain stem function. EEG showed a diffused slowing of wave length with periodic lateralised epileptiform discharges, while a repeat EEG about three weeks later revealed prominent bilateral discharges on a background of diffused slowing. The patient remained in a vegetative state for about six months after the onset of her problems. The CJD was confirmed by biopsy.

A 16 -year clinical duration of the illness has been reported in a male mathematician patient which appears to be the longest documented case of CJD (Cutler et al, 1984). According to the description provided by his wife, when the patient was 31, he showed mild clumsiness, difficulty in screwing a light bulb into a socket and manipulating carpentry tools (Cutler et al, 1984). At the age of 34, the patient became aware of troubles with complex maths and had to give up his teaching job. Routine tasks took longer and he would lose his way in familiar surroundings. Over the next 5 years, the patient attempted less demanding jobs, but his level of physical functioning deteriorated to a stage of merely maintaining basic personal and hygienic requirements. His speech was clear but his vocabulary gradually deteriorated. The results recorded that his condition stabilised during the next several years. In 1982, 16 years after the onset of the first symptoms, he became bedridden, uncommunicative and incontinent. His neurological examination revealed generalised rigidity and myoclonus. Coarse tremors were present at rest and exacerbated by increased activity. The rest of the findings from general physical and neurological examination were normal. Pathological examination of his brain revealed spongiform changes, which were severe in the occipital cortex and molecular layer of the cerebellum. None of the pathological changes seen in AD could be demonstrated in this case.

Another case, reported by Brown et al (1984) was a male 55 year-old retired auto mechanic who was noted by his wife as having undergone an unpleasant personality change, using increasingly foul language, drinking and bringing home pornographic material. He remained unchanged for the next four years, but then the patient noted numbness in his right hand and clumsiness of the right arm. He developed a staggering gait and slurred speech. On admission to hospital three months later, he was found to be mentally slow, unable to read or write and a stammer developed. He had poor coordination and extremity rigidity with weakness. He rapidly deteriorated over a two months period with the appearance of twitching of muscles (myoclonus), and slow wave EEG activity, and died some four and half years after the onset of the symptoms.

Kamin and Patten (1984) noted another patient of long duration who was a 45-year-old restaurant owner who experienced problems with forgetfulness on re-

218

turning to work from holiday. Within three weeks, he exhibited bizarre behaviour, hiding objects in unusual places and forgetting where they were. He became nervous and edgy, with temper outbursts and periods of confusion. His symptoms continued to worsen, he lost interest in work, became hypersexual, had trouble sleeping, and acted more and more irrationally. He was admitted to hospital about three months after the onset of these symptoms. He was found to have serious loss of memory, episodic confusion, and unpredictable and sudden changes of behaviour. His EEG showed only slow wave activity. Over several months, he had progressive intellectual loss and experienced episodic trembling, gait disturbance, and generalised myoclonus. Following a brain biopsy, he continued to exist in a more or less vegetative state for the next three years with increasing muscular rigidity but still able to eat and follow simple commands, until finally dying of pneumonia four years after the onset of symptoms.

Clinical Stages of CJD

The onset is abrupt, there being usually no difficulty in assessing the exact commencement of symptoms. Nevin et al, (1960) and later Kirschbaum (1968) reviewed 150 cases from the literature and suggested that the clinical course of the neurological syndrome in CJD, although varying greatly in duration and symptomatology, can be divided into three stages.

The First Stage of the Disease

The first stage is an ingravescent stage (entrance of individual into eclipse) in which symptoms build up over several weeks. These are initiated by vague complaints, such as headaches, tiredness, physical discomfort, odd and painful sensations in the limbs which often present at the onset but are never conspicuous. Apart from these general complaints, mild apprehension, fatigue, morbid anxiety about one's health (hypochondria), inability to concentrate and forgetfulness are also observed. Other presenting symptoms include the impairment or distortion of vision, diplopia, stiffness, paræsthesiæ, weakness or loss of control of a limb consisting of a lack of coordination, failure to arrange words in their proper order (dysphasia), inability to think clearly, blunting of memory, depression, irritability, drowsiness or inability to sleep (insomnia) and also unsteadiness in walking and involuntary movements, especially myoclonus. Incoordination of movements and slight changes of gait and speech, accompanied by dizziness, also persist. There may be an organically tainted depressive mental reaction, with an illusion of movement, a sensation as if the external world were revolving around the patient (vertigo) and involuntary rapid movements of the eyeball, which may be horizontal, vertical, rotary, or mixed (nystagmus). There may be short spells of confusion. Alertness and consciousness may be diminished. Once started, the disease progresses steadily without intermission. The initial disturbances increase in severity, new symptoms appear and old ones in turn increase in intensity after a period of eight to twelve weeks, or even as short as three to six weeks. At the height of the illness, there may appear a gross impairment of cerebral function.

The Second Stage of the Disease

The second stage starts with greater mental abnormality and unbalance as well as major neurological symptomatology, with cortical, pyramidal, and extrapyramidal dysfunctions. There is general intellectual decline, followed by emotional weakness, which can be very rapid in some patients, before a depressive phase becomes apparent. The symptoms vary from apathy, unrest with delusions, a delirious phase, general mental enfeeblement, semistupor or unawareness, to profound dementia. This has been described as 'organic psychotic reaction'. The deficits that appear include an inability to recognise (agnostic), loss of ability to carry out familiar, purposeful movements in the absence of paralysis (apractic), and loss of power of expression by speech (aphasic). These manifest concurrently, overhang or alternate. The characteristics and sequence of events may vary exceptionally. The patient is ultimately unable to continue with daily routine business activities.

The second and third stages are marked by aggravation of the symptoms. Characteristically, the syndrome may last from a few weeks to several months or, in some cases, may present for as long as one and a half years. In these cases, it is important to find individual differences in the appearances and various combinations. Kirschbaum (1968) in the summary list includes varying neurological findings, among them transient and permanent mono- or hemiparesis, sensory symptoms, altered muscular state of tension (tonicity), a form of spasm in which the head and the heels are bent backward and the body bowed forward (opisthotonus), postural changes such as rigid positions of neck, limbs, fingers, abnormally decreased motor function (hypokinesia), athetotic movements, or ataxia, disturbance of muscular coordination (dyssynergia), or pyramidal symptoms and progressive muscular atrophies. There were a number of individual cases where variations in the duration of illness and symptoms were reported. Loss of the sense of smell in one of the nostrils (heamianopsia), or dissociation of the eye movements combined with, or without, uncontrollable tremor (palsies) signs. Reflexes are altered, muscles become stiff and movements are awkward (spastic), or weak (flaccid), with slight or incomplete paralysis (pareses). These are suggestive of pyramidal type features.

A temporary suspension of consciousness due to generalised cerebral ischemia (syncopes) may not be apparent at the beginning, but can become marked in the later stages. Myoclonic, shock-like contractions of portions of muscles are common in the upper half of the body, and rather common in the second or third stages. These might appear as a type of epileptic seizure. There is repetitive lack of coordination among parts of the body, or there may be disturbances of that proper association in the contraction of muscles, which assure that the different components of a movement follow in proper sequence at the proper moment and are of the proper degree, so that the action is executed accurately

220

(asynergic). Asymmetric muscular jerks are often evoked by external stimuli, or occur spontaneously and coincide with spike/wave discharges of the electroencephalogram. A number of cases have been described as amyotrophic lateral sclerosis associated with pyramidal tract disease.

The Third Stage of the Disease

The third stage of the illness lasts from a few weeks to months. Most patients have a mere vegetative existence with gradual progression of the symptoms of the second stage. They are characterised by sound sleep (sopor), inability or refusal to speak (mutism), temporary paralysis (akinesis), myoclonic and epileptic seizures, disturbances of autonomic regulations, postural changes, cerebral function being reduced, rigidity and a stupor from which a patient might be aroused (semicoma). It is a kind of living death.

An Ataxic form of Subacute CJD

Foley et al (1955) reported three cases of subacute progressive Encephalopathy occurring in middle aged patients under the heading The Ataxic-Cerebellar Form of CJD. Later Brownwell et al (1965), described an additional four cases of the ataxic-cerebellar form of CJD, and reviewed six previous cases. The outstanding clinical features, in order of their appearance reported, were rapidly progressive ataxia of cerebellar, with imperfect articulation of speech due to disturbances of muscular control (dysarthria) which result from damage to the central or peripheral nervous system; involuntary rhythmic jerking movements, dementia, progressing to coma and, finally, a state of generalised muscular rigidity in which the involuntary movements tended to disappear. In the final stage, speech was totally lost. The duration of the disease in these cases was about 13 months with a mean of seven months.

Kott et al (1967), described another identical case in which the patient noticed that he was easily becoming tired and that his legs were weak. He would lose his balance and often fall. It became difficult for him to walk. He lost his appetite and weight, and spent many hours of the day sleeping. His speech was recorded to be dysarthric. His finger-to-nose test showed marked ataxia. Deep tendon bilateral reflexes were exaggerated. The lower extremities showed constant myoclonic movements. There was a rapid deterioration of his mental condition, and he became completely disorientated. He shouted, repeated the same sentence for hours, then stopped and began to laugh. EEG results showed some slow activity. The patient died after a four month illness. All these cases were sporadic with a duration of illness lasting under 13 months. Subsequently, several further cases with initially ataxic symptoms of CJD, have been reported in Europe, the USA and Japan.

In this ataxic-cerebellar form of CJD, the symptoms appear to start in the same way as those observed in kuru patients. Ataxia becomes more marked with awkward placement of the feet and a swaying and weaving gait, the patient tending to trip and stumble. As the ataxia becomes more progressively severe, a distinctive tremor becomes apparent. Alema et al (1959), Khochneviss (1960) and Siedler et al (1963) noted 60 to 70 cases of the ataxic-cerebellar form (which had appeared in the literature), but there is no agreement as to which of these cases should be included in the CJD group. Khochneviss (1960) placed these in a separate category of "subacute SE", a term introduced by Jacob et al (1958), leaving open the question whether the vascular pathology in such cases, or the secondary effects of the patient's terminal state, or just mere coincidence is the principal cause of the cerebral changes. Since status spongiosus has been repeatedly observed in these mixed cases, without vascular changes usually being demonstrable, vascular changes cannot thgerefore be the primary cause. It is well known that the strain of the agent can modify the clinical presentation and the virulence on serial passage within the same species. CJD still leaves us with many unresolved questions.

New Strain CJD Cases

A new variant of CJD has been identified in the UK, and it is unique in that it affects young people. The clinical course of the disease in the new strain is distinct from that usually seen in sporadic CJD. The clinical symptoms in these cases are similar to those seen in growth hormone treated patients. Some of the early symptoms include behavioural and mood changes along with depression. Balancing and walking become difficult and the patients feel as if they are going to fall and need support. These symptoms are the same as those seen in the ataxic-cerebellar form of CJD, becoming more marked with a swaying and weaving gait, the patient tending to trip and stumble. Memory impairment becomes apparent with the progression of disease. None of these cases had the typical Electroencephalograph (EEG) patterns traditionally associated with CJD. During the last stage, EEG results showed some slow amplitude activity. Symptoms were so different from typical CJD cases as to cause these patients to be referred to a psychiatrist. As early as 1988, I observed a series of patients presenting with atypical clinical history who also had pathology closely resembling that seen in BSE. Because of these new features, I described them as atypical CJD. Initial diagnosis in all these cases was made by demonstrating nemavirus and SAF in their brains. Based on conventional and accepted diagnostic criteria for CJD, none of these cases would be even classified as "probable" cases of CJD on clinical grounds. Peter Hall, of these patients, who was suffering with a neurological disorder for about a year, was being treated by a neurologist who, because of unusual symptoms, did not even suspect he had CJD. His parents asked me in December 1995 to diagnose Peter using my urine test. This I did and found him positive by this test for CJD.   Peter Hall died aged 20 in February 1996. His death sparked a major investigation which led to the acknowledgment that he died of the "new strain" of CJD, which had been officially previously not recognised. If I had not tested Peter, no-one would have known about the new aty-

222

pical strain of CJD. Out of historical precedence, and for ease of classification, and to avoid confusion, it has been proposed that this "atypical" "new variant" strain be termed hereafter Narang Disease (ND).

The Familial form of CJD

The proportion of patients with familial CJD represent approximately 5 to 15% of the total CJD cases (Masters et al, 1979). The major distinguishing features of familial disease are the earlier age at onset and the longer duration of illness. The problem with familial cases comes when one finds cases within a family where the relationship is by marriage (Will and Matthews, 1982; Brown,1986). In general, the patients with familial CJD do not differ appreciably in their clinical symptomatology, neurological and neuropathological features from sporadic CJD. There may be variations in the clinical features within families but similarities in the clinical features within a given family far outweigh any differences (Masters et al, 1979).

There is no evidence that mothers are more frequently affected than fathers. In all these studies, the parameters determined include ages at death, sex distribution, duration of the illness and the rates of occurrence of the disease among siblings and cousins. Genealogical evidence shows skipped generations where there is no CJD case, single-generation occurrence, matrimony and twin occurrence and evidence of preponderance in maternal or paternal line relations. All these have made understanding difficult. Geographical spatial separations and death intervals between affected family members, and differences between ages at death of affected siblings were also described. In some studies, two important differences between familial and sporadic cases have been observed: 1) Age at death is 10 to 15 years lower in familial than in sporadic cases of CJD. Gálvez (1983), however, showed in this study that the mean age at death in familial CJD cases (54.45 years) was identical to that of the sporadic CJD. However, there was a tendency toward female preponderance in the familial CJD, while males were more common in sporadic CJD. 2) The disease duration is longer in familial than in sporadic CJD. However, some surveys suggested that the average duration of the disease is not significantly different in familial and sporadic CJD (Gálvez et al, 1983; Masters et al, 1981). A study of the average age might have been influenced by three cases with extremely long durations of the illness, two of which were 60 months and another one 120 months (Brown et al, 1986). It is important to state that the patient with the longest duration of the illness of 120 months was one of the histologically confirmed cases. Another more critical interpretation for this difference was that they may have included an occasional case of Alzheimer's disease within CJD families (Brown et al, 1986).

For purposes of these studies, family histories are established on factual and anecdotal evidence with the grandparents generation classified as 'first' generation. Masters et al (1979) from the occupational viewpoint described a family of particular interest. Two affected brothers who developed the disease were in

223

the second generation. They owned and worked in a butcher's shop. They had an affected sister and an affected son. Those who developed the clinical disease were from the third generation who also worked in that shop. Another member, who frequently played as a child in the butcher's shop, also developed CJD, while yet another member, whose relationship has not been established, also caught the disease. Six other members of the family studied, who did not contract the disease, and were regarded as unaffected, were in the second and third generation, and had little or no contact with the shop or meat trade. The authors of this study, however, cited another unconfirmed CJD case as the business partner of the affected butcher's family. That patient died of progressive dementia with myoclonus. These examples could be taken as evidence of an environmental source of infection, presumably scrapie-infected meat. The patients were known to eat poorly cooked sheep and beef brains.

The familial clustering of infectious disease, such as CJD, permits a search for evidence of lateral transmission through close physical contact, or for evidence of exposure to some common environmental source of infection. There is one instance with eight or nine affected siblings in the second generation. Direct questioning of the only surviving non-affected member revealed that he had left home at the age of 21, and subsequently had little contact with his brothers and sisters (Master et al, 1981). In contrast all the affected siblings lived in the same area, and were described as "close" in terms of their physical relationship. There are similar other examples of affected siblings living together, while those unaffected had moved away at some early stage.

Where affected siblings died at approximately the same time, this type of evidence suggests a common exposure to the infection at the same time, assuming rather uniform incubation period. In another family, there were five neurologically affected parents in the third generation. Four of them had neurological disease with dementia and they had 16 children of whom nine were affected. The other fifth case was without dementia and had a son and two daughters and their subsequent children were healthy. These nine patients died between the ages of 43-66, a difference of some 20 years; but their deaths all occurred between 1968 and 1973, a period of five years. There is no evidence that affected siblings tended to die at the same time but in terms of a slow virus developing in humans, a variation in the incubation period of about five years would not be unexpected.

During the course of the studies, the authors noticed that one of their third generation cases, a 42 year old male who was well until early 1972, started having errors of judgment and he noticed pain and "flashing lights" in both eyes and lost the ability to discriminate distances. His balance became poor and he staggered. By October, although his physical condition was normal, he generally became unresponsive, although he occasionally repeated the same phrases. His condition deteriorated and an EEG recording showed a diffused slowing with triphasic waves. A second EEG taken two weeks before death, showed periodic biphasic and polyphasic discharges about once every three seconds on a relative

224

low signal background. In the last two months myoclonic jerks became more evident and eventually he became comatose and died of bronchopneumonia.

There is remarkable heterogenous symptomatology in the cases as they are presented. In one case, for instance, the neurologist described mild Parkinsonism, particularly in the facial expression. The gait was ataxic. Three of the patients noticed weakness and dragging of one leg and difficulty in walking. One complained of paresthesias in the left leg and both hands. A year later she was noticed to have left-sided hemiparesis with increased reflexes. In three years, the patient could not support her weight and slowly developed progressive bilateral pyramidal tract dysfunction and incontinence and died at the age of 65. Her sister, 57, had paresthesias over the right side of her face. As the patient deteriorated, she developed ataxia. Later her speech became stammerous and gait slow and shuffling. She too died at the age of 65.

Examining the pedigree, four of six females and one out of the two males in the second generation were affected; thus Rosenthal et al (1976) suggested an autosomal dominant transmission of a factor that is associated with susceptibility to neurological disease. In the third generation descendants of the second-generation affected parents, five of 11 females and two out of seven males developed neurological diseases. One of the relatives died of other causes at the age of 28 , while others had not reached the traditionally expected CJD age.

Another family, with seven affected individuals from three generations in a kindred having over 250 members,has been identified by Bertoni et al (1983). This is the largest reported kindred of CJD. Most of the affected patients were farmers. They reported that a farmer at the age of 58 developed a progressive dementing illness. The family recalled that his illness was identical to that seen in his son, with ataxia and subacute incapacitating dementia. He had eight children and at least 42 grandchildren. The pedigree included 97 great-grandchildren, 107 great-great-grandchildren and 12 great-great-great-grandchildren.

Cartier et al (1985) reported a familial cluster of three cases of the ataxic form of CJD from Chile. In these three familial cases, early symptoms shown were progressive cerebellar ataxia, with a late onset of dementia. In all the three patients, the clinical features were similar, starting with progressive unstable gait due to a predominantly truncal ataxia. Myoclonic jerks were observed in one of the patients. EEGs revealed unspecific and diffused slowing in two of the patients. Pathologically, typical spongiform lesions were observed. The majority of cases of sporadic CJD are not genetically interconnected and appear to be distributed world wide. Genealogical investigations, however, have revealed a small minority of 5 to 15% of CJD cases within related families. In this group of familial cases, interpersonal contact between affected individuals can be consistently established which may elucidate the natural mode of transmission of the CJD agent.

Haltia et al (1991), described 30 patients who died with a diagnosis of CJD during 1974-1984 in Finland. Six were familial cases, all belonging to the same kindred. In another study covering the period 1958-1990, they diagnosed 12 new CJD patients all from the same family, five men and seven women. All patients had spent their childhood in a small community in southern Finland. The mean age at the onset of the disease was 47 years (range 26-56 years), and the mean duration in 10 deceased patients was 27.5 months (range 16-51 months). The periodic EEG activity had not been observed and the patients showed myoclonic muscular twitching which increased during arousal, and intentional muscle activity.

Over one third of the CJD cases worldwide reviewed by Masters et al (1979) occurred in persons directly or indirectly associated with agriculture or food handling. Twenty-four (8%) of 308 persons were farmers or the wives of farmers. Although the association in these families may have been coincidental, it should not be ignored. Increased incidence of the infectious disease could be explained by increased exposure to the agent, thus allowing the opportunity for increased entry of the agent into the host. Farmers and food handlers frequently suffer minor hand wounds such as cuts, abrasions, and cracked-dry or blistered skin. These would serve as ideal portals for the entry of the infectious agent coming in contact with the skin. Other modes of entry would be inhalation and swallowing of the agent with dust from animal food or from animal wastes around about buildings.

The increased incidence in some families who are not farmers or butchers may be due to some families eating brain tissue more than others, since oral transmission of scrapie, kuru and CJD has been demonstrated in squirrel, monkeys and mice, and now, by accidental transmission of BSE, to cows. In some patients, the portal entry may be through bad teeth or peptic ulcers. In animal exposures where infection has been documented after high doses of infected tissue feed, transmission was so irregular that the question arises as to whether the true portal was either the gastrointestinal tract itself, or through areas of mucosal abrasions. Ulcerations in the lips, gums and intestines may also play a role. Studying the effect of gingival scarification on an oral route of infection, demonstrated that 70% of nonscarified compared with 100% of scarificated mice developed the disease and with a significantly shorter incubation time. Single episodes of oral ingestion of the agent alone, therefore, may not transmit SEs and it is likely that other factors play an important role, including the dose of the agent and the length of the incubation period.

Infection caused by the process of accidental inoculation

It is known that CJD is rapidly transmissible by a direct inoculation of infectious material from human to human, with incubation periods from two to five years. The differences in the incubation period for disease observed in these cases may be attributable, in part, to the route of inoculation, the dose of infectious material and the source of infection.

Gerstmann-Sträussler-Scheinker Syndrome

Gerstmann-Sträussler-Scheinker syndrome, (GSSS) a rare variant of CJD, was first described in an Austrian family in 1936. GSSS, which is pathologically similar to CJD, in almost all cases appears to show a pattern that is consistent with the autosomal dominant inheritance pattern (Masters et al, 1981). However, the disease is infectious which suggests that the agent may be carried via a germline as in AIDs and not be a genetic disease. A single-gene point mutation is considered to be the cause of the disease in GSSS cases and, although the hypothesis is widely favoured, unfortunately, it has in fact never been tested. Subsequently, GSSS has been reported in about a dozen other unrelated families as well as in sporadic form. But the fact is that most of the cases of GSSS described are familial.

In GSSS patients, clinically spino-cerebellar signs precede dementia and the disease has certain distinct features. Many of the symptoms, clinically and pathologically, overlap kuru and CJD. The disease presents as an atypical dementia with spino cerebellar ataxia. EEG in these cases is within normal limits. Histopathologically, a large number of unusual forms of amyloid plaques are seen throughout the brain. The presence of amyloid plaques, on first examination, suggest a diagnosis as AD. Spongiform changes in the cortex are modest and variable. GSSS cases have been demonstrated to be infectious by experimental transmission of disease to non-human primates with extracts of brain tissue from human patients. The disease as produced in the non-human primates is indistinguishable from CJD (Masters et al, 1981).

The coding region of the PrP gene was amplified and all the four affected members and 11 out of 29 unaffected members of that Austrian family, had a point mutation in the PrP codon 178. Three of the unaffected members with the mutation, were between 61 to 63 years. This point mutation has been observed in some other familial cases. Some workers in the field have considered that, in these cases where mutations are present, the disease is genetically determined. Usually the disease affects an age group between 35 and 55 years, with an illness duration of two to ten years, compared to CJD where the mean age is 65 and the duration of the illness is three to six months from the onset of symptoms. It still remains to be seen whether the fatal familial insomnia cases, like GSSS, are transmissible. The presence of a transmissible agent in the fatal familial insomnia cases would widen the spectrum of the SEs, and would support the contention that the disease is more common than previously suspected.

Fatal Familial Insomnia and CJD

In 1986, Lugaresi et al, reported two cases of familial insomnia, a rapidly progressive familial disease clinically characterised by untreatable insomnia, total absence of motor coordination (dysautonomia), and motor signs, and pathological, by selective atrophy of the anterior ventral and mediodorsal thalamic nuclei. The entire kindred has always lived in the northern part of Italy. In more advanced stages, these patients had complex hallucinations, and at terminal stages, had stupor and coma. Ataxia, imperfect articulation of speech, stammer, myoclonus, and pyramidal signs have also been described in these patients. Spongiosis of the cerebral cortex was observed in only one member of the family. The mean age at the onset of the disease was 49 years (range, 13-65) with a mean duration of the illness of 13 months. A total of 288 members have been recorded in the pedigree of six generations of this family. Subsequently, Lugaresi et al, examined five other affected members of the family, with 29 other members who may have been affected in over five generations (Medori et al, 1992). They considered that the pattern of inheritance was similar to that seen in autosomal dominant transmission of the disease and termed the disease "fatal familial insomnia." Based on the broader neuropathological changes observed in these cases, they suggested that fatal familial insomnia could be a "prion" disease like CJD. Protease-resistant protein (PrP), a molecular biological marker was demonstrated in two of these fatal cases, but the size and number of protease-resistant fragments were different from those seen in CJD.

Diagnosis and Classification of CJD Cases

There are no pathognomonic clinical or laboratory findings available to make diagnosis of the disorder unequivocal. A subacute clinical course may be characteristic of a majority of CJD cases. There are certain clinical features which would not be expected in other dementias, but there are still many cases where categoric diagnosis is not possible. The order of clinical manifestation may vary significantly from case to case.

Masters et al (1979), provided a classification that has been used in many subsequent studies to assess the patients according to the degree of diagnostic certainty. Brown and associates (1986) from a considerable number of accumulated studies, proposed a simplified scheme for the clinical diagnosis of CJD as follows:

Definite cases: having mental deterioration, myoclonus and 1-2 cycles/second periodic EEG complexes with the illness duration of under 12 months.

Probable cases: having mental deterioration with myoclonus and 1-2 cycles/second periodic EEG complexes with the illness duration of under 18 months.

Possible cases: having mental deterioration with any type of movement disorder or EEG periodic activity with the illness duration under 24 months.

The Potential for Misdiagnosis

The potential for misdiagnosis has been well illustrated in a few studies, some of which have been described by Brown (1989). In his study, the first patient was thought to have CJD; the next two patients were difficult to separate, although CJD was favoured in the patient with periodic EEG, while AD was favoured in the patients with non-specific EEG abnormalities. The last was considered to be definitely a patient of AD. The results of neuropathological examination completely reversed the clinical impressions: the first two cases were found to have had AD, and the last two cases had CJD, as were confirmed by transmission studies.

The situation becomes even more complicated when familial AD cases are considered. Surprisingly, a large proportion of affected members in some of the families having dementing illnesses of comparatively short duration, were associated with pyramidal, extrapyramidal, or cerebellar signs, and even periodic EEG complexes, which suggested the diagnosis of CJD (Masters et al, 1981). Of equal interest is the existence of AD families in which one member had been pathologically verified as having CJD (Masters et al, 1981). From the published accounts, there are doubts as to the certainty of the diagnosis in some of these familial cases. There is no question about the coexistence of AD and CJD in at least a few families (Masters et al, 1979). The frequent overlap in clinical symptoms and the demonstration of familial concurrence of AD and CJD, suggests a relationship between them, and indicates the need for further study into this area, to ensure finer tuning of the diagnostic process.

The classic AD and CJD pathology has occasionally been observed in the same patient (Oppenheimer, 1975; Gaches et al, 1977; Liberski et al, 1987; Brown 1989). The case described by Brown (1989), was a 73 year-old woman who died after nine months of the illness, characterised by progressive dementia, cerebellar signs, myoclonus and a periodic EEG entirely typical of CJD. Neuropathological examination of the brain from this case revealed a diffusely distributed spongiosis, gliosis and neuronal loss, as observed in a typical case of CJD. However, large numbers of neurotic plaques and neurofibrillary tangles in a cortical and hippocampal distribution, characteristic of AD, were also observed. Inoculation of the brain tissue suspension into primates, transmitted CJD.

Some other CJD cases present with Parkinsonian features or chorea-atherkinesia prominent. Variations in degree and succession might allow for many modifications of the clinical picture. The most common presentation was usually, behaviour, mood alteration, errors in judgment and simple memory loss. Even Jakob's own original observation revealed certain differences in the symptomatology, but the cases were not subgrouped. In some patients, there is concurrent overlap or the type of events alternate and vary greatly.

Histological sections from the brains of 66 patients (aged 55 to 94 years; mean 77 years) with a clinical history of progressive dementia, and with a diagnosis of AD, were re-examined by Smith et al (1987). In the original histological diagnosis, AD had been established by the presence of numerous neurotic plaques and the number depended on the age of the patient (Khachaturian, 1985). Smith et al (1987), in the retrospective neuropathologic study of brains from 66 patients with AD, demonstrated vacuolar changes in 50 (76%) cases which they described as almost indistinguishable histologically from the spongiform changes characteristic of CJD. However, the degree of vacuolation varied from slight (54%), moderate (24%), to severe (22%) while none of the non-demented age-matched control cases showed vacuolar changes. Smith et al (1987) in "end stage" AD cases, did not demonstrate any significant association between vacuolar changes and the density of plaques. Duffy et al (1988), in 27 consecutive cases that fulfilled the clinical and pathologically accepted criteria for AD, reported four of these cases as having severe vacuolar changes. These four were familial cases from two different families. The symptoms were associated with dementia and occurrences of myoclonus jerks, and with becoming mute before death. Neither myoclonus nor spongiform changes are specific in either familial or sporadic Alzheimer's patients.

The differential diagnosis must rule out cerebrovascular disease. Chronically elevated blood pressure, previous syncopal attacks, remitting course, more unilaterally localised symptomatology, cerebral angiographic changes and unusual general neurological findings favour arteriosclerosis or other vascular conditions. Disseminated or diffused manifestations of chronic cerebral infections, chronic exogenous intoxications, chronic alcoholism, nutritive deficiencies and other metabolic disturbances, must be distinguished and differentiated. The sequelae of viral encephalitides seldom gives rise to a CJD syndrome.

Traub et al (1977) investigated by inoculating brain tissue from 220 cases with a wide range of neurological conditions into non-human primates. Of the 78 transmissions which occurred, three cases were diagnosed as having AD, enabling the researchers to assert that AD was transmissible. Re-examination of these brain sections revealed amyloid senile plaques with spongiform changes. However, the presence of spongiform changes were to be considered, while senile plaques were to take second place in the diagnosis, the 22% with severe AD and may be some more of the 24% moderate vacuolation cases in the Smith et al study should also be classified as CJD. Brown et al (1990) reported the co-existence of CJD and AD in the same 73 year-old patient, who died 10 months after the onset of her illness. CJD was diagnosed by the neuropathologic findings of widespread spongiform changes, astrogliosis, protease-resistant protein and the experimental transmission of SE to primates inoculated with the brain tissue. Masters et al (1979) also reported transmission of a SE from experimental inoculation of the brain tissue from two cases of familial AD. However, senile plaques, the "hall mark" and the criteria for AD, were also demonstrated.

There have been three other reports suggesting coexistence of CJD and AD (Masters et al, 1981). Further, in a previous study, a few cases, clinically and histologically diagnosed as Alzheimer's disease, produced SE on transmission to animals. Senile plaques, although regarded as the hallmark of AD, are not unique to the condition and there is no agreement as to what the excessive numbers of plaques mean. Duffy (1988) reported four cases with myoclonus jerks, a feature of CJD. However, brain examination revealed no spongy changes, but showed senile plaques, suggesting a diagnosis of AD was made. In these four cases, experimental transmission to animals was not attempted. It is possible that the two diseases CJD and AD coexist in the same individual. In view of their many overlapping clinical features, it would be essential to demonstrate tubulofilamentous particles and scrapie - associated fibrils (SAF) in brains, which are seen only in CJD cases and other SEs. The controversy over the transmissibility of AD, and the evidence for it, remains, at least for the time being, and will continue so, until other tests are available to distinguish the two disorders. This is where both the touch technique developed for the demonstration of tubulofilamentous particles and scrapie-associated fibrils could be used to advantage.

Electroencephalograph (EEG)

Electroencephalograph (EEG) is a technique for recording the electrical activity of the brain through the intact skull. The technique is simple, and gives valuable diagnostic information about epilepsy and encephalopathies, including CJD, and has been considered sufficiently distinctive to help in the diagnosis of the disease. Levy et al, (1986) in an article entitled "Early evolution and incidence of electroencephalographic abnormalities in the CJD", suggested that 82% of patients with CJD exhibit periodic sharp wave complexes within 12 weeks of the onset of the clinical symptoms. EEG evidence of periodicity is an important diagnostic indicator of the disease. Periodic sharp wave complexes may also appear late in the clinical course. The timing and frequency of recordings thus become important when discussing the absence of characteristic activity (Tietjen et al, 1990). A number of electrodes are applied to the scalp and the potential charges so recorded are amplified and presented for interpretation. The activity can be recorded from different areas of the head simultaneously, using different channels. Electrophysiological recordings have also been recorded from cats, as they are nearly inaccessible to direct symptomatic examination, and the technique permits a strong indication of the disease.

CJD patients show a generalised repetitive stereotyped bilateral synchronous sharp wave, which usually occurs at frequency of 1 to 2 Hz. These have often been observed associated with myoclonic jerks. Synchronous bilateral paroxysmal discharges, occur in other diffuse neurological diseases. Other abnormal EEG discharges, which may be physiologically related, are seen in a wide range of different encephalopathies, but periodic discharges have been consistently observed in only two groups: subacute spongiform encephalopathy (SSPE) and CJD. References to abnormal electroencephalograph have also been made in other encephalopathies such as herpes and infectious mononucleosis, phothepatic encephalopathy and cerebral lipidoses (Cobb et al, 1952). Abnormal electroencephalograph also occurs in selected cases of post-herpetic encephalitis and hepatitis. Poursines et al, (1953) and de Ajuriaguerra et al, (1953) noticed the special features of the EEG records with the CJD syndrome, while Jones et al (1954) emphasised the consistent polyphasic high voltage, in their two cases of subacute vascular encephalopathies. However, the characteristic of the periodic complexes observed differ strikingly in these two disease conditions. Specific

231

wave pattern complexes of CJD consist of a single wave, usually triphasic in configuration lasting 100 to 600 milliseconds (average 360 milliseconds) with an amplitude of about 100 μV (microvolts). This is usually followed by a burst of rhythmical discharges at 3 to 7 Hz, or alternatively, a period of flattening for 1 second. The complexes repeat at intervals ranging from 0.5 to 4 seconds (average 1 second). These patterns may not be present at the beginning of the clinical disease, but rather appear relatively late in the development of the disease. Thus, repeated examination reveals correspondence with the development stage of CJD and rate of progress of the disease.

The initial clue to the differentiation of CJD from other dementias has come from periodic EEG activity results which played an important role in differential diagnosis although EEG activity may be lacking in as many as 50% of the patients. Brown et al (1984), in a series of 300 cases, in which EEGs were recorded at least once in almost all patients, showed that, in the early course of the disease, the EEG was often normal, or showed only nonspecific slow wave activity, or mild background disorganisation. Later in the illness, EEG abnormalities became more pronounced, and approximately half of their patients showed either one or two types of semi-periodic slow wave patterns. In some cases of CJD, no EEG is carried out, and in others only a single tracing is obtained early in the course of the illness. The chances of obtaining a characteristic record are enhanced if EEG is repeated, and, therefore, the likelihood of correct diagnosis increases. The awareness of the condition and repetitive, approximately 1 cycle/second biphasic or triphasic EEG complexes, sometimes unilateral but eventually diffuse, have been observed (Au et al, 1980; Chiofalo et al, 1980; Jones et al, 1985). Combined involuntary movements and periodic EEG activity are extremely unusual (Brown et al, 1986). In some of the studies, it was acknowledged that the recognisability of these, the complexes, nearly doubled the rate of accurate diagnosis between the retrospective and prospective phase, with serial tracings of typical patterns. In a Chilean study, patterns were seen in 90% of the patients (Chiofalo et al, 1980).

In AD, there is a slow asymmetrical theta and delta activity which is present continuously throughout the duration of the prolonged course of the disease, and is unrelated to the severity of the clinical picture. In this respect, the EEG differs from the usual pattern in CJD and AD. During the later stages of the disease, this EEG pattern may continue, but frequently, periodic synchronous high voltage wave spike discharges interfere at intervals of one to several seconds, accompanied by myoclonic contractions. In some patients, it has been observed that, at the end, the intervening slow wave activity may disappear, while the random high amplitude spike discharges continue, leaving between them a featureless low voltage tracing. With the worsening of the patient's condition, the periodic synchronous high amplitude spike and wave discharges diminish in frequency. According to Abbott (1959), to start with, the patients have 21 amplitude occurrences in 10 seconds up to 350 μV, diminishing to three times in 10 seconds towards the final stage. Once these patterns appear, a rapid clinical deterioration is observed and death follows within weeks.

Most scientists assume that the synchronous periodic spike wave bursts result from discharges in the brain stem centres due to failing interconnections with cortical cerebral neurons. Nelson and Leffman (1963) followed a case of CJD with severe cortical and cerebellar neuronal loss, but showing relative preservation of the brain stem. The recordings in the patient during the comatose phase of the illness showed an isoelectric background with pseudorhythmic, diffuse discharges. The characteristics of EEGs are considered to be related to bilateral synchronous spikes from all regions of the scalp. Histopathological examination at autopsy, revealed extensive losses of cortical and cerebellar neurons and pathological lesions were observed, with relative preservation of the brain stem, reticular formation and nonspecific nuclei. Diffused bilaterally synchronous EEG discharges could be regularly evoked by many types of sensory stimulation, rhythmic photic, auditory, muscle stretching, or nerve-tendon stimuli. The discharges appeared 65 to 85 milliseconds after stimulation and their configuration differed slightly after each type of stimulus, and spontaneous discharges were almost completely suppressed during the rhythmical stimulation (Nelson and Leffman, 1963).

Unlike kuru (the type with shivering tremor), CJD patients show myoclonic jerking, associated with a very characteristic electroencephalographic pattern of periodic triphasic slow wave spikes. From a few large studies, it has become apparent that about 50% of sporadic CJD cases show marked progressive bursts of high voltage slow waves on electroencephalograph. These periodic bursts of slow-wave activity are a characteristic pattern of high-voltage spikes at a frequency of 1 to 2 cycles per second. This regular high amplitude, spiking discharge observed is seen only in CJD. In another 25% of the sporadic CJD cases, the EEG show other types of irregular abnormal pattern of diffuse slow-wave, while in the remaining 25% of cases, EEG shows slow-wave abnormality within the normal pattern. Based on a large series of patients with neuropathologically verified CJD, it has been suggested that the absence of both periodic sharp wave complexes and involuntary movements virtually excludes the diagnosis of CJD from consideration (Brown et al, 1986; Tietjen et al, 1990).

No comprehensive evaluation of EEG characteristics in familial cases exists. However, from the limited studies, it appears that periodic sharp wave complexes are less common in familial than in sporadic CJD cases (Tietjen et al, 1990). The underlying mechanism of periodic sharp wave complexes is unknown, however, and it has been suggested that they occur consistently only with diffuse cortical and subcortical gray matter involvement (Zochodne et al, 1988; Tietjen et al, 1990). The absence of periodic sharp wave complexes in familial cases may be due to the distribution of the lesions in the brain. The observations that patients with CJD and prominent cerebellar symptoms are less likely to exhibit periodic sharp wave complexes may be secondary to reduced cerebral cortical involvement (Cartier et al, 1985). Kuru, a SE with marked features of cerebellar signs, shows that, with late dementia, the periodic sharp wave complexes and myoclonic are absent even just before death (Cobb et al, 1973). The kuru-infected brains, when inoculated into rhesus monkeys, produced myoclonus and generalised spike-wave complexes in recordings from dural electrodes. This suggests that factors other than the strain of the agent or lesions in the brain may be responsible.

In GSSS, which is characterised by ataxia and dementia of a long duration, myoclonus seldom occurs, and the EEGs are normal or only mildly abnormal, without the periodic sharp wave complexes. Pathological features in these familial cases are quite distinct from those seen in sporadic CJD cases. Although a clinical picture of typical CJD emerges from this analysis, exceptions to these typical clinical evolutions are not uncommon. The CJD cases might exhibit slow progressive disturbance and minimal movement abnormalities, and the EEG may show only nonspecific generalised slowing. On the other hand, patients with AD may have severe abnormal neurological experiences and an EEG indistinguishable from the characteristic pattern of CJD. Thus, in summary, there is an overlap, with " a grey zone", between these two disease conditions. As previously mentioned, this certainly makes diagnosis very difficult in the earlier stages, or even throughout the duration of the illness. To a lesser extent, the symptomatology and clinical evolution is further complicated by many other neurological conditions.

Drug Effect on the Discharging System

Several drugs are known to effect transmission in the diffusely projecting system(s). Nelson and Leffman (1963) reported consistent effects on at least two occasions. They reported that intravenous administration of amobarbital profoundly reduced auditory-evoked discharges by one per second. After a single dose of 100 mg, there was a rapid decrease in discharge amplitude after a 58 second delay. Spontaneous discharges also disappeared. After intravenous administration of Metrazol (pentylenetetrazol), the effect of barbiturates-blocked potentials are quickly reversed. They also reported that the frequent spontaneous discharges also resumed in the patient, with an abrupt return of random movements and rigidity. Occlusive effects were noticed with all combinations of stimuli and during spontaneous discharges limited to a 50 to 100 milliseconds interval. After the intravenous administration of 75 mg of chlorpromazine, a marked increase in spontaneous activity was also noticed, without altering the threshold for the evoked discharge (Nelson and Leffman, 1963).

Laboratory Diagnosis of Creutzfeldt-Jakob Disease

Macroscopic examinations of the brain in CJD usually yield little in the way of specific findings. Most cases of CJD exhibit cortical atrophy in a global distribution, often accompanied by cerebellar atrophy, particularly in the superior vermis. GSSS and iatrogenic CJD cases may show disproportionate atrophy of the cerebellar hemispheres, in addition to the vermis, often with relative sparing of the cerebral cortex. In more elderly CJD individuals, the brain may exhibit a more severe degree of age-related changes, both on external inspection and on microscopy.

Pathology

On gross examination, CJD brains usually appeared normal, or showed a mild to moderate degree of ventricular enlargement and diffuse or focal atrophy of the cerebral mantle. Occasionally, however, severe focal or diffuse atrophic changes have been reported as with other SEs. No lesions have been demonstrated in any organ outside the CNS.

CJD is diagnosed by histopathological microscopical examination of the brain sections. The pathological changes are distinctive. They consist of widespread loss of nerve cells with vacuolation in all layers. A particularly striking feature is the damaged cerebral cortex, especially in the occipital lobes. This damage is not like that seen in secondary nerve loss after the absence of oxygen supply to tissue, despite adequate perfusion of the tissue by blood (anoxia). The disease presents in varying manifestations in individual cases and, therefore, the neuropathological characteristics, though markedly different in individual cases, should not come as a surprise. Nevertheless, spongiform changes, accompanied by neuronal loss and reactive gliosis, are striking features, which confirm the diagnosis in the majority of cases. Variation in the intensity, the distribution of lesions and the stage of development from case to case is evident from the reported cases. There is sufficient evidence of similarities, however, common to most cases, to suggest strongly that the degeneration has been caused by the same or similar virus.

A state of confusion has existed over CJD pathology because a wide range of degenerated neurons may be present. All parts of the central nervous system may not be equally effected. From case to case the neuronal damage may be very widespread throughout the central nervous system or it may be local. Concern arises when insufficient neuropathological microscopic changes are seen, or the spongiform changes are hard to find in cases with otherwise typical clinical signs. Histopathological criteria for diagnosis were first established in 1921 by Dr Jakob. There is a marked topographical distribution of degenerative changes with relatively normal cortical areas. These may alternate with severely affected patches of lesions. Damage is so severe with large vacuoles in some stretches that the architecture is almost completely destroyed.

Besnoit and Morel in 1898, by microscopical examination of scrapie sheep brain, described vacuolation in the anterior horn cells of the spinal cord and intense neuritis involving the smaller motor nerves. From that first description of neuronal vacuolation, it took nearly sixty years to recognise these vacuoles as characteristic changes of scrapie in sheep. Now, vacuolation of the central ner-

235

vous system, as observed in histological sections, is used as a criterion for confirmation of the diagnosis. Vacuolated cells may occur anywhere, but they are especially common in the medulla among the large nerve cells in the brain, especially near the midline, which are nearly always affected to some degree. Vacuolated lesions are common in the pons, thalamus and in the hippocampus. In the spinal cord anterior horn cells are frequently affected. Lesions are also seen in basal ganglia.

The spongiform degeneration is characterised by fine microscopical vacuoles in the grey matter. The essential neuropathological pattern consists of degenerative processes in which vacuoles are observed in nerve cells. The cortical lesions consist essentially of destruction and loss of nerve cells in all layers occurring without obvious patterns, and may be mild to severe. In earlier and less severe stages of the disease, the completely destroyed neurons may not be numerous, but many of those remaining neurons show pathological changes of an acute kind, consisting of chromatolysis, fragmentation and dissolution of the layer cells and shrinkage of the smaller cells. The astrocytes and the oligodendroglia are destroyed in the softened areas of cortex and in other parts. One may see partial dissolution of the astrocytes or regressive changes characterised by swelling or loss of processes. An intense proliferation of the astrocytes is the most striking feature of a damaged cortex.

The diverse formats of hospital neuropathological reports have not been helpful in providing a precise tabulation of the topographic distribution, and the extent of the different lesions in the brain. This may be because only a limited number of cases are examined by each neuropathologist. Lesions, typically have been seen in the basal ganglia, thalamus and cerebellar cortex. Cerebellar involvement is present in most cases, although the severity and distribution of vacuolation within cerebellum is markedly variable. Cerebellar pathology always involves the outer molecular layer. Confluent spongiform changes are very unusual in the cerebellum in sporadic CJD cases. In the electron microscope, vacuoles are seen to be separated by the cell membrane. The diagnosis of CJD often presents problems because of the time taken to process brain tissue for histological examination. As briefly mentioned before, status spongiosus is also seen in AD, with a large neuronal loss.

Apart from the presence of ischaemic softening (oxygen starved tissue) the white matter has been relatively little affected in the cases so far described. However, secondary degeneration of the myelin of the cerebral hemispheres and the brain stem consequent upon atrophy of the cerebrum and cerebral cortex have been reported (Foley et al, 1955, Nevin et al, 1960). Destruction of myelinated fibrils and axis cylinders may be little evident, apart from in the areas of status spongiosus, but where the disease has been severe, considerable destruction of the fibril bundles of the cortex may occur. The cerebellum may also be severely affected (Foley et al, 1955).

It is clear that status spongiosus can occur in the cerebral grey matter under a

236

variety of pathological conditions. These fall into two main groups: (1) those where destruction of neurons follows a degenerative or a toxic metabolic process, such as Pick's disease, Alper's disease, etc. (2) those where a vascular factor is probably present such as in arteriosclerotic brain and in air embolism, and may combine with nutritional failure to give the spongiose lesions (Hallervorden, 1952). The specific lesion in the cerebral grey matter in this disease is such as could arise on a vascular basis, and has been understood on that basis for a long time (Jones et al, 1954; Nevin et al, 1960).

There were no structural changes in the blood vessels which could directly impair the blood flow and could explain how vascular disturbance arose. It has been seen, however, that the nerve cells are damaged in subacute SE, in areas of the cortex where cavitation is minimal and there is, in fact, no direct relationship between the severity of the symptoms and the status spongiosus. The patchy nature of the lesions, with the presence of such gross destructive lesions without cuffing in most instances, makes this disease different from other known viral infections.

In the CNS, in addition to vacuolation, other microscopical changes seen became easier to interpret with the development of experimental models. There is general agreement that the earliest change to be observed is a proliferation of astrocytes, a type of cell which has large branching processes. These cells are believed to be concerned with metabolic transport in the nervous system. In brains of normal animals, astrocytes and their processes are very pale and do not stain well. Once the animals are inoculated and the disease processes start, the first noticed morphological microscopical change is enlargement of astrocytes, their cell processes becoming prominent. The stain readily impregnates making the processes stand out clearly. So precocious and characteristic are these processes that it gives them the appearance of "spiders", hence the common name "spider" cells. Once the astroglial hypertrophy starts, it spreads to all parts of the brain and spinal cord. At this stage, the appearances of these cells with their sucker feet give the tissue a very wild angry look under the microscope. Hypertrophy and proliferation of astrocytes could be the initial response to a non-specific injury, and, although the change occurs very early, or soon after infection of the CNS, this change by no means is a specific indicator to scrapie or CJD and, therefore, it cannot be used as a marker of any specific disease. On the whole, it appears that, there is not much to support the view that the primary trouble lies with the astrocytes.

Astrocytes have been shown to line blood vessels and take part in myelination of some axons, the nerve fibres. Some neurologists consider that morphological changes in these cells and in their processes might result in some functional disturbance, particularly caused by alteration in their sucker feet. Dysfunction might result from interference in the absorption of nutrition from the blood brain barrier and the transportation of essentials in and out of the brain, causing neuronal malnutrition. Gardner (1968) considers that astrocytes and mi-

237

croglial cells can become phagocytes.

Plaques

AD tends to develop in middle to later life, and is characterised neuropatholo- gically by the extracellular deposition of insoluble protein fibril material which accumulates to form plaques in the brain and its blood vessels, and is a neuropathological hallmark of AD and Down's syndrome. Small numbers of plaques are also present in normal old age cases. About 15% of CJD cases show a small numbers of amyloid plaques which are similar in appearance histologically to those seen in AD. In later studies, it was found that the protein plaques seen in AD were different from those seen in CJD.

Immunohistochemical studies

By electron microscopy, it has been shown that there are marked differences in the ultrastructure of these plaques. Based on immunohistochemical staining process, two types of plaques have been identified in the brain tissue.

(i) amyloid ß-protein positive (APP) plaques termed amyloid plaques, are a "hallmark" of AD. The gene coding for the precursor APP is a normal host gene and has been cloned (Goldgaber et al, 1987) and mapped to human chromosome 21 (Robakis et al, 1987), and on the homologous murine chromosome 16 (Lovett et al, 1987). The APP gene is highly conserved in evolution, transcriptionally active, and is expressed in a variety of tissues and cell types (Goldgaber et al, 1987; Tanzi et al, 1987). Amyloid ß-protein positive senile plaques are also seen in Down's syndrome and in some normal aging humans. Amyloid plaques are also seen in cases of CJD, kuru, Parkinson's disease, and in some strains of experimentally induced scrapie in mice (Roberts et al, 1988; Kitamoto et al, 1988; Snow et al, 1989). In a limited series of cases, amyloid plaques have been observed in 55% of natural scrapie of sheep (Gilmour et al, 1986) and in 62% of infected mule deer (Bahmanyar et al, 1985). However, amyloid plaques have been observed in only 1 BSE case out of 20 examined (Wells et al, 1990).

(ii) Protease-resistant protein (PrP 27-30 kDa) positive plaques are seen in CJD, kuru, natural scrapie of sheep and in some strains of experimentally induced scrapie in mice. PrP 27-30 kDa (PrP-sc) is derived from PrP33-35 kDa precursor protein (PrP-c) coded by a normal gene, assigned in mice to chromosome 2, and in humans to the short arm of the chromosome 20 (Robakis et al, 1986; Liao et al, 1986; Sparkes et al, 1986). Once a host is infected, a post-translation conversion of PrP-c to PrP-sc process starts in the host brain and appears, to be a secondary process, involving a fusion protein (Narang, 1992; 1996). PrP-sc molecules aggregate to form SAF, PrP plaques. Specific PrP antibodies have been used to demonstrate PrP plaques in SEs (Bendheim et al, 1984). PrP plaques have only been found in brains of animals suffering from SEs. It is important to point out that PrP positive plaques have not been observed in AD or Down's syndrome or any other non-–SE neurological disorder.

PrP plaques have been found in about 10% of sporadic CJD cases, 50% to 70% kuru patients and all GSSS patients (Kitamoto et al, 1988). Plaques are identified in the cerebellum in a minority of these cases in the thalamus, basal ganglia or cerebral cortex. According to some researchers, occurrence of plaques is related to PrP genotype, and is associated with codon 129 polymorphism (Gibbs et al, 1985), and in familial CJD with several PrP gene mutations (Prusiner et al, 1991). Kitamoto et al (1988) suggested that the total positive rate might change with the length of the clinical course. New variant strain of CJD cases all have PrP plaques in their brains; in all these cases duration is 12 months or more and there appears to be some correlation with the length of the clinical course in these patients and density of plaques. Therefore, I do not consider that more PrP plaques are seen in CJD cases with PrP mutation, but are more related to the duration of illness.

Masters et al (1978) pointed out that neuronal loss and gliosis predominated in pathologic change of long survivors with CJD, while there was no definite spongiform changes remaining in the cerebral cortex, but "status spongiosus" was present in four cases with a longer duration. In addition, there is a particular problem in interpretation of cortical biopsies in cases of suspected CJD, and therefore, biopsy in such cases is now discouraged. It is now known that CJD and related diseases are associated with accumulation in the brain of PrP plaques and a reliable accurate immunohistochemical technique for staining in animal models has been developed (Kitamoto et al, 1988; 1992; Piccardo et al, 1990). The presence of PrP plaques in suspected cases would be confirmation of the disease. Kitamoto et al (1988) proposed that examination of PrP plaques which are specific for CJD and other SEs should be carried out as an additional confirmatory test. In suspect cases, where there is a clinical history of SE, and spongiform changes cannot be demonstrated in the brain, it is essential that this test should be performed. PrP plaque staining can be confirmed by using interspecies cross-reactivity anti-mouse-CJD serum, and this is how I was able to confirm SE diagnosis in two hens. Specificity of immunostaining of this antisera is very reliable.

Neuropathologically familial CJD cases differed only from sporadic CJD in the absence of significant spongiform changes in some affected members of families, while multicentric amyloid plaques were present in all affected members of families suffering from GSSS. Brown et al reported 100% transmission of disease to nonhuman primates from tissue preparations with iatrogenic CJD. Neuropathology in iatrogenic patients was indistinguishable from that of sporadic CJD.

To consider and classify, it is important to be aware of the classification and identification used in the diagnosis of such cases. For CJD patients, three diagnostic categories have been used as follows:
1) Definite CJD: histologically verified cases showing typical spongiosis.
2) Probable CJD: cases with a typical clinical picture and a duration of illness

239

less than two years, but lacking histological verification. In this category are included relatives of definite CJD cases who, according to the clinical descriptions and testimony given by collateral family members, who knew them, also died of a similar disease.

3) Possible CJD cases: these were relatives of definite CJD cases. For those, the clinical records, descriptions and testimony of collateral family members were lacking, while the information collected from other sources, revealed that they had died of a dementing disease, similar to that of a verified case. Thus, where a demented patient was a relative of a definitely diagnosed CJD patient, in the first, second or third generation, the patient could be classified as a possible case of familial CJD.

Routine Diagnosis and Confirmation of CJD Cases

The diagnosis of CJD often presents problems, because of the time taken to process tissues for histological examination. Confirming the condition by transmission of the disease into animals because of its long incubation periods extends the required time even further. This is made more difficult by the unusual format of the CJD amyotrophic form, characterised by motor system disturbances without any spongiform changes in the brain. It has also been shown that occasionally CJD may be associated with other underlying diseases such as tumours, brain abscess, AD, and strokes as demonstrated by transmission of the disease from these cases into animals. The difficulties faced in reaching the correct diagnosis may partially explain the low incidence of the disease and the current known cases perhaps represent only the tip of the iceberg. It is conceivable that large segments of the population are infected without any, or with only trivial or subclinical signs, or the true nature of the disease maybe concealed by some other co-existing disease.

This point is further well illustrated where clinically and histologically diagnosed AD cases have on transmission produced SE in primates, and is further highlighted by iatrogenic transmission, from corneal transplantation (Duffy et al, 1974), by contaminated electrode implantation (Bernoulli et al, 1977) and by virus-contaminated batches of human growth hormone prepared from pooled, apparently healthy pituitary glands. A large number of cases have been reported as a result of earlier therapy with hGH detailed in next section.

The problems of accurate diagnosis certainly add to the difficulties of conducting epidemiological surveys. It is, therefore, important to use all available diagnostic procedures including electron microscopy of thin sections, and the simple touch impression technique to confirm CJD cases. A study should have been previously organised, with a view to obtaining pathological specimens from all suspected CJD cases for such confirmation (Narang, 1990). Tissue from other neurological diseases and normal cases should also be examined for control and clinically misdiagnosed cases. Parallel neurohistopathological studies of these cases should also be carried out in age matched normal individuals who died of

240

other causes. The relatively simple impression technique can provide a means of rapid diagnosis of CJD, with minimal tissue handling and reduced exposure risks.

Nemavirus Particles in Creutzfeldt-Jakob Disease Brains

Examination of CJD brains by cutting thin sections revealed tubulofilamentous particles termed Nemavirus particles (NVP), similar to those seen in natural scrapie of sheep and experimental scrapie in mice, rats and hamsters, and are described in detail in a separate section. These are seen in all transmissible SEs including BSE. The number and distribution of NVP may vary from one case to another, and even, in the same case, from one area of the brain to another. Further, it has been demonstrated that scrapie-associated fibrils (SAF) form the core of these particles and that, as with scrapie, the Nemavirus in the outer coat contains a single-stranded DNA protected by an unknown protein layer.

Development of Touch Impression Technique

To simplify the examination of experimentally infected animal tissues by EM, a simple impression technique has been developed to demonstrate NVP/SAF (Narang et al, 1987; 1988) and this method was validated by experiments, using a variety of known human and animal viruses. This method was applied to experimental scrapie CJD brains. NVP ha\s been identified in all scrapie and CJD cases so far examined. The method was also applied to tissue samples taken from hamsters at various stages of the incubational period of the disease, and from uninfected tissues, without the researcher knowing which samples were from normal and which were from infected animals. The status of all tissues under test was correctly identified, on the basis of the presence or absence of NVP. Furthermore, the samples taken 20 days post-inoculation, which is a quarter of the way through the incubation period, gave consistently positive results by the touch method. However, histological examination of these brains revealed no spongiform changes. It would seem reasonable to conclude from this that the technique could be applied for routine sample screening of suspected animals for diagnostic purposes.

Relationship of Tubulofilamentous particles to SAF/PrP

In a number of my recent studies on CJD cases, it has been demonstrated that SAF/PrP form the core of these tubulofilamentous particles. A single stranded DNA (ssDNA) wraps around SAF/PrP, and is protected by an outer protein coat, to form tubulofilamentous particles. For detail see scrapie section.

Transmissibility, spongiform changes and PrP

Brown et al (1993) tested a total of 44 neuropathologically examined and experimentally inoculated patients, for the presence of protease-resistant protein (PrP-sc or PrP) in brain tissue by Western immunoblots. These included 28

241

cases of sporadic CJD; 10 cases of familial CJD, fatal familial insomnia, or GSSS , two cases of iatrogenic CJD due to contaminated growth hormone and four cases of kuru. Of the 44 cases, 30 (68%) had consistent results, that is, 29 were uniformly positive and one (the case of GSSS) was uniformly negative. Four transmitted cases had spongiform changes without detectable PrP, and 10 untransmitted cases had either spongiform changes (2 cases), PrP (2 cases) or both.

Using these numbers (Brown et al, 1993), simple calculations revealed that the presence or absence of spongiform changes correlated with at least one of the other tests (transmission study or presence of PrP) in 95% of cases whereas transmissibility, or PrP correlated with at least one other test in 86% of cases. Considering only the 33 transmitted cases, 100% showed spongiform changes and 29 (88%) had detectable PrP.

Significance of SAF/PrP

SAF are morphological structures composed of small protein molecules termed "PrP", which is a normal modified host derived protein. The molecules of this normal protein are more likely to be joined together, by a regulatory protein molecule termed *Nemo corrupta*, from the genome of the scrapie agent to form morphological structures, SAF. SAF/PrP was considered to be the infectious agent, but now we know, through a number of studies, that infectivity can be separated from the entity SAF/PrP. The host gene for PrP protein is expressed at similar levels both in uninfected and in SE infected animals. The importance of SAF and PrP are discussed in detail in a separate part of this book.

Transmission of Disease to other Species

It was in 1968 that Drs. Gibbs and Gajdusek transmitted human CJD to chimpanzees, which became ill and developed similar histopathological degenerative lesions in the brain, as in the human condition. Subsequently, the disease was transmitted from chimpanzee to chimpanzee. The disease has been regularly transmitted from CJD patients to chimpanzees, New and Old World monkeys and domestic cats (Gajdusek, 1978). The pathology in the animals is indistinguishable at the microscopical level from that of the natural disease or of experimental kuru and scrapie (Beck et al, 1969; Lampert et al, 1972). Like scrapie, there are different strains of CJD which vary greatly. Chimpanzees, squirrel monkeys, and spider monkeys proved to be the most susceptible species. Over-all, the duration of the incubation period appears related to the life expectancy of the host. In a given species, the same inoculum injected into multiple animals often produced a range of incubation periods (Brown et al 1993). In a serial passage, the incubation period for the transmissible agents like the scrapie agent, typically becomes shorter and then stabilises.

The disease manifests after either intracerebral or peripheral routes of inoculation. In non-human primates, the disease may develop after over two years of an asymptomatic period. The clinical disease produced in spider monkeys after in-oculation closely mimics the human disease, with an incubation period of some two years or more (Gajdusek, 1977). Also, the sequence of the clinical disease progression imitates that in man, extending from several months to over a year until death. The histopathology in these experimentally inoculated animals is indistinguishable, at the microscopical level, from that in the natural SEs of animals or humans. Like kuru, the human brain tissue from CJD, when inoculated into goats at a high dilution, produces a disease which is indistinguishable from scrapie.

It is known that the slow virus infection may show no histopathological changes at all in many of the organ tissues of the host's body, while many of the apparently normal looking tissues may be highly infectious. Several puzzling long-drawn-out human diseases have had to be reassessed in the light of this slow virus concept, and unsuccessful experiments re-evaluated. Although only a limited number of other tissues besides brains have been adequately tested for the presence of the CJD agent, it has been demonstrated in all tissues, including blood and spinal fluids. CJD patients' blood has more often been shown to contain the infective agent than blood of scrapie sheep (Klein et al, 1993). With the development of a mouse model for CJD, it has been possible to obtain valuable information on persistent viremia and preferential replication of the virus at low-density in lymphocytes (Kuroda et al, 1983).

The brain homogenates from only 21 (51%) of 41 human patients transmitted the disease to the domestic cat, after an average incubation period of 36 months, but this included two cases that did not transmit to primates (Brown et al, 1993). These findings show that some, but not all, CJD strains are transmissible to the domestic cat (Gibbs, Gajdusek, 1979). In the laboratory, the disease has been transmitted from man to guinea pigs, and serially propagated in this convenient host. Ten (14%) of 71 cases transmitted to the guinea pig, after an average incubation period of 36 months, and these included cases that did not transmit to primates. This is further evidence that, even where disease cannot be transmitted to non-human primates, tissues may still contain the infective agent. CJD has also been transmitted to Syrian hamsters (Manuelidis 1977) and laboratory mice (Tateishi et al, 1983).

Brown et al (1993) reported experimental transmission rates of the disease to non-human primates were highest (100%) for iatrogenic CJD, kuru (95%) and sporadic CJD (90%), and considerably lower for familial CJD (68%). The incubation period as well as the duration and character of the illness varied greatly, even in animals receiving the same inoculum, mirroring the spectrum of clinical disease seen in humans (Brown et al, 1993). In the group of patients whose SE was not transmissible to non-human primates, the patients did not display any particular clinical or pathological differences from those where the disease was transmitted (Brown et al, 1993). The researchers state that in half of the untransmitted cases, only a single primate was inoculated, whereas most of the trans-

243

mitted cases were inoculated into multiple animals. In many cases, disease was transmitted to only one of a pair of inoculated animals. Three further cases, which were reported as non-transmissible to primates, were later transmitted to non-primate species in other laboratories. Had more animals been inoculated, it is likely that many of the untransmitted cases, particularly those with spongiform changes, would have transmitted.

Brain Infectivity Titres

End-point infectivity dilutions have not been calculated for individual cases, because of the limited number of primates available. Brown et al (1993) reported infectivity titres from 27 patients which included 21 with sporadic CJD, one with familial CJD, two with GSSS and three with kuru. Based on the inoculation of squirrel monkeys, the mean infectivity per gram of tissue, calculated in their study from a total of 27 patients, was approximately 100,000 units, and incubation periods showed a trend to lengthen with increasing dilutions of the brain inocula, from two years using 10^1 or 10^2 dilution to four or more years following 10^5 dilutions. They calculated that most brains tested contained at least 10,000 infectivity units/gm of tissue, and in a few cases, levels of infectivity reached at least 1,000,000 units. For several cases they also obtained infectivity levels on passage (inoculation fro animal to animal) to the brain tissues; the titres were equal to and often higher than those in human tissue, typically ranging from 100,000 to 10,000,000 infectious units/gm of tissue.

The route of the inoculation has a significant effect on the apparent infectivity and the induction of disease. Brown et al (1993) reported that inocula which reproducibly transmitted disease by the intracerebral route, transmitted only irregularly by peripheral inoculation. When transmission did occur, incubation periods could be comparatively shorter. High doses overcame the comparative inefficiency of peripheral routes of infection, whereas low doses transmitted disease only after extremely long incubation periods, or not at all.

Transmission rates were reported to be comparatively low, following the inoculation of either formalin fixed brain tissue (34%, 14 out of 41) or cultured brain tissue (38%, 10 out of 26) Brown et al, 1993].

The occurrence of viremia (virus in blood) in encephalopathies, as with conventional viruses, is well recognised (Johnson et al, 1968). Viremia in scrapie has not been demonstrated in some of the studies, where serum or whole blood were used for inoculation (Pattison et al, 1962; Hadlow et al, 1974), while other studies have indicated a titre of 1000 units of infectivity per gram in the scrapie blood. In experimentally induced CJD in guinea pigs, viremia has been demonstrated by the use of buffy-coat and whole blood (Manuelidis et al, 1978). Tateishi (1985) and Klein et al (1993) also transmitted CJD using blood, cornea, and urine samples of a patient. This appears to be an important difference between scrapie and CJD, and it should be tested using BSE tissues, which may give clues to any change in the strain variation of the agent. From the hGH-associated CJD cases, we have learnt that, following peripheral inoculation of the infectious agent, it probably enters the brain via the blood stream. This implies the infective agent is small enough to cross the blood-brain barrier.

Distribution of Infectivity in the Body

In a number of studies, apart from the brain, spinal cord and eye, infectivity was only detected irregularly in other body tissues, and the disease transmission from 20% homogenates of non-central nervous system tissues was irregular. Infectivity levels can be presumed much lower (Brown et al, 1993). In the limited studies in kuru patients, both the kidney, spleen and pool of kidney, spleen and liver were found positive. In the CJD patient, the liver has been found positive at a dilution of 10^3.

A Possible Oral Transmission

In humans, in a comparative case-control study of CJD, dietary risk factors were studied in the USA (Davanipour et al, 1985). In this study, links between the consumption of under-done food and a possible oral transmission was demonstrated. The transmissible agent of SE is remarkably stable over a wide range of physical and chemical conditions. But it has been reported to be destroyed when heated to $121^{\circ}C$ for one hour (Gajdusek et al, 1978; Rohwer, 1984). However, some of the infectivity may still survive even after such a prolonged treatment. The author left half of a hamster scrapie-infected brain overnight at $121^{\circ}C$. A dilution was then made in 1:10 weight by volume. Out of eight hamsters inoculated with this material, one hamster developed scrapie after a 285 day incubation period. Hamsters inoculated with the untreated infected material, with dilutions of 1000, however, produced scrapie with an incubation period of 90 days while the incubation period increased to 175 days with a million fold dilution. Other workers have reported that the infectivity titre of the infectious agent decreases by 100 to 1,000 fold following heating at $80^{\circ}C$ to $100^{\circ}C$ for 30 minutes (Walker et al, 1983). Differential heating of food portions may account for differences in the attack rate among family members, who presumably ate the same contaminated food. Oral ingestion alone may not be sufficient to transmit SE, or, if it is to do so, a higher dose may be required or the incubation period extends (Prusiner et al, 1982). The effect of gingival scarification on transmission indicates that lesions in the mouth or in the oral cavity could play a major role in the oral transmission of SEs (Carp, 1982).

Neuropathologically, same strain of CJD virus may cause severe status spongiosus lesions in many areas of the brain particularly the cerebral cortex. In chimpanzees and spider monkeys, the same strain of the agent may cause minimal involvement of brain stem or spinal cord. In the squirrel monkey, however, the same virus strain may cause extensive brain stem and spinal lesions.

The length of incubation period in a range of hosts, or the distribution of the severity of lesions in the brain and spinal cord, cannot be used as criteria to dis-

245

tinguish the CJD virus from scrapie, BSE or kuru. One must appreciate the significance of the SEs agents as they affect humans and animal.

Mode of Natural Transmission

Despite intensive efforts, there is still no full understanding of the natural mode of transmission of CJD. This, of course, is critical for preventing the spread of the disease to those who may be at risk. The mode of natural transmission of CJD remains unclear and incubation periods are difficult to estimate. The mechanism of the disease transmission is known only in those rare disastrous cases of accidental infection by direct inoculation from contaminated instruments, tissue, or hGH respectively. This is also true for naturally occurring SEs. We do not know clearly the mode of dissemination or maintenance from one host to another. The incubation periods in those cases studied ranged from 15 months to a few years.

For kuru, there is some explanation of the spread within close kinsmen, but how it started remains a mystery. Kuru is gradually disappearing with the cessation of cannibalism. There has been a report of a spontaneous case of CJD in a 26 year old native of New Guinea from the Central Highland. The clinical diagnosis in this patient was confirmed by histopathological examination of the brain (Hornabrook and Wagner, 1975).

Iatrogenic (Accidental) Transmission

Iatrogenic CJD remains uncommon. It continues to appear in new and unforeseen circumstances. Originally ascribed to contaminated instruments and grafts, the disease more recently turned up in a group of patients given growth hormone treatment. Since 1985, more than 65 cases of CJD have been described among recipients of pituitary-derived hGH. These cases have been reported in USA, UK and France. It would appear that the hormone treatment patients were exposed to very low doses of the contaminated materials injected subcutaneously. The highest experimental transmission from patients with hGH cases of CJD suggests that the infectious agent in human to human-acquired disease is more "virulent" than in naturally occurring sporadic disease.

Transmission of CJD from Human Tissue Graft

A 55 year old man died following a case history of two months of incoordination, memory deficiency, involuntary movements and myoclonia. CJD was confirmed by histopathological examination of the brain. Soon after his death, a corneal transplant was performed from this donor to a 55 year old woman. Approximately 18 months later she developed lethargy, nausea and ataxia. During the next eight months, neurological deterioration progressed and walking and swallowing difficulties developed. She died eight months from the onset of the disease, and CJD was confirmed after the neuropathological examination of the brain (Duffy et al, 1974). In France between 1992 and 1994, four patients died.

246

They all had received dura matter graft between four and seven years before the onset of CJD.

Two patients, a young man of 17 and a woman of 23, underwent surgical excision for intractable epilepsy. Both developed CJD 2.5 years and 2.25 years, after stereotactic electroencephalographic exploration using silver electrodes. In both cases, two out of nine of the electrodes used had been previously implanted in the brain of a 69 year-old woman who had suffered from CJD. The electrodes used had been sterilised with 70% alcohol and formaldehyde for inactivation of the CJD virus. At that time, the surgeons were not aware of the resistance of the CJD virus to 70% alcohol and formaldehyde. Both biopsy and autopsy confirmed the diagnosis of CJD in the patient who had the electrodes planted. The young man died demented, aged 19 of CJD, while the clinical diagnosis was confirmed in the woman, by EEG (Bernoulli et al, 1977). The inoculated brain suspension from both infected patients also transmitted SE to primates after an incubation period of 15-25 months. Also, one of the electrodes subsequently transmitted SE to a chimpanzee 18 months after an implantation in the cerebral cortex (Brown, 1992).

A 28 year old woman developed CJD 19 months after a neurological operation which involved the grafting of commercially available dura mater (Thadani, et al, 1988). An additional case was reported in a 25 year old man in New Zealand, who rapidly developed progressive dementia 31 months after neurosurgery for head injuries sustained during a fall (Nisbet et al, 1989). Dura mater tears were repaired with commercially prepared imported cadaveric human dura mater graft. CJD was confirmed after the neuropathological examination of the brain. The patient had no family history of degenerative neurological disease, nor had he received hGH treatment. Several further cases raised suspicion, and gave conclusive proof of accidental transmission from person to person. Another 28 year old female underwent the resection of her right ear and a dural graft was placed in the right temporal area. The woman while pregnant, complained of nausea, vomiting and over the following four weeks developed unsteady gait and slurred speech. Mental status deterioration was present, and the patient was unable to walk. Repeated EEG over a period of time showed marked slowing with sharp periodic waves typical of CJD. The patient died and the disease was confirmed from biopsy.

Transmission of CJD from Human Growth Hormone

Gibbs et al (1985), in the USA reported the first case of CJD amongst recipients of pituitary-derived hGH. The age at which the disease appears was primarily considered a major indicator of the transmission of the disease to humans. Three cases with typical histopathological features of spongiosis occurred in 1985 in the USA, all within a year, one after the other. The patients were not classified as CJD cases, because they were all under 30, while CJD is predominantly a disease known to occur between 35 and 86 years. Fradkin et al, (1991) from the figures available, calculated that the worldwide incidence of sporadic CJD in the general population is of the order of 1 per million. For sporadic CJD in people under the age of 40, the incidence is more appropriately about 1 per 20 million. The diagnosis of CJD in the three cases in the United States was considered, but rejected on the basis of the patients' ages. Further investigation of these cases produced vital clues in assessing the modes of transmission of CJD in under-age patients, and led the investigators to discover contaminated hGH to be the cause of the disease in these patients. This story has been well illustrated by Dr Paul Brown.

Brown (1988) described the discovery of the connection between hGH therapy to CJD in a drama set in three Acts. The drama is about a boy who was born about 1963, when research on hGH had reached the point at which large-scale clinical trials could be envisaged. In the first two years of his life, the boy was found to have deficiencies of the thyroid hormone, insulin, and growth hormone. He was put on "replacement therapy". As a child, he was happy, optimistic and talkative.

Scene I

"In May 1984, the young man and his family flew from San Francisco to Atlanta en route to Maine to visit his grandparents. As he rose from his seat to change planes, he complained of dizziness. His mother, who was experienced in the diagnosis of hypoglycemia, gave him some candy and watched him closely for the rest of the trip. Nothing more happened and the incident was forgotten. Several days later, however, in Maine, he turned down an offer to go for a spin on the lake in his grandfather's motorboat, saying that 'he didn't need to go for a spin because he was already dizzy.' On his return from Maine, the patient went back to school, but his dizziness persisted, and then his speech seemed slightly changed. He was seen by a local practitioner, who was unable to find any physical basis for the complaint, but was concerned and suggested that he be seen at Stanford, where he was already being monitored for his endocrine problems."

His mother, on 17 June, called Dr Raymond Hintz, their paediatric endocrinologist, who saw the boy in the Stanford emergency room. The patient was found to have subtle impairment of coordination and speech and appeared to have an involuntary movement of the eyeball (nystagmus). An appointment to the neurology clinic was arranged and, in the interim period, several laboratory tests were scheduled, including a computerised tomography (CT scan), auditory-and sensory-evoked potentials, and tests of vestibular function.

By the middle of August, the patient's cerebellar symptoms had worsened considerably and he was now showing some muscular rigidity, shock-like contractions of a portion of a muscle (myoclonus) and a suggestion of mild mental deterioration. The patient was admitted under Dr Bruce Berg of the University of California in San Francisco, and during the course of intensive laboratory evaluation, the patient was presented at a paediatric EEG conference. At this meeting, Michael Aminoff raised the notion that the patient might be suffering from CJD. After much discussion, the diagnosis of CJD was rejected as highly improbable because of the patient's age. The patient was discharged from the hospital without any consensus as to the cause of his disorder.

As the patient's condition continued to worsen, while his diagnosis remained unclear, preparations were made by Drs. Gravina and Berg to obtain a post mortem examination of the brain. On a November day, the patient died and a University of San Francisco pathology resident was dispatched to courier the brain back to San Francisco, where examination subsequently revealed the pathological changes similar to those seen in CJD (Koch et al, 1985). Brown (1988), stressed that without the combined efforts of all of the physicians involved with this patient (including the anonymous pathology resident), and the co-operation of the family, his story might never have come to light.

The patient had received hGH within the first two years of his life. In May 1984, he complained for the first time of dizziness, and soon his speech seemed to change. His paediatric endocrinologist, Dr Hintz, recorded subtle impairment of coordination and speech. The neurological examination which followed, suggested muscular rigidity and mild mental deterioration. Further investigation which followed - particularly the results of the EEG - raised the possibility of CJD. At the same time, there were two other cases, one in Dallas and another in Buffalo, which were being investigated with similar scenarios. In both cases, a diagnosis of CJD was not considered on the grounds of the patients' ages.

The role that the paediatric endocrinologist Dr Hintz played on learning that the histopathological findings were consistent with CJD, was very crucial. Although, after much discussion at an earlier conference, the diagnosis of CJD was rejected because of the patient's age, Dr. Hintz on March 4, 1985, wrote to the Food and Drug Administration (FDA) that the death of his patient might be related to the treatment with hGH, and that this factor should be considered.

Four days later, the National Institute of Health (NIH), responsible for the distribution of the growth hormone, convened a meeting of officials and scientists from the NIH, National Hormone and Pituitary Program, and the FDA, for the purpose of evaluating the likelihood of the causal relationship, between the hGH and CJD. At the very first meeting, their recommendations included a notification to physicians about the existence of a possible problem, and the establishment of a search for other possible similar cases in the recipient population, and cancellation of all non-therapeutic use of the hormone. Suspension of the therapeutic use of the hormone was thought to be inadvisable, until independent verification of the relationship of hGH and disease was established, and other sources of exposure to the CJD virus had been excluded.

While these initiatives were being carried out, alarm bells were ringing rapidly throughout the community of paediatric endocrinologists about the case of CJD, and would continue until a decision has been reached on the hGH. Many paediatric endocrinologists, however, voiced concern about the adverse conse-

249

quences of halting hGH distribution because of a single case of CJD, and considered the link between the therapy to CJD a matter of speculation. According to Dr Brown, retrenchment and reconsideration were in order.

Scene II

Scene II moves from California to Texas. There a few months earlier, a similar scenario was unfolding (Brown, 1988). In Dallas, a 32-year-old patient with hypopituitary function disorder had been noticed by his mother to stagger slightly when he walked, and to tremble when he tried to lift a cup to his lips. The patient's lack of coordination increased, but he continued to work in a music store where a customer, who was also a physician, strongly advised him to see a neurologist, which he did. At first, the most likely diagnosis was thought to be a diffused white mater disease: multiple sclerosis, leukodystrophy, or a pontocerebellar degeneration. He never developed myoclonus or any periodic EEG activity. He was still playing games of "Trivial Pursuit" until shortly before his death in February 1985. At the time, a diagnosis of CJD was not even considered (Tintner et al, 1986). partially it is understood, because of his comparatively young age.

Scene III

Meanwhile, in Buffalo, NY, a 22-year-old patient with hypopituitary function disorder was walking along a street when he had an unexplained episode of veering to the right. Within a few weeks, he began having strange sensations in his head and was progressively finding difficulty with his balance and periodic double vision. At his first examination, an ENT specialist believed he was malingering, but later at Buffalo General Hospital, his assessment disclosed a severe cerebellar syndrome, it was thought most likely caused by a demyelinating process. The patient did not have any myoclonus. He had normal EEG findings and a minimal mental deterioration and, again, diagnosis of CJD was not considered (Gibbs et al, 1985). In this patient, his age being again a factor in that possible diagnosis was continually disregarded.

This patient had been on hGH treatment starting in June 1969, and he was on standard doses for eight years until October 1977, when he was 15 years old. During the course of this treatment, he received 150 vials of at least 15 different lots of hGH manufactured and distributed through the National Pituitary Agency. Eleven of the 15 lots were prepared by the method of Wilhelmi (1961) and the remaining four were prepared by the method of Raben (1957). The Wilhelmi (1961) method for preparing hGH essentially consisted of a series of acetone and ammonium sulphate extractions being interspersed with low speed centrifugation. The product of the Raben (1957) method, however, contained acetone-extracted dried pituitary powder, which was further extracted with glacial acetic acid at 70°C. At that time, it was known that the scrapie agent was present in high titres of infectivity in the hypothalamus and pituitary glands of infected

250

animals. Both glacial acetic acid and acetone provided strong bactericidal and viricidal action in the extraction of hGH. However, the highly resistant CJD agent might have escaped inactivation.

At this stage, Drs. Robert Blizzard and Margaret MacGillivray, the two doctors in Dallas and Buffalo, were separately convinced as to the condition of their patients, and reported the clinical histories etc. to the NIH on the 11 and 18 April 1985. The clinical histories of these two cases from Dallas and Buffalo arrived at the NIH .. on the 19 April 1985, and the hormone was officially banned from therapeutic use the next day.

The American scene remained quiescent and there ensued a period of consolidation. A full-scale investigation of the problem was being set in motion along two lines of inquiry: first, laboratory investigation designed to test the risk of infection from processed human pituitary glands and second, an epidemiological study designed to track down any remaining cases of CJD in patients who had received growth hormone distributed under the National Hormone and Pituitary Program.

During this period, an additional case was reported in England. The patient had been treated with hGH prepared from pituitary glands collected and extracted in Great Britain (Powell-Jackson et al, 1985). It was at this stage that the scientific community realised contamination was generalised to possible worldwide proportions.

Another interesting case reported was that of a 16 year old girl who was born in 1963. At the age of five, she showed a good metabolic response to hGH, and regular therapy was started in February 1969. She received regular injections of hGH till she was seven and half years old, then intermittently for four years, and then a regular therapy was reinstituted and continued until her hospitalisation at the age of 16. She received hGH from 17 different batches. Three lots were shared with the Buffalo CJD patient, and three lots were shared with another CJD case. No lots, however, were shared with the Baltimore or Philadelphia CJD patients.

During the course of treatment, at the age of nine, her normal EEG tracing began to show background disorganisation and diffused slowing with occasional sharp waves, suggesting generalised cerebral dysfunction, with sudden recurrence of spasm or seizure (paroxysmal) features. Repeat EEGs during the next four years all showed the same abnormalities, with no periodic activity, and no progression. The patient had specific learning difficulties in visual and auditory memory, perception, integration and conceptualisation. At the age of 15, she attended a special school for disabled children. The patient while still under the hormone treatment in 1979, developed bilateral pneumonia, and died three days later, following an acute upper respiratory illness.

Initial neurohistopathological examination showed an extreme degree of neuronal loss in the tubero-infundibular nuclear group of the hypothalamus, loose-textured, with an excess of astroglia in the damaged area of the central ner-

251

vous system (gliosis).

Another 37 year-old man developed CJD following hGH therapy. The patient received replacement therapy, beginning at the age of 14, from February 1963 until November 1967. His initial neurological examination revealed minimal head titubation and truncal ataxia. His cerebellar function deteriorated further, with severe ataxia, especially of the legs, and the course of his illness was dominated by cerebellar signs. These symptoms seen in hGH recipient were typical of kuru cases (Gajdusek et al, 1959). The EEG was consistent with a diffuse encephalopathy, although periodic discharges were absent. Initially, the EEG may have been within the normal range, but then there was increased theta activity, and finally the increase showed a slow activity. The clinical presentation of these hGH patients also resembles that of the "new strain" of CJD. These findings suggest that kuru and the "new strain" of CJD may be the same or similar.

As a response to the epidemiological study seeking to track down any additional cases of CJD, Dr. Maria New went through the notes of all patients treated with hGH in her clinic. One patient, aged 16, was one of nearly 100 patients under her care who had received hGH intermittent therapy for 10 years at Cornell Medical Centre in New York City. Dr. New had personally contacted and checked on the recipients of growth hormone treatment and, during the course of investigations, amongst the notes of the patients who had died, she found the 16 year old girl's case history. Microscopic examination of her brain had shown only severe overgrowth of the organ (hypertrophic atrophy). Dr New suggested that the slides should be re-examined, in case CJD pathology had been overlooked. On re-examination of all the stored slides, SE was confirmed, although these changes were not seen in all of the slides (New, et al, 1988). The discovery of CJD in this patient seven years after her death was made only after her medical records and slides were re-examined by Dr New in the light of the recent outbreak of CJD in patients treated with hGH. The significance of this case is that no patient treated with natural hGH can be assumed to have escaped infection with the virus of CJD. No matter what the cause of the death, without a complete neuropathological examination directed specifically at the detection of SE, it would be difficult to rule out CJD as the cause.

One case of CJD was identified amongst 180 patients treated with pituitary-derived hGH in New Zealand (Croxson et al, 1988). The patient, a 31 year old woman, was treated with hGH between the age of 16 and 19, from October 1970 until October 1973. The patient was treated with six lots of growth hormone, obtained from the United States from batches of pooled pituitary glands. None of the lots of hormone used in this patient were shared with any of the USA CJD patients (Croxson et al, 1988). She developed severe ataxia and mild nystagmus. Six months from the onset of these symptoms, she had become sleepy and mute. Brief myoclonic jerks were seen for the first time. The initial EEG showed a severe generalised abnormality, with diffused high-amplitude irregular delta activity, but no periodic complexes. Serial EEGs showed a progressive deterioration in background activity.

Cases with pituitary-derived hGH have occurred in the USA, UK, France, Australia, New Zealand and Brazil. Cadaver-derived hGH was used in the UK between 1958-1986, and during that period more than 1,900 children were treated while in France, more than 1,700 children were treated between 1972 and 1988. In the UK and France, the numbers of confirmed hGH-linked CJD cases have been 17 and 24, respectively. The first UK case, that of a 23 year old woman, was reported in 1985 (Powell-Jackson et al, 1985). According to the case report published, the patient, had had a tumor removed when two years-old in 1964. She received human pituitary-derived growth hormone twice weekly from July 1972 until July 1976. In March 1984, a subacute dementing illness developed with neurological signs which included ataxia. A neurological review in October 1984 confirmed the progression of physical signs. No myoclonic movements were observed. The EEG was abnormal, with high-amplitude poorly formed alpha activity. The patient died in February 1985. Histopathological diagnosis of CJD was confirmed. The patient received hGH prepared in the Department of Biochemistry Laboratory, Cambridge. Pituitary glands were of UK origin, and hGH was prepared by the Raben (1957) and Wilhelmi methods (1961), from acetone-dried pituitaries.

One of the British patients treated with human growth hormone but who is still alive, had his growth hormone injections during 1976 to 1981. He was always cheerful, with good humour. He started to show signs of illness in about September 1994, not so much physical symptoms but complaining of feeling dizzy from time to time and occasionally falling over. By Christmas 1994 there were a lot of mental and behavioural changes which became more marked.

He would weave quite badly. He could drive better than he could walk. At first, he wanted a stick for going out because he was staggering when he went to the pub and people thought he was drunk. He used the stick for psychological reasons. It was in early January 1995 that he developed flu-like symptoms and complained of feeling generally unwell. He had been to the GP, and was advised that he needed rest. Over the next few weeks, his dizziness and balance problems increased. He was having more problems riding his motor bike to ride to deliver letters for his living. Latterly there had been difficulties when he had been working. He had gone to places he had known, and suddenly been lost and unable to find his way. For a courier in a place he knew well, this was frightening. He was becoming quite unsteady on his feet and actually fell off his bike. The last time, he was working, he rang up his wife and said "I'm not very well, come and get me." That would have been in February 1995, and after that he did not go back to work. In early autumn 1995, he stopped riding his motorcycle completely although he continued driving his Land Rover occasionally right up until October 1995.

253

He was referred to a Neurologist at Gt. Ormond Street Hospital where by process of elimination and because he had had hGH injections, a week later, a diagnosis of CJD was confirmed. Short term memory loss had become prevalent and he could not remember what happened ten minutes ago. If you asked him what he had had for breakfast, he would not know. He could chew and eat food put in his mouth and sometimes, when given something like a biscuit or a slice of toast he could manage it, but often when it was a knife and fork meal, that proved beyond him, he had to be fed.

To assess the extent of the incidence of CJD among recipients of hGH, Fradkin et al, (1991) conducted an epidemiological follow-up of the recipients of hGH in the USA, through the National Hormone and Pituitary Program (NHPP). Their primary goal was to identify and ascertain the current health of, every individual ever treated with hormone distributed by the NHPP. This tremendous task was carried out diligently and thoroughly. Through a painstaking procedure of cross-checking records from several hundred physicians and treatment centres, they identified 6284 recipients of hGH - 68% were male and 32% were female. In this study, the data provided by the treating physicians revealed that 254 deaths had occurred in recipients of the hGH, but neuropathological slides were available for only 94 of these 254 cases.

A similar study was undertaken in France by Goujard et al (1988). The primary goal of their study was to identify and ascertain the current health status of every individual ever treated for growth failure with the hormone distributed by the NHPP. The study was designed to go well beyond the simple determination of neurological evaluation and to provide a collective knowledge for follow up information, on the social and mental status, of the recipients of the growth hormone. To start with, there were four laboratories producing hGH, but from 1977, the production had been switched to one laboratory.

Circumstantial evidence gathered by Dr Brown revealed that the first seven CJD American cases occurred amongst the nearly 700 hGH recipients who started therapy before 1970 (Fradkin at al, 1991). These patients represent 10% of those who received the original hGH, which may have been infected, with an average incubation period of 15 years (Brown, 1988). The evidence was produced from a late realisation of the risk inherent in different methods of processing pituitary glands for preparation of different lot of hGH. No single lot, however, could be identified as the common source of infection, even in the first three cases. But further investigation revealed that a single batch of glands was not ordinarily processed into a single corresponding lot of hormone. Various fractions of the processed glands were often remaindered and later reprocessed with other batches of glands, with the result that material extracted from a given batch of glands often found its way into several different lots of distributed hormone. Thus, the lots of hormone used contained various fractions or reprocessed remainders derived from a single batch of glands that was originally produced in 1966. British and New Zealand cases however, cannot be connected with the

American cases.

From collective studies, it appears that there have been at least five or more contaminated batches prepared in three different countries. A single batch of hGH was prepared from a single batch of 5,000 to 20,000 human pituitary glands. From this study, it appears that a single lot of hGH was distributed in small amounts to many physicians. Results show that 74 lots distributed between 1963 and 1979 were received by a great many of the patients then undergoing treatment. Months and years after shipment, tracing of these recipients must have been a painstaking assignment. This exercise of cross-checking NHPP records against hundreds of physicians' treatment records, identified 8157 possible persons of whom information on 6284 was available. Of the identified recipients, 5240 (84%) were successfully contacted and interviewed personally, or assessed through mail questionnaires. The majority of the patients were under 18 years old and were questioned through their parents; older patients were interviewed directly. Information on their overall current health and neurological status was recorded. Reports on all 254 deaths which had occurred amongst the recipients between 1979-1986 were examined by the authors. No deaths were found in this group which could be related to CJD.

Fradkin et al (1991) reported two additional cases of CJD which were notified by the physicians and relatives of the patients. A 32 year old white woman was treated with hGH from 1963 to 1973. When she was interviewed in 1988, there were no neurological symptoms suggestive of CJD. One month after the interview, however, she began to show a wide-based gait, and felt off-balance. She subsequently had rapid neurological deterioration and developed rigidity and myoclonus and an EEG showed diffused slowing and bursts of theta activity. She died in August 1988, and neuropathological examination revealed extensive spongiform changes.

A second case, notified during the Fradkin et al (1991) study, was that of a 26 year-old black man who was treated with growth hormone from 1968 until 1983. In 1988, shortly after his family was contacted for the interview, his mother and his physician notified the NIH that he had developed an ataxic gait, followed by slurred speech, impaired memory, nystagmus and myoclonus. An EEG taken early in the patient's illness showed high-amplitude slow waves without periodicity. The brain biopsy revealed mild spongiform changes.

The average age at which hGH therapy was given was 9.6 years, with an average treatment duration of 2.9 years. It has not been possible to say precisely which lots were contaminated and thus the incubation period could not be established. Compared with the unaffected recipients, the patients who developed CJD had markedly longer duration of treatment with a mean of 100 months compared with 41 months in the unaffected group. Different incubation periods for patients who received growth hormone prepared in the United States, UK and France, have been observed, and these differences may be due to levels of infectivity in the three preparations, the greater the infective dose, the shorter the incuba-

255

tion period (Brown, 1992). The incubation periods have not been determined precisely, but deaths have occurred from as little as two years to as much as 28 years or even more.

When the infectious agent is introduced into or near the brain, the incubation periods are measured in months, whereas peripheral infection produces incubation periods of years or even decades, a contrast that closely parallels the situation in experimentally infected non-human primates. It would appear that the majority of the recipients have not yet attained even the minimum incubation period required for the development of the disease.

It was calculated that about 30,000 human pituitary glands were required annually to meet the needs of approximately 800 UK recipients. Of these about 20 have died of CJD. Although CJD is rare, there is a reasonable probability that pituitary glands from patients with CJD might be included in the batch process. The potential consequences of such an event were recognised, and a project to asses the risk was considered in 1970s in the UK by some members of the Medical Research Council (MRC), to examine the risk that some hGH batches might be contaminated with the CJD agent. A study was commissioned by the MRC. The group working on the slow virus research, based at the Edinburgh Neuropathogenesis Unit, undertook to monitor the efficacy of the method followed for the preparation of hGH.

In the UK, hGH for therapeutic use has been prepared under licence in several laboratories by various techniques (Jones et al, 1979; Raben, 1957; Wilhelmi,1961). There were major differences between the methods: frozen pituitaries were the starting materials for the Raben and the Wilhelmi method, while for the Lowry technique, acetone-dried glands, which necessitated severe chemical treatments, were used. The Lowry process produced highly purified hGH, which was less immunogenic than the other processes (McLean et al, 1981). For evaluation purposes, tissues used for the preparation were deliberately contaminated by adding the scrapie agent and the process was shown to remove the contaminants successfully, even when added at high concentration.

Taylor et al (1985) demonstrated that infectivity had dropped to undetectable levels in the final purification step. However, after the event, they argued, it was likely that the batches of hGH could have become contaminated in any production process where cross contamination was not understood. It is important to point out that the laboratories producing hGH for human use never handled contaminated scrapie or CJD tissues, therefore the source of contamination in these laboratories must have been a contaminated pituitary gland. Further, Taylor (1985) suggested that the hGH products could be made safe by using 25 nm pore-size membrane filters, assuming that the virus was over 25 nm in diameter.

Although, according to Brown (1985), experimental work (Taylor et al, 1985) was finished in 1983, the results were not published until August 1985, four months after the human cases were reported. Further, he wrote a note in The Lancet "Free from contamination with unconventional slow viruses" criticising

256

Taylor and his colleagues (1985) on the preparation of hGH. Although their study might have been done with impeccable scientific care, it has nevertheless not been able to confirm the complete freedom from contamination indicated by the title of the article. Taylor et al, have certainly demonstrated a very substantial reduction in the virus infectivity during the preparation of growth hormone, according to the Lowry protocol; the experiments, however, were done in a way that leaves unanswered questions as to whether full sterility was in fact achieved.

There are a number of drawbacks and problems with this kind of experiment. A limited amount of the total material is inoculated, possibly once or twice in these experiments and the level of the virus may remain undetectable. This does not imply necessarily the complete absence of virus. Further, because of the slow nature of the virus activity, the disease is undetected since the animals are killed or die before the clinical symptoms appear. In some instances, tissue from the first set of animals, who have reached the end of their life span, is passaged into fresh groups of animals. In such experiments, it is always a problem when to terminate the experiment and how to interpret negative results as is very obvious from the CJD cases associated with hGH.

Since the publication of Fradkin et al (1991), Brown (1992) has reviewed 23 known CJD cases attributable to treatment with cadaver-derived hGH in the USA. He calculated the risk of dying from CJD in the treated hypopituitary population, of the order of 1 in 200 patients, compared with 1 per million sporadic incidence in the general population. The total exposure time   to hGH therapy may be the single most important determinant of the risk of the recipient of human growth factor contracting CJD. In most countries, pituitary-derived hGH was replaced by synthetic preparations in 1985, but a few countries, inexplicably, continue to use the natural product. Brown (1992) recommended that the practice should cease. Recipients of hGH will unfortunately, however, remain at risk for some decades to come, because incubation periods may be as long as 30 to 40 years.

Human Growth Hormone distributed by the National Hormone and Pituitary Program from 1963 to 1985 was prepared from a total of 1.4 million human pituitary glands obtained from cadavers (Fradkin et al, 1991), although pituitary glands from patients suffering from encephalitic syndrome or viral infections were not excluded from the materials used. It has been estimated that these glands might include up to 140 taken from CJD cases, while Brown considers between 25 to 250 to be the possible figures. The same authors have suggested that in the USA, one in 10,000 deaths may be due to CJD, with the true incidence proving higher if more autopsies were performed.

Human Pituitary-derived Gonadotrophin and CJD

A 40 year old woman in New Zealand began developing unsteady gait 13 years after receiving an eight-month course of human pituitary-derived gonadotrophin (hormones which influence an ovary or testis) injections as treatment

257

for infertility. Over the next 10 months, she developed disturbance of her short term memory and obvious clumsiness of her limbs, face, trunk, and ataxia. She developed profound dementia and died 10 months after the onset of her illness. Histopathological examination confirmed CJD. The CJD case was due to the administration, 13 years earlier, of contaminated material. So far there are four Australian cases of CJD following treatment with human gonadotrophin (Cochius et al, 1991; Brown, 1994). There are approximately 90 women who received their injections from this particular batch. This further adds to the growing concern over the use of human derived products. It is possible that more cases will come to light over the next few years, due to the contaminated pituitary-derived human gonadotrophin hormone.

Clinical pattern in the human growth hormone recipients

The clinical presentation in the hGH recipients of CJD cases starts with cerebellar syndrome similar to that observed in instrument and transplant cases, while mental deterioration is a late manifestation. In sporadic CJD cases, however, mental deterioration has been observed as the initial symptom in about two-thirds of cases, the other one-third having cerebellar presentation. Exactly why the growth-hormone treatment and instrument/transplant CJD patients differ so strikingly from sporadic CJD patients is not understood. The early age of infection in the iatrogenic patients is not the only explanation: sporadic CJD patients with atypically early onset are, in all other respects, identical to the overall population of the sporadic cases of CJD. Like kuru cases, where human to human transmission was identified, the illness also began with cerebellar ataxia. The clinical similarities between hGH recipient CJD patients, and kuru, would suggest that, during the passage of the infectious agent, the humans have selected a strain of CJD.

Incidence of CJD in the General Population

The natural incidence of clinically and laboratory diagnosed CJD worldwide in the general population is about 0.3 - 1 per million, based on the number of CJD cases. In the recipients of hGH, the overall risk of CJD in both the USA and UK has been revised and calculated at about one case of CJD for every 1,000 hGH recipients. Originally, it was suggested that only 11% of these recipients - those who began treatment before 1970 - might have received the contaminated product, but the diagnosis of new cases makes it appear that the true risk may be greater than one in 100 treated patients. From a study just completed in the USA, there are about 7,000 children who had received hGH.

Dr Brown estimated the probability of CJD in the USA, which has a population of 250 million. The annual mortality rate from CJD is about one per million, or 250 deaths per year. The annual mortality rate from all causes is 1% of the total population, or 2.5 million deaths each year. It follows that 250 divided by 2.5 million, or one in 10,000 deaths is due to CJD in the USA. The proportion of autopsies on patients with CJD is likely to be even higher, and, in fact, results of an informal survey of several large university pathology departments suggest that a figure of one per 1,000 is a reasonable estimate.

It is important to point out differences between the iatrogenic infections as compared with sporadic cases of CJD. The clinical similarities in the iatrogenic group as previously mentioned, are very marked, particularly gait, speech, dementia and ataxia. Another point to note is that when the agent is introduced into the CNS, incubation periods are measured in months, whereas in peripheral infection, the incubation period can be years or even decades as has been illustrated by experimentally-infected primates (Brown, 1988). It also appears, from several studies, that the CNS inoculation is associated with primary dementia, a clinical syndrome similar to sporadic CJD cases, while the peripheral inoculation predominantly results in cerebellar syndrome similar to kuru and BSE in cows. The outbreak of CJD amongst recipients of hGH has not reached the high levels that were feared when the problem first came to light (Brown, 1988), but in view of the long incubation period, no one can estimate with confidence the future numbers which may appear due to hGH treatment. It has been suggested that changes in the preparation techniques, involving the 'column' purification step from 1977, may not completely eliminate but can significantly reduce the agent of CJD. Therefore, even though the newer lots may not be completely safe, contamination levels may be so low as not to produce the clinical symptoms of CJD in the lifespan of the patient.

Estimates of the future number of cases of CJD attributed to hGH in the recipient population cannot at present be made with confidence, in view of the long incubation periods between the infection and the illness. It has been well illustrated by Fradkin et al (1991) that within a few months of their interview, two recipients developed CJD and died. Assuming that all infected individuals will develop CJD and that contamination has been random, as the recently treated recipients move through to their incubation period, the number of cases may increase. Since the first case was reported in the UK, there have been on average two new CJD/hGH cases every year.

Representatives samples of all the 15 lots of hGH used on the first diagnosed CJD case in the USA were available at NIH. The patients had each received more than 150 vials in total over the years from these 15 lots. Chimpanzees and squirrel monkeys were inoculated with each lot. After the minimum incubation period of two years for CJD, none of the inoculated animals had developed the disease (Gibbs et al, 1985). However, low doses may be associated with incubation periods exceeding nine years in chimpanzees and three years in squirrel monkeys.

The evidence is ambiguous as to whether exposure to the infectious agent of CJD invariably leads to disease and death, or that death occurs due to other causes while patients are still incubating the disease. Under some experimental conditions, with a small dose introduced by a peripheral route, the clinical disease may not always develop. One should conclude that there is no easy solution to the

259

trade-off between therapeutic benefit and the risk inherent in the inter-human transfer of tissues and tissue products. These risks might be much higher with appearance of BSE and the "new strain variant" of CJD. In simple words, eating self is cannibalism, and the injection of human derived products to human is also a form of cannibalism. The risks must be weighed against each other in each particular case, and even when the treatment is essential, it must be understood that a small risk may eventually become real, and subsequently cause trouble and suffering.

CJD and Blood Transfusion

Persistent viraemia (presence of virus in blood) and preferential replication of the virus in low-density lymphocytes have been demonstrated by two different groups (Kuroda et al, 1983; Tateishi et al, 1980). Previously, low levels of scrapie infectivity had been demonstrated in blood from terminally sick scrapie infected animals (Dickinson et al, 1969; Field et al, 1968) and in hamster scrapie (Diringer, 1984). Manuelidis et al (1985) reported transmission of CJD to animals, histologically verified from blood from two patients. They inoculated intracerebrally four guinea pigs with 50 μl of 10% of the brain homogenate suspension, and four guinea pigs with buffy-coat blood with 50% suspension homogenate in saline. In their experiment, two of the guinea pigs inoculated intracerebrally, were found dead, 251 and 311 days after the inoculation, and one which appeared depressed, was killed 293 days after the inoculation. The fourth guinea pig, 423 days after the inoculation became paralysed, and was killed. Histological examination confirmed characteristic symptoms of CJD. In their study, out of the four guinea pigs inoculated with buffy-coat blood, three died from the disease half-way through the experiment. The one which survived, showed clinical signs for 15 days, 840 days after the inoculation and CJD was histologically confirmed in this animal.

Tateishi (1985) and Klein et al (1993) independently transmitted the disease from blood samples of a patient (and mice) infected with CJD. He also inoculated mice with 20 μl of 10% crude suspension made in normal saline of the brain, cornea, and untreated cerebrospinal fluid (CSF) and urine from this patient. Animals infected by above sources of material showed clinical signs and common pathological changes; the incubation period varied, the brain, 789 ± 112 days; cornea, 1037 days; blood, 1080 ± 69 days; urine 880 ±55 days while animals inoculated with CSF only remained healthy. Mouse-to-mouse transmission through blood inoculation has been successful after a mean incubation period of 365 days (Tateishi, 1980). Previously, infectivity via the CSF of infected rats has been shown to be positive (Tateishi, 1980).

Blood Transfusion: Incidence

Esmondé et al (1993), in one epidemiological study in the UK of 202 definite and probable cases, identified 21 CJD patients who had received a blood transfusion, and 29 who had donated blood. With a definite history of blood transfusion and comparison with controls, they found no significant difference. The mean interval from blood transfusion to the onset of the clinical symptoms of CJD, was reported to be 174 months, median 114, ±18, range 2 to 588. The clinical features recorded in the blood transfusion CJD recipients were similar to those observed in the sporadic cases, and therefore, Esmonde et al suggested that blood transfusion is not a major risk factor for CJD. However, he concluded that epidemiological evidence does not exclude the possibility that isolated cases of CJD are caused by the transmission of the causative agent through transfused blood. Further, every precaution should be taken to ensure that blood and blood products are not obtained from individuals having CJD, or from high risk members of CJD families, or people who have been treated with hGH. More efficient methods must be developed to detect pathogens. As viraemia has been proved in guinea pigs, mice and CJD patients, blood for transfusion and blood products for medical use must be fully tested.

Role of PrP, protein

It has been suggested that the scrapie agent is composed exclusively of the host-coded PrP, without a scrapie-specific nucleic acid, and the term "prion" for this was proposed (Prusiner, 1982). The most important discovery in this field, has been that the protein being considered the agent is in fact, is, encoded by the host DNA and not non-host DNA. The question has to be asked, "Why does a normal protein act as the agent? The hypothesis was first advanced that the protein can self-replicate, and that hypothesis has since been supported by increasingly persuasive amounts of theoretical romanticism, based on wild assumptions derived from experimental data. Models which involve "the protein only" hypothesis are in direct conflict with the existence of distinct scrapie strains. What is the role of this normal host protein? Is it a major component of the infectious agent? Is it the essential component of the agent?

Prion protein PrP is derived from PrP33-35 kDa precursor protein coded by a normal gene assigned to human chromosome 20. There is only a single PrP gene, expressed to equal extent in normal and infected humans, giving rise to the same primary translation product in normal and scrapie-infected brain. A comparative backbone amino-acid sequence of precursor proteins, a 254 amino-acids protein, is similar to that sequenced from other mammalian species, and has been discussed in detail in separate chapters. There are different amino acids at some places in the sequence in different animal species. Once it was realised that the PrP was host derived, molecular genetics entered on the scene and a search began for mutations in the corresponding PrP human gene among infected families.

Role of Mutations in the PrP gene

In humans, it is estimated that only about 10% of CJD cases occur in family members, while almost all GSSS cases appear to be familial. Some of the fa-

261

milial GSSS cases have mutations in the gene which codes for the precursor protein of 254 amino-acids. Surprisingly, the protein isolated from normal individuals does not differ in any of the biochemical or immunological features from the protein isolated from affected individuals. Therefore, it is obvious that the mutations observed in CJD cases are not caused by the SEs agent. The significance of these amino-acid differences in different species remains to be determined. However, once the protein was identified, imagination ran as far as experimental techniques will permit. The significance of mutation has been discussed in a separate chapter.

The infection does not create a *de novo* mutation in the PrP gene. Almost twenty-five years of knowledge that familial, as well as sporadic varieties of CJD, can be transmitted to experimental animals (Ferber et al, 1974) reveal the infectious nature of both disorders. Transmission studies demonstrate that the infective agent is present in the patient's tissue. Since tissues from the familial patients inoculated into laboratory animals transmitted the disease, we are now faced with the problem of explaining how a genetic disease can be infectious. Is it just a coincidence that these families have a mutation in the sequence of the PrP gene? This finding does not support the idea of GSSS being a simple genetic disease. Since PrP is involved in the pathogenesis process (Narang, 1992), these mutations in the PrP gene in some familial patients may be important for two reasons, (i) the mutation reflects an increased susceptibility or (ii) the mutation has occurred in patients subsequent to infection.

According to Brown (1994), in spite of the great temptations of molecular genetics, the heyday of mutation hunters has probably come and gone. It is unlikely that the next dozen, mutations will add very much more to what we have come to appreciate from the first dozen which is that mutations are at the least predisposing. Sporadic CJD cases, which form the majority, do not have these mutations.

Genetic Predisposition of Recipient Host

The discovery that there is a mutation in the PrP gene which might be linked to the occurrence of familial disease has stimulated new interest. Susceptibility to disease from exposure to exogenous infection is apparently also influenced by the host genotypes. It is known that, in experimental scrapie, different host-strain combinations are associated with different incubation periods and lesion distribution (Bruce and Dickinson, 1985; Bruce et al, 1991). It is most likely that in human disease, different mutations in the PrP gene would also influence these variables. Such host-strain differences have been cited as strong evidence for the involvement of a foreign nucleic acid in the infectious process. This led to the molecular-genetic analysis of iatrogenic CJD, to asses whether the distribution of cases reflects genetic factors, and to determine that it is not merely a random contamination of hormone preparations which is responsible for the disease.

262

Not a single one of 27 patients in the USA in whom DNA was tested, has had any of the known disease-specific mutations, and in five of them, full sequencing of the translated region of the PrP gene has revealed a completely normal sequence (Collinge et al, 1991; Goldfarb et al, 1992). An over representation, however, has been reported for the valine allele homozygosity at codon 129 in both British (50%) cases, in contrast to its polymorphic frequency of only 10% in the normal population in the UK. The normally polymorphic valine-methionine codon 129 has been found in four out of seven patients with iatrogenic CJD, but in only 12% of 106 normal individuals, leading to the proposal that the presence of homozygous valine genotype predisposes the individual to iatrogenic CJD (Collinge et al, 1991).

Results from the USA and France have been different. In France all cases have instead been homozygous for methionine (Brown, 1994). In the USA, the normal population in North America has a polymorphic ratio of 11% valine-valine, 51% methionine-valine, and 38% methionine-methionine (Brown, 1992). Thus, valine homozygosity is clearly not required for the development of the clinical CJD in recipients of growth hormone patients. Brown (1992) also reported that eight of the 16 patients tested in the USA, UK and France were either heterozygous or homozygous for methionine, and suggested that valine homozygosity might possibly increase susceptibility to the disease. Results from these studies suggest that this factor may have a statistical significance, though biologically it is not important.

Case to Case Transmission

For the vast majority of cases, there is no obvious iatrogenic source, no family history of any neurological disease, and no connection with other cases of CJD. The source of infection in these cases remains unknown. So far, there has been no firm evidence to suggest that in the general population, the agent of the disease is transmitted from person to person, but transmission through environmental means and via the food chain is now evident.

Epidemiological Surveys

England and Wales : In a retrospective study of CJD cases (Wills et al, 1986), covering the period 1970-1979 in England and Wales, 152 cases of CJD were identified of which 121 (65%) were definite cases. The average annual recorded incidence was 0.3 per million for this period. Of the 152 cases, family history records were available in only 98 cases. Six patients described had a positive family history of one other member having medically confirmed with CJD/AD symptoms. The familial cases figures appeared comparable to those observed in France. The mother of four siblings who died of symptoms of CJD had relatives who also died possibly of CJD. In the England and Wales study, Wills et al (1986), however, do not give the numbers of families involved.

Masters et al, (1979, 1981) in their epidemiological study of more than 1400

263

cases of CJD, found familial cases from 37 families with two or more affected members per family. They estimated that across the world, familial CJD represented 10% to 15% of the total cases of CJD. In 1968, infectious aetiology of CJD was first demonstrated. In their analysis of worldwide CJD cases diagnosed during a period from 1968 to 1979, they found 218 families with dementias. They classified these cases into 12 groups of dementias detailed below.

Group 1, 2, and 3 included transmitted, definite, probable and possible familial cases, respectively. Group 4 contained familial "amyotrophic" form of CJD, 15 families in which two or more members were affected with the so-called amyotrophic form of CJD. Group 5: familial AD with at least one member affected with definite CJD while two or more members had AD (three families with 19 members affected). Group 6: Seventeen families where one or more members had a clinical syndrome resembling CJD, while two or more members had AD. At least one case in each family was pathologically confirmed in whom the appearance of abnormal movements, especially myoclonus together with pyramidal, extrapyramidal or cerebellar signs or sharp wave complexes on EEG might have led to the clinical diagnosis of CJD. Group 7: transmitted familial AD in experimental primates (two families with eight members affected). Group 8: contained familial AD (50 families with 221 members affected) and groups 9 to 12 had no CJD patients in their families.

France: Brown et al (1986), carried out a survey of CJD cases in France covering the period 1968-1982. In this study, they identified 329 cases, of which 232 (71%) were definite CJD cases. The annual mortality rate of CJD in France for the 15-years period was 0.42 per million population. The definite familial cases in their study account for only 4% of the total series and another 4% of the cases fall possibly into the familial class but where clinical and neuropathological information was insufficient to establish the diagnosis. Of the 329 CJD cases, 19 were familial (about 6%) occurring within six families. Eight of these cases belonged to three families of Mediterranean Jewish origin, while the rest were native non-Jewish French families. In France as a whole, CJD occurred more frequently in the foreign-born population, particularly North African residents (annual mortality rate 0.77 per million), than in the native-born French population (annual mortality rate 0.38 per million).

They also observed in 21 geographic regions of France a significant relationship between the mortality rate and population density. During the period of their study, the population of continental France numbered 52.6 million people, of whom 4.8 million were foreign-born. They identified 329 French residents who had died of CJD during the period, 1968-1982; of these 19 (6%), were familial, and 56 (17%) were foreign-born cases (particularly North African). In a further breakdown of the annual mortality, they found that the mortality rates were higher in foreign-born residents, particularly, 4.90 per million from Tunis, 2.03 per million from Poland, and 1.03 per million of Algerian origin. The lowest mortality rates occurred in rural areas, intermediate rates occurred in provincial urban areas, and the highest rates occurred in the Paris metropolis. This phenomenon is probably related either to the higher population density of foreign-born cases in Paris, or to the better facilities available for case ascertainment. Since the disease occurred more frequently in foreign-born residents (0.77 per million) than in the French-born population (0.38 per million), foreign-born residents tended to be concentrated in the densely populated urban areas.

Chile : The incidence of CJD in Chile is similar (Gálvez et al, 1980; 1982) to that found in the United States (Master et al, 1979) and France (Brown et al, 1979). Gálvez et al (1983), however, reported more exact figures; 39 (45%) were familial from a total of 87 cases of CJD in Chile between 1931-1983. These reported cases occurred in 11 families, with an average of 3.5 affected members per family. Most of these cases occurred, however, within a single generation (four families), or in that generation grandparents generation (six families). Only one family showed affected members in three successive generations. Three pairs of affected members in three different families died at the same time, possibly indicating a common exposure to CJD agent. Most of the familial cases reported in this study lived in the central region of the country. It has been suggested that the variations in these figures may be due to insufficiently obtained family histories in some cases and due to extensive investigations in others. The documentation of CJD in a woman related by marriage to one of the affected families, and other similarly related cases which occurred in France (Brown et al, 1979), produced strong evidence for lateral transmission resulting from the high intrafamilial concentration of cases, or from an unusually virulent virus strain. These findings justify further epidemiologic investigation of CJD.

In all these studies, the parameters set included ages at death, sex distribution, duration of illness and rates of occurrence of disease among siblings and cousins. Genealogical evidence of skipped generations, single-generation happening, matrimony and twin occurrence, evidence of preponderance in maternal or paternal line relations, and evidence of increased awareness of the disease have been collected. Wide geographical separations between affected family members, death intervals, and differences between ages at death of affected siblings were also described. In some studies, two important differences between familial and sporadic cases have been observed: 1) Age at death is 10 to 15 years lower in familial than in sporadic cases of CJD. But Gálvez (1983) results from Chile showed, that the mean age at death in familial cases (54.45 years) was identical to that of the sporadic CJD cases (54. 88 years), with however, a tendency toward female preponderance in the familial cases, and males more common in sporadic CJD. 2) The disease duration is longer in familial than in sporadic CJD. However, some surveys suggest the average duration of the disease was also not significantly different in familial and sporadic CJD (Gálvez et al, 1983; Masters et al, 1981). The most comprehensive survey in England and Wales of CJD cases was between 1968-1982, which reported a female preponderance of 2:1 in most years, with overall ratio of 1.68:1, with an annual incidence rate of 0.3 per million.

CJD has a maximum world-wide annual incidence of about 1 case per million people (Brown et al, 1987) estimated in 1987 on information available at that time.

Brown et al (1986) reported that the average duration of the illness might have been influenced by three cases with extremely long incubation period, two of which were 60 months and the other one, 120 months. Particularly important is the fact that the patient with the longest duration of the illness of 120 months is one of the histologically confirmed cases. Another more critical interpretation for this difference was suggested by Brown et al that an occasional case of AD within CJD families might have been included in these families.

Source of Infection

O ver the past many years , epidemiological studies have revealed the existence of three groups: (1) Familial: these cases occur within the same family; (2) Iatrogenic, caused by accidental inoculation; (3) Sporadic. Sporadic, familial or iatrogenic cases have one thing is common; all have the infective causative agent in their tissues, particularly in the brain, and that agent is transmissible, as is the case with all other animal SEs.

Epidemiological surveys have so far failed to reveal any natural mechanism of transmission within the affected families. This has raised questions beyond external aetiological factors. The existence of vertical transmission in humans seems very unlikely while environmental factors, particularly the natural source of the causative agent and the route of infection remain unknown. Some of the evidence points to genetic factors playing a role in providing a portal entry to extraneous infective agents, thus precipitating the clinical onset in a familial group which may be classified as "high risk". Clinical and histopathological findings are similar in both familial and sporadic cases, and it has been important to distinguish the two groups. Some of the genetically determined CJD cases appear to be in a class of their own.

In 1985, contaminated batches of hGH in the USA, when inoculated into animals, also produced SE. In this, it resembles kuru, the major difference between CJD and kuru being epidemiological. Kuru is highly focused in a small community, while the majority of CJD cases occur almost in a dispersed pattern of sporadic cases, the annual rate varying from 0.25 to 30 per million per year (Masters et al, 1979), with 5 to 10% cases within families. In most places, no more than one case per million of the population might be expected. In France, 329 cases of CJD were diagnosed between 1968 and 1982. Six percent of these were familial cases with males and females equally affected, which suggested the likelihood of an autosomal dominance (Baron et al, 1986). A detailed study of these families has shown wide variations in individual pedigrees, particularly the occurrence of CJD in a genetically unrelated woman, married to an uninfected branch of the CJD family. The fact that she was raised by the affected branch of the family, argues in favour of horizontal transmission early in life. As members of a given family tend to die at the same age, the data fails to discriminate between vertical and horizontal transmission.

From published studies of the epidemiology of CJD, and the hypothesis proposed to explain sporadic cases, Brown & Cathala (1979) concluded, that the scrapie agent from sheep produces CJD in man. Indeed, emphasising this point, they reported that a patient developed symptoms of CJD three months after receiving a course of rabies vaccine prepared from the brain of sheep. No further details have been published on this case.

The prevalence of CJD in different countries varies markedly in time and place. The rate per million in the USA is 0.26, (Masters et al, 1979), France, 0.32, (Brown et al, 1979), and England 0.09 (Matthews, 1975). On average, 1 CJD case per annum in a population of three million had been seen during a period, 1970-1987, in the northern region of the UK, and unexpectedly from 1988 onward, on average, four cases were being diagnosed each year.

Over one third of CJD cases reviewed by Masters et al, (1979) occurred in persons directly or indirectly involved with agriculture or food handling. Twenty-four (8%) of the 308 persons affected were farmers or the wives of farmers. Although the association in these families may have been coincidental, it cannot be ignored. Increased incidence of the infectious disease could be explained by increased exposure to the agent with increased likelihood of infection. Farmers and food handlers frequently suffer minor hand wounds, such as cuts, abrasions, and cracked, dry or blistered skin. These could serve as ideal portals for the entry of the infectious agent in contact with the skin. Other modes of entry would be inhalation and swallowing of the agent in dust. There is an increased incidence in some particular families, who are not farmers, or butchers. It may be that some families have a practice of eating brain tissues more than others, since oral transmission of scrapie, kuru and CJD has been demonstrated in squirrel monkeys and mice, and now there is the food-born transmission of BSE to cows. In some patients, the portal route of entry may be through bad teeth or peptic ulcers. In animal exposures where infection has been documented after oral feed, transmission was so irregular that the question arises as to whether the true portal was either the gastrointestinal tract itself or through areas of mucosal abrasions. Ulcerations in the lips, gums and intestines may also play a role. Studying the effect of gingival scarification on the oral route of infection demonstrated that 70% of nonscarified, compared with 100% of scarificated mice, developed the disease, and with a significantly shorter incubation time (Carp, 1982). Single episodes of oral ingestion of the agent may not transmit SEs, and it is likely that other factors play an important role, especially the dose of the agent.

However, it is known that CJD is rapidly transmissible by direct inoculation of the infectious material from human to human, with incubation periods between two and five years. A long incubation period for disease expression in these cases may be partly attributable to the route of the inoculation, the amount of dose of the infectious material and crossing from one species to another.

267

Cluster CJD Cases

In the context of uncertainty about the origin of the majority of cases of CJD, there have been a few reports of case clusters from several countries (Kahana et al, 1974; Matthews, 1975; Mayer, et al, 1977; Lechi et al, 1983; Araya et al, 1983; Trabattoni et al, 1990). Once, some occasional cases are observed within an area, the interest and awareness stimulated leads to a more careful search for additional cases in the same area, suggesting a cluster. The existence of familial clustering does seem fairly certain. Significant clustering has been described among Libyan-born Israelis (Kahana et al, 1974; Neugut et al, 1979). Most of these studies have concentrated on linking either person-to-person transmission, or an environmental common point source for the disease. Equally important, it is entirely possible for a number of unrelated cases to occur close together simply by chance. Further, with long incubation periods, data has been collected retrospectively in most of the studies and may not reflect the true facts. As the disease agent is very common in the environment (sheep and cattle tissues), an appropriate mechanism by which the disease might be acquired, has to be considered, such as an inherited genetic susceptibility to the disease.

Matthews (1979) in the UK, conducted a study by asking neuropathologists to notify cases with verified histopathological diagnosis during the decade, 1964 -1973. Forty-six patients were identified with an annual incidence rate of 0.09 per million. Fourteen patients, according to their relatives, were thought to have never eaten sheep brain. Five were known to have done so. In three cases, he recorded that a sibling was reported to have had an identical disease, although the evidence was not substantiated with histopathology or clinical backup. Matthews also described two clusters of three patients each. In each instance, he tried to investigate further, through personal contacts with the patients when they were alive. From the epidemiological viewpoint, the three cases had occurred in a small community living a short distance from each other. Matthews suggested that there was a good chance that the patients had had some social contact, but it is highly improbable that transmission could have been effected by any casual contact. It was more likely that there had been a common exposure through a common source of food. In the second cluster based on the local population, the annual incidence rate of CJD for the decade was 1.3 per million, 10 times the overall rate for England and Wales.

Will et al (1982), in a retrospective study, described three cases of probable accidental transmission of CJD, each patient having undergone some neurosurgical procedure in the past. They also described three more cases of CJD, in a closed geographical group in Eastern England, possibly connected by dental procedures. They described that in 1965, a patient died of CJD which histopathology confirmed. In 1968, another patient developed CJD and died. Both these patients shared the same general practitioner and lived within 250 metres of each other. Unfortunately, their medical records were destroyed. Another patient, a dentist, used his house as a surgery and lived midway between these two patients. He died in 1980, and CJD was confirmed neuropathologically. Dental records were found to be incomplete, and although the possibility that the patients were treated by the same dentist, was considered, further information was not available.

Will et al (1984) described another CJD case in the UK who had previous social contact with a group of three cases representing a familial cluster. Two of these were sisters who lived in the same house until their early twenties. The third case was their first cousin with whom they had close social contacts during her teens and early twenties. They regularly met, went on holidays together and worked in the same factory. The fourth case was related by marriage, and knew the first cousin with whom she had regular meetings, and was even said to have visited her during her final admission.

CJD has also been documented in Chile and France, among patients who had contact with cases of familial CJD, but who were not genetically related. These cases showed a much longer incubation period, about 13 years, before developing the disease. Brown et al (1986) in France, also described, two instances of CJD cases occurred within a short distance. In the first instance in small villages within a radius of six km and population of only 300 to 700, two cases occurred within few months of each other and a third case was reported nine years later. All the three cases were known to each other. In the second instance, another two cases occurred in 1978 and 1980 within a single hamlet of 50 inhabitants in a region of rural France, and their houses were located 70 m apart. The two patients were known to each other, and one of them worked in the village restaurant. Later, they found the home of yet another patient less than 100 m away. Her clinical onset and death virtually coincided with those of her former neighbour. The last two patients did not know each other, but shared many of the same shops and at one time were looked after and received injections from the same visiting nurse who sterilised needles and syringes by boiling.

Trabattoni et al (1990), in their study described 13 cases of CJD which occurred between 1975 to 1984 in the region of Parma, Italy, with a population of 1,448,000. The suspicion of CJD had not been raised in any of the cases prior to the time they were investigated by these authors. It was reported that all patients experienced a range of neurotic-like symptoms, anxiety, depression, change of mood. A second period followed, with a mixture of symptoms, namely cerebellar and focal impairment. Dementia was, for all, the most relevant component of the last stage. At the last stage, these patients developed myoclonic jerks and the EEG patterns were typical from the early full stage onward.

None of the patients were genetically related, or had any family background of neurological or psychiatric illness. Trabattoni et al (1990) described the occupations and relationships, to other patients as follows: Six of the patients were farmers; three housewives (two on farms), 1 miller, 1 blacksmith, and 1 lorry driver. One had worked in a military powder warehouse before becoming a cook and later a cloakroom attendant. This patient was born in a large village close to

269

that in which another patient had been born. The lorry driver and the patient who worked in the powder warehouse had been brought up on farms and most of their relatives and friends were farmers and lived out of town. One of the patients who had been on holidays, stayed in a pension run by nuns. This pension was in the same village as that in which another of the patients lived. Three other patients' occupations were different at the time they developed CJD, but they were brought up on farms. Twelve of the 13 patients came from low to middle class families with small landholdings. Thus, Trabattoni et al (1990) established that 12 of their patients had a direct connection with agriculture and came into contact with animals. Only one out of 13 had no such connection. According to the authors, the locals had several characteristic feeding habits with a high consumption of horse meat and some eating cats as a traditional delicacy. Mutton and lamb was not commonly eaten.

These investigators claimed that this group of patients resembled no other one, since there was a predominantly rural case concentration (Chatelain et al, 1981). They excluded the possibility that scrapie might have been involved in disease transmission, since sheep were uncommon in the particular area, and scrapie was rare in Italy. Matthews (1975) was skeptical about the possibility that casual contacts had caused the illness in three patients he studied, who were living in the same small community. Trabattoni et al (1990), however, preferred the alternative explanation based upon common environmental conditions. This they based on the fact that the regularity, monotony and similarity of their lives seemed remarkable enough to justify a meticulous research into "conditions shared by all of them". However, they suggested that for two pairs of patients, person-to person horizontal transmission cannot be excluded, and were cautious in defining the difference between a "transmissible" and a "contagious" disease.

Brown et al (1986), however, observed a significant association between mortality rate and population density. Geographically in France, the lowest mortality rate occurred in rural areas and the highest rates occurred in the Paris metropolis. Possible explanations, ethnic composition, age distribution, and case finding artifacts for these differences. They also found that there were relatively more people in the older, (higher risk) age groups in Paris than in its suburbs. This phenomenon is probably explained by the higher density of foreign-born people with elevated case incidence of CJD in Paris. Better facilities for case ascertainment might explain at least some of the differences between the Paris area and rest of France, but it does not account for the high rate in Paris relative to its suburbs, since the availability of neurological services is uniformly high in the Paris area. Brown et al (1986), suggested a neurosurgical iatrogenic transmission occurrence on one occasion, and casual contacts between presymptomatic patients occurring on two occasions. They could not establish contacts between the great majority of the cases, or any links between CJD and socioeconomic factors, or exposure to animal sources of infection.

Significance of Autosomal Dominant Inheritance

According to Brown et al (1986), the overall frequency of occurrence of CJD among affected siblings is 47.3%, which is consistent with a pattern of an autosomal dominant transmission. For some time, since the earliest descriptions of familial CJD, most genealogies have been interpreted as showing autosomal dominant inheritance of the disease on the bases of approximately equal involvement of both sexes and occurrence in approximately half of the siblings in affected families (Asher et al, 1983). However, within a family, it varies from 26.7% to 80%. Further, no affected parents were identified in two of the affected families which would contradict the hypothesis of single gene autosomal dominant transmission with complete penetrance (Brown et al, 1986).

There was an occurrence of a few families, with two to four siblings, where all had died of kuru. Within a single family where parents were affected with the illness, there were deaths of two of four siblings, the children dying at the same age. In kuru, the coincidence of mother-child cases appeared more common. The age distribution and the ratio in male to female was 1:1 in children and 1:13 in adults, with a short period from the onset to death. The distribution of the disease was considered genetically related to the local population compared to the centre of the region. This gave a wrong lead in thinking that kuru was more likely a heredo-ataxia ataxia. Gajdusek suggested it to be be some genetic determinant of the disease. At that time the genetic hypothesis was difficult to accept and later it was proved to be an infectious disease. Knowing that CJD can be transmitted to primates and nonprimates by the intracerebral inoculation of brain homogenates from individuals with CJD and GSSS, paradoxically and confusingly, we are unable to abandon the old contradictory dogma that these diseases have a genetic basis related to the mutations seen in the PrP gene.

In these studies, cases were reported from three successive generations of one family only, where the proportional incidence or "rate of occurrence" calculated on the basis of the number of affected and non-affected siblings and cousins aged 40 years or more within any generation, should be of the order of 58%, which appeared to be consistent with a pattern of autosomal dominant transmission. In another 11 families, however, the authors identified five affected fathers and two affected mothers of the affected children, but failed to identify affected parents in four of the families. The restriction of CJD cases to a single generation in four of the affected families, and the observation of one instance of skipping a generation in another family, highlights the limitations of the inheritance theories and their validity in human genetics. It may well be that these limitations are due to insufficient information on the cause of death of other members of the affected families. In the group of 11 families, seven families had affected members in two or three succeeding generations and thus a tendency for increased awareness of the symptoms was observed.

Ten instances where the age of the offspring at death was equal to or less than the parental age at death have been recorded, while three cases died where the offsprings' ages at death exceed that of the respective parent. The number of cases of familial CJD in which complete medical and surgical histories were available were few and there was similar lack of information as to dietary habits. It is known that one of the familial patients had eaten uncooked sheep blood and poorly-cooked sheep's brain. There were three such examples sited for the sporadic cases of CJD.

There are a number of other important points in the Gálvez et al study, which are worth discussing. A family which originated in Los Angeles, Chile (Gálvez et al, 1979) had three affected members in two successive generations. The same clinical disease occurred at the same time in two of the patients while the patients' ages were different, 40 and 49, respectively, and one of whom had left home some 21 years previously, and subsequently had no physical contact with her relatives. This suggests a common exposure to the CJD agent at least 21 years before the clinical onset of the disease.

There has been so far no evidence for the vertical transmission of naturally occurring kuru (Gajdusek, 1977). Vertical transmission, a possible source from an affected father who died at the age of 61 years of possible CJD, with illness of two years duration was considered. However, none of the parents in this family in the first generation appeared to have had CJD, or a similar disease. In the same study, two affected sisters are reported to have died at the same time and at about the same age after living all the time in a close physical relationship. Another family in the study showed a pair of cousins developing CJD at the ages of 57 and 63, respectively, in 1981-82. In the previous generation two siblings had died in the years 1969 and 1977 at the ages of 55 and 73, respectively. Since a physical contact existed between both pairs of affected family members for five years, the authors speculated that the first two siblings could have been the source of infection in the later affected cousins. This suggested a minimum incubation period of five years. From the overall study, from the mean death interval of 14.5 years or 9.3 years, they calculated the minimum incubation periods to be between five and 37 years or two to 23 years respectively, for person-to-person transmission occurring within the affected families.

The occurrence of CJD in a woman in the year 1972 at the age of 40 years, related by marriage to the familial cases, has been reported (Masters et al, 1979). She married into a CJD family, 13 years before the onset of her illness, and had been in close contact with 2 affected members who died in the years 1968 and 1970 at the ages of 49 and 47 years, respectively (Gálvez et al, 1983). These results strongly suggested a common source of horizontal transmission. A similar case has been reported in which a business associate of the affected butcher's familial cases also died of progressive dementia with myoclonus, probably CJD (Brown et al, 1986; Masters et al, 1979).

272

Relationship of occupation

Masters et al (1979), from the occupational view point gave a very interesting account of a family with CJD. Two affected brothers owned and worked in a butcher shop, where their affected sister and a son also worked. Another member, who developed CJD, played in the butcher shop, frequently, as a child. The occupational history of another affected member, diagnosed as having CJD, remains unknown. They have identified six non-affected members in the second and third generations as those who had little or no contact with the meat business. Further, they reported that a business partner of this affected butcher family had also died of a progressive dementia with myoclonus, probably CJD (Brown et al, 1986; Masters et al, 1979). Such examples could be taken as evidence of an environmental source of infection, presumably scrapie-infected meat. These patients were known to eat poorly cooked sheep and beef brains.

These authors reported a similar occupational situation with an almost identical history in an AD family, where three brothers with AD worked in a butcher's shop for 25 years, and were known to eat poorly cooked sheep and beef brains. Their three unaffected siblings were reported never to have worked in the butcher shop.

Masters et al (1979) also studied the occupation of the CJD patients in group 1 and 2 consisting of 67 CJD cases. Of these, two were health workers, three in the agriculture/meat professions, 20 were food handlers (housewives/domestic servants), eleven clerical workers, 10 professional workers and seven transport workers. The remaining 14 cases represented many different professions. Similar data was not available in patients with familial AD.

Husband and Wife Cases of CJD

There are two reports of conjugal disease in which husband and wife died of CJD within a few years of each other (Garzuly et al, 1971). There is a reported case of a husband and wife both developing the disease, but the diagnosis was only definitely confirmed for one of them (Matthews, 1975; Jellinger et al, 1972). Masters et al, (1979) also described a conjugal pair, where, however, the diagnosis of CJD was based on a poor history of dementia and therefore considered only a possible case. Conjugal occurrence of CJD could be taken as strong evidence in favour of a common source of infection if the spouses were ill at about the same time, or for lateral transmission with contagion, if the case preceded the others by several years. Personally, I have seen a case in a woman who was diagnosed and confirmed as CJD case. Her husband died less than two years later, but was clinically diagnosed as dying from a stroke after an illness of about five months. At the time of his death, the attending physician was not aware of the cause of his wife's death. A postmortem was not performed. However, once it was realised that his wife had died of a definite CJD, based on a poor history of dementia occurring, a possible case of CJD was considered. No conjugal cases have been observed in AD. Thus, it would appear that person-to-person

273

contact is not enough to transmit the disease, because, if so, even the sporadic families would be at risk. There is another aspect in the equation in situations where members live close together and   probably eat similar food from the same sources. Even when families move from the country of origin, they carry the same eating and cooking habits with them, while the scrapie agent is present world wide.

Cases Within Families

While, in general, patients with familial CJD did not differ appreciably in their clinical symptomatology and neuropathological features from cases of sporadic CJD, variations between families do occur, but the similarities in the clinical features within any given family far outweigh the differences (Masters, et al, 1979; Bernoulli et al, 1979). Rosenthal et al, 1976) reported a family with several affected members with a neurological syndrome characterised by varied motor system abnormalities of long duration, with or without dementia. Several of the affected members had syndromes of spino-cerebellar ataxia. Three other affected members in the same generation were reported to have had rather slow progressive dementias without myoclonus, and prominent motor impairment. Two of these cases had confirmed pathological SE, and had kuru-like amyloid plaques, particularly in the cerebellum (Masters et al, 1979). In the family, clinically and pathologically, therefore, the disease strongly resembled GSSS.

Masters et al (1979) cited from the literature three families where definite CJD occurred in one member while two or more members had AD. They also summarised results of 17 other families where two or more members had AD, at least one of which was pathologically confirmed. A total of 88 affected members were identified in the group, 30 of whom had abnormal movements, especially myoclonus, together with pyramidal, extrapyramidal or cerebellar signs which led to the clinical diagnosis of CJD. The mean age of of all affected members was 46.1 years compared to 47.7 years in affected members with myoclonus or other movement disorders. The mean duration of the disease in these atypical members with myoclonus was 56 months compared to 85 months in typical AD cases. When brain tissue from one member. from each of two families with two or more members having AD, was inoculated into nonhuman primates they found the tissue induced SE   with an incubation period similar to that of sporadic CJD cases. No cases of sporadic AD has transmitted to nonhuman primates from 19 cases where the brain inoculation has been on test for four years or longer (Masters et al, 1979).

Gerstmann-Sträussler-Scheinker syndrome (GSSS) which is pathologically similar to CJD in almost all cases, appears to show characteristics consistent with autosomal dominant inheritance pattern (Masters et al, 1981). The disease, however, is infectious which suggests that the agent may be carried in the germline. Unfortunately, the hypothesis of a single-gene inheritance, although widely considered, has in fact never been tested. The problem with familial cases comes when cases are found within the family but the relationship is by marriage (Will et al, 1982; Brown,1986).

There is no evidence for maternal lineage in CJD distribution or transmission. However, there are suggestions against maternal vertical passage and transplacental or breast milk routes of infection. On the other hand, the finding that deaths within a family occur within the same age bracket, supports vertical transmission. Brown et al (1986) describe the occurrence of CJD in the wife of a healthy member of an affected family, who had spent a part of her childhood with her future in-laws, two of whom died of CJD. All three deaths occurred at a similar age, 59 (wife), 60 and 61 (relatives by marriage). This is a strong evidence in favour of horizontal or common source transmission in early childhood. The data so presented fails to discriminate between vertical transmission and common source exposure within the affected families. The occurrence of CJD in a woman related by marriage to an affected branch argues in favour of horizontal transmission early in life. The mean age at death in familial CJD is 51.9 years as compared to 61.2 years for sporadic CJD. It is strange to note that with a few exceptions, members of a given family have a tendency to die within the same age group. Two brothers in a family died at the ages of 47 and 48 years, despite their deaths occurring in years 1972 and 1977; while in another family, a brother and sister died nine years apart at the ages of 58 and 59 years (Brown et al, 1986). However, there are instances where deaths of affected family members have occurred at approximately the same time with wider variations in the age at death (Brown et al, 1986). Thus, depending on the age group of the patients at the time of death, they have been categorised into "Young", "Middle-Aged" and "Elderly" CJD families. Where affected members of the family die at the same age but not at the same time, this points to a vertical transmission or infection acquired early in life as opposed to exposure to a common environmental source of contamination. This would indicate that the incubation period is constant and that is highly unlikely for the SE agent. Most of the familial cases described have occurred in the same generation. However, cases have been reported in second, third and fourth generation.

Rosenthal et al (1976) described a familial neurological disease in a family which originated from Bedfordshire, England. The father migrated to the United States at the age of 24, and died 28 years later of a chronic neurological disease that was not typical of CJD. A son died 32 years after the death of his father in which the diagnosis of CJD was confirmed by neuropathological examination of the brain. The disease was also transmissible into primates (from this case) and several relatives living in England also died of CJD. The family history given by Rosenthal et al (1976) describes 118 members in the pedigree of "W" family. Some members of the family live in England and others are now scattered throughout the USA. A daughter in the second generation maintains that her mother and her aunt were identical twins and both died at the age of 55 and the cause of death was certified as "disseminated sclerosis".

275

In the second generation, there were eight brothers and sisters of whom five developed a neurological disease. The patients' ages at death ranged from 49 to 69 years. The actual years of their deaths has not been mentioned. The illness in most cases started with weakness, dragging of one leg, and slurred speech. The family members deny any signs of dementia or memory loss until shortly before death. One patient developed headaches and another had trouble swallowing food or liquids.

In the third generation, of the five affected parents, four had 16 children out of whom 9 were affected, while the fifth affected case had a son and two daughters, and their subsequent children were not affected. These nine patients died between the age of 43 and 66, a difference of some 20 years; but their deaths occurred between 1968 and 1973, a difference of five years. Four of the affected members had a neurological disease with dementia, while the other five were without dementia.

One of the cases in this generation was a 42 year old male who was well until early 1972, when he started making errors of judgment. He noticed pain and "flashing lights" in both eyes, and lost the ability to discriminate distances. His balance became poor, and he staggered. He had delusions, nightmares and became confused. Although his physical condition in October 1972, was normal, he generally became unresponsive and occasionally repeated same phrases. There were no horizontal or vertical eye movement. The patient occasionally moved his hand awkwardly across his forehead. Rigidity was present, and this became symmetrical in the elbows, knees and neck. His condition deteriorated and EEG showed a diffused slowing with triphasic waves. A second repeat of EEG taken two weeks before death showed periodic biphasic and polyphasic discharges about once every three seconds on a relative flat background. In the last two months, myoclonic jerks became more evident. The patient became less responsive eventually comatose, and died of bronchopneumonia.

There is a remarkable heterogeneous symptomatology in the cases as presented. In one case, the neurologist described mild Parkinsonism, particularly in the facial expression. The gait was ataxic. Three of the patients noticed weakness and dragging of one leg and difficulty in walking. One complained of paresthesias in the left leg and both hands. A year later, she was noticed to have left-sided hemiparesis with increased reflexes. In three years, the patient could not support her weight and she slowly developed progressive bilateral pyramidal tract dysfunction and incontinence, and died at the age of 65. Her sister, 57, had paresthesias over the right side of her face. As she deteriorated, she had ataxia, later she stammered, and her gait became slow and shuffling. She died at the age of 65.

Examining the pedigree, four of six females and one of two males in the second generation were affected. This led Rosenthal et al (1976) to suggest an autosomal dominant transmission of a factor associated with susceptibility to neurological diseases. In the third generation, five of 11 females and two of seven

276

males developed neurological diseases. One of the relatives died of other causes at the age of 28, while others had not reached the expected CJD age.

Another family with seven affected individuals from three generations in a kindred having over 250 members has been identified by Bertoni et al (1983). This is the largest reported kindred of CJD. Most of the affected patients were farmers. Bertoni et al (1983), reported that a farmer at the age of 58, developed a progressive dementing illness. The family recalled that his illness was identical to that seen in his son, with ataxia and subacute incapacitating dementia. He had eight children and at least 42 grandchildren. The pedigree included 97 great-grandchildren, 107 great-great-grandchildren and 12 great-great-great-grandchildren.

Compared to Rosenthal et al (1976) most of the cases had more or less homogeneous symptomatology. A typical case experienced the gradual development of tremor of the arms and staggering gait and confusion, inability to repeat more than three numbers, slurred speech, slow and weak pupillary reactions to both light and adjustment, absence of convergence, marked impairment of upward and downward gaze on command, and an inability to stand with the feet together even with eyes open. Tremor of hands increased, and gait became more ataxic. Hallucination developed and mental condition deteriorated progressively till death. In cases where brains were examined, the spongiform changes were reported to be most severe in the thalamus, pons, and cerebellar cortex.

The case reports which were obtained from the family members in the absence of medical records, were compared to the frequency of signs observed in order of appearance, dementia and ataxia of gait by Bertoni et al (1983). In the original five cases reported by Jakob (1921), apart from dementia which may start late, the most frequent signs and symptoms were gait disorder, dizziness or illusion of movement and vertigo. Gait problems were present in about one third of cases, while Kirschbaum (1968) included gait and coordination disturbances in the typical early stages of CJD. Kirschbaum (1968) mentions oculomotor palsies and dissociation of eye movements and more variable signs as late symptoms.

The differential diagnosis must rule out stroke-like presentation, viral encephalopathies which seldom give rise to CJD like symptoms. Disseminated or diffused manifestations of chronic cerebral infections must be ruled out. AD can also develop as a spongiform state in the brain which may contribute to the difficulty in distinguishing the changes from those observed in CJD. From the historical viewpoint also, the two disorders primarily lead to dementia. Since one of them is transmissible, it is important to differentiate CJD from AD, both clinically and pathologically. Thus, to confirm CJD, it is often essential to transmit the disease experimentally. Transmission studies are carried out using tissue from a wide range of neurological conditions including CJD, AD, Huntington's chorea, Pick's disease, MS and a number of other undiagnosed disorders. Traub et al, (1977) presented results from 220 such cases where brain tis-

277

sue was injected into non-human primates. Transmission occurred in 78, of which 75 were CJD, and the remaining three were AD cases. Upon reexamination of these cases, the histopathological picture always appears to be similar to SEs, which was initially thought not to be significant. According to Corsellis (1986), this was the start of the controversy over the transmissibility of AD. In one case, the diagnosis had been made after death, and in the other, it was based on biopsy (Rewcastle et al, 1978). Therefore, it was considered that AD might have a transmissible agent. In AD, a transmissible agent has not yet been demonstrated with certainty. But, based on their clinical, pathological and biological findings, a number of workers consider there is ample justification believing AD to have similar pathogenesis to SEs. In the light of scrapie having long and short incubation strains, AD might belong to a long incubation strain. The short incubation strain of scrapie produces clinical symptoms in mice in about 150 days as opposed to over 600 days in the long incubation period strain.

Since the major clinical feature of CJD is progressive dementia , the term, "transmissible virus dementia" was proposed for CJD (Gajdusek, 1985). Both AD and CJD affect males and females with equal frequency. The age of onset and frequency distribution are remarkably similar. The average age in AD is 67 years compared to 60 years in CJD. Although the duration of the illness is much longer - eight years versus eight months with considerable overlap - some AD cases die following a very short duration of illness, and some CJD cases live as long as 10 years.

Alzheimer's disease presents a progressive mental deterioration, with a slow onset starting with behavioural changes, memory and speech loss. With the progression of the disease, higher cortical functions are disoriented, and speech can become be restricted to a few words. Many of the CJD cases present and progress as AD cases, but subsequently become associated with one or more additional neurological abnormalities.

The major difference between CJD and kuru probably lies in their epidemiological patterns. Unlike the highly focused and geographically constricted incidence of kuru, CJD occurs in an almost completely disperse pattern of sporadic cases worldwide at an annual incidence of only about one case per million people, distributed equally among men and women in the age group 50 to 75.

Since the SEAC in Britain have considered 10 cases of CJD which have occurred in people aged under 42, this has raised the possibility that BSE may be transmissible to humans. Furthermore, the SEAC considered that most likely explanation is exposure to BSE infection before 1989, in other words, before the control measures to protect humans, were introduced. What is hard to understand, if this had already happened and control measures were in place, is why SEAC should be recommending additional control measures? Is it not just guess work? Most of the measures should have been in place from 1988. Yet calf brain under six months is allowed into human food chain - just consider work done by Stamp and colleagues in 1959.

Therapeutic Treatment of CJD Cases

Therapeutic trials with a wide range of drugs and extensive treatment have shown little beneficial results. Antibiotics, steroids, or anti-histamines: none of them altered the course of the disease and knowing its inevitably fatal outcome, every possible therapy, no matter how unlikely to prove successful, was considered. The impossibility of diagnosing the disease in its preclinical stage, and the variety of clinical features in each case during the progression of the disease make it difficult to follow the effects of drugs. Without knowing the nature of the agent or the cause of the transmissible encephalopathy, attempts at treatment were presumptions, shots in the dark, and the question remains, does therapeutic intervention help. The agents that cause the SEs have for a long time been known, and considered by many to be closely associated with plasma membranes. Therefore, it is not surprising that some of the first therapeutic drugs studied were membrane related. A vast variety of anti-infective and other drugs have been studied in animal models including some with membrane-active compounds, a few of which prolong the course of infection, and a few others appear to prevent the illness. However, no form of therapy has been effective when given after the disease becomes clinically manifest, and because there is no laboratory test to detect preclinical infection, treatment has been unsuccessful.

Although no humoral or cellular immune response in the infected host has ever been shown to appear, the infectious agent has been considered to be a virus or virus-like agent. Hence, the first drugs to be tried were immunosuppresants, steroids, anti-lymphocytic serum and archis oil, immunomodulating drugs, interferon, interferon inducers; immunostimulants, vaccine virus, BCG, and bacterial polysaccharides. For viral infections, amantadine, cytosine and adenosine arabinoside, phosphonacetic acid, sodium butyrate, sodium thiocyanate, and many other drugs were tried on SEs.

Therapeutic trials with antiviral drugs in CJD have been limited by the rarity of CJD cases and none have yielded reproducible success. The first antiviral drug to be used was amantadine on seven patients, and reports were published between 1971 and 1979. Two of the patients experienced a temporary clinical improvement and two showed permanent improvement. One of these two patients died five years later with unrelated causes, and the fate of the other is not known. The problem with the living patient lies in that neuropathological diagnosis has not been verified and the clinical history suggests it is not CJD. These early successes were not repeated and the drug is no longer considered worthy of attention.

There are reports of a patient being treated with vidarabine, who benefited from transient symptomatic remission on each of the five occasions when the drug was used, but then progressively deteriorated, and died nine months later. Recently a patient with a mild impairment of memory, speech and co-ordination, whose mother had died of CJD, was treated with a transfer factor, and has shown some clinical improvement.

Over the past many years, a number of chemotherapeutic agents have also been used to treat experimental scrapie and CJD. The trials included many drugs active against known infections; niclosamide, diiodohydroxyquin, chloroquin, metronidazole, amphotericin B, griseofulvin, sinefungin, tetracycline, sulphamethoxazole, trimethoprim, thiamphenicol, rifampicin and many others which are know to have some activity agent.

In the literature of the last few years, isolated cases of CJD have been reported to have improved after treatment with amantadine hydrochloride (Sanders, 1979). Following treatment with amantadine hydrochloride, a transient improvement in the patient's wakefulness and mentality, and EEG changes have been observed (Braham, 1971), although amantadine did not ensure a longer survival than that obtained with no therapy (Terzano et al, 1983).

First CJD Case Report in Germany in the 1920s

Jakob's first case was a 52 year old housewife who, without previous medical history, complained of cramps and aching of legs and feet for a few years. The year before her illness, her son had died and she became depressed, tired, dizzy and forgetful. The pains and numbness of her legs lessened, but she developed a spastic ataxic gait. She became unable to stand and walk. A state of fright and delirious confusion appeared. In the final stages, disorientation and dementia accompanied by loss of voice (aphonia), difficulty in swallowing (dysphagia) and other bulbar symptoms developed. She died after about a year of the illness. Syphilitic infection was considered but rejected, and the paper was published under the title, "The disorder was diagnosed as disseminated Encephalomyelopathy, spastic pseudo-sclerosis".

Over the years, a number of papers on further cases were published. The observations emphasised variations of clinical and neurological stages in these cases. Similar symptoms might have occurred in one or the other order, but overall similarities were apparent. Aronyk et al (1984), described a CJD case in a 68 year old female. She developed apraxia of the left hand and intermittent partial elementary motor seizures in the left upper extremity. Within a few weeks, her mental status had begun to decline, and her left-sided seizures had become almost constant. She became increasingly lethargic and finally went into partial or complete unconsciousness (stuporous). Her seizures remained primarily left sided. Her head and eyes deviated to the left, and rhythmical twitching involved the left side of the face, left arm and leg. Occasional myoclonic jerks of the right arm were observed. No spontaneous movements other than the seizure activity were recorded. Muscle tone was generally reported to be increased, while cranial nerve examination revealed intact brain stem function. The first EEG showed a diffused slowing with periodic lateralised epileptiform discharges while a repeat EEG after three weeks revealed prominent bilateral discharges on a background of diffused slowing. The patient remained in a vegetative state for about six months after the start of her problems. CJD was confirmed by biopsy.

In two familial cases of CJD, a woman with diabetes developed generalised malaise in July, 1985, and over the next three months, she became demented and increasingly ataxic. Within six months, the patient became incontinent and was confined to bed, unable to recognise family and friends. Records of family history revealed that her paternal grandfather, father, two parental uncles and three cousins had suffered from progressive dementia. Her 59 year old sister, about three years later, complained of blurred vision, and became forgetful. Within two weeks, she was ataxic and had imperfect articulation of speech due to disturbances of muscular control (dysarthric); at six weeks she was confined to bed and was unable to feed herself. Myoclonus was not shown to have developed in these patients. The serial electroencephalograms which were performed late in their illness which failed to show periodic sharp wave complexes. All members were farmers and ate a homemade sausage containing hog brain.

Selected confirmed Case Reports

Female, 60: duration of illness: 5 months. Before her illness the patient showed a normal interest in all affairs of the home; no oddness or peculiarity of any manner had ever been noticed. Nineteen years previously, after the birth of her only child, she had pelvic cellulitis. She had complained of miscellaneous pains which were attributed to rheumatism. Her present illness appeared three months prior to hospitalisation, with complaints of dizziness. It was noticed that she had ataxic gait, scanning speech, depression, agitation, forgetfulness and confusion. A diagnosis of disseminated sclerosis was made by the physician. She returned home and developed general muscular weakness, spasticity, exaggerated deep reflexes, and missing abdominal reflexes. She could not walk without assistance. At this stage, mental deterioration was noticed , a period of depression gave way to restlessness and confusion. She would laugh, scream for no reason and spit. She was incontinent of urine and required every care and attention. The mental state was one of confusion and apathy. One minute, she said she had a boy of two and few minutes later, she had two children, a boy and girl. The patient was grossly disoriented in both time and place. She could not recollect her husband's visit a few hours after he had left. She expressed a great desire to go to Egypt, and said that she had just returned from China. She insisted that she was only eight years old. She exhibited uncoordinated movements, constant grimacing, fast progressing dementia, impairment of speech (dysphasia). The progress of the illness was downhill and rapid. She had some difficulty towards the end in swallowing fluids. Death occurred suddenly after about four and half months illness.

Male, 53: duration of illness: 17 months. The patient was first examined at the age of 52. While walking, he found himself unable to walk in a straight line. A week later, he developed double vision seeing two images side by side. He developed ataxic gait, and temporary diplopia progressed to generalised incoordination, imperfect articulation of speech due to disturbances of muscular control resulting from damage to the central or peripheral nervous system

281

(dysarthria), difficulty in swallowing (dysphagia), and tremor. The patient was found to have subsequent impairment of coordination and speech and some suggestion of an involuntary movement of the eyeball (nystagmus), with crying and dizzy spells. Abdominal reflexes were present, and he had overactive tendon reflexes . Generalised rigidity with flexed arms, extended legs, arched neck and back were evident. There is no further record of mental change in this patient.

Female, 66: duration of illness 4 months. Ten weeks before the admission to hospital, she became easily fatigued and short of breath, giddy with slight unsteadiness in walking and subject to double vision at times, particularly in the morning. She occasionally became forgetful. After admission, she became delusioned and disorientated and was unable to recognise her son except for a brief moment. The patient was restless, grimacing, shouting, talking and was quiet for brief periods only. She seemed to hallucinate and spoke as if to domestic animals in the room. She was disorientated, uncooperative, and only occasionally would obey simple commands. She was incontinent of urine and faeces. She moved her limbs freely and no motor abnormality was manifest. The patient gradually grew worse in hospital and no longer spoke coherently although remaining noisy and hyperactive. Late bilateral Babinski reflex, extrapyramidal signs, temporary paralysis of muscles (akinesia) and coma were present.

Female, 41: duration of illness 24 months. The patient was 39 when she first experienced stiffness of the right leg. She then developed an illusion of movement, a sensation as if the external world were revolving around her (vertigo), difficulty in walking and dragging of the right leg. She had a fixed face with weakness of the right side of it Examination revealed an increase in the normal tone of muscles (spasticity) of the affected side with the foot scraping when walking. There was a tendency for the right foot to assume an equinovarous posture. Slight paralysis (paresis) of the affected leg extended to both upper and lower extremities with Parkinsonian rigidity and temporary paralysis of muscles (akinesia). Hyperactive tendon reflexes were present throughout. The patient often complained of dizziness and was emotional, irritable and apprehensive and at times undemonstrative (apathetic). She showed no interest in her surroundings but made great demands on the family. This is a very unusual case because of the familial incidence. Her two brothers aged 32 and 50, also developed the disease with similar patterns, starting from leg complaint.

Female 59: duration of illness 9 months. The patient had after childbirth (postpartum), thrombosis of the leg at the age of 26 and was operated on for a uterine muscular tumor (myoma) and appendicitis. At 43, she suffered a head injury without complications. For a year before her present condition she complained of giddiness, but continued to work normally until the onset of the illness. Apparently otherwise the patient was well, when, for the first time just, before her present illness, she had a peculiar sensation as if her head was "empty or filled with air". She also noticed unsteadiness of gait and difficulty in controlling the movements of her left arm. There was no obvious weakness or loss of sensation. A few days later, she noticed stiffness in her left leg which began to drag while walking, but she was still able to walk with support. She recorded occasional headaches. At this stage, she was hospitalised. Her gait was found insecure, but there was no difficulty with speech. There were notes to suggest moderate paralysis (paresis) in the left abducens, and a moderate aural adaptation, impairment of coordination and speech, and some suggestion of an involuntary movement of the eyeball (nystagmus). There was slight hearing loss, but otherwise the neurological examination showed no abnormalities. Three weeks later, jerky uncontrollable movements in her left arm, were noticed. The motor power in the left arm and leg was reduced, and finger-nose and knee-heel tests showed disturbance of the power to control the range of movement act (dysmetria) in the right arm and leg. Over the next few weeks, the movements of her legs and arm became increasingly clumsy, especially on the left side. The tendon reflexes in the upper extremities were found to be normal. She was only able to stand or walk with support, unsteadily, and with feet wide apart. She had difficulty in finding words to speak although replies were still adequate, and eventually it became difficult to obtain contact with the patient. Two and a half months after hospital admission, she became incontinent of urine and faeces. Gerstmann's syndrome was diagnosed. The patient lost finger power to recognise (agnosia), and was unable to do simple arithmetic calculations (acalculia), and to distinguish between right and left, up and down.

Male 62: duration of illness four months. The patient, a farmer had always been well except for probable epidemic influenza without a sequential outcome, at the age of 21 during military training. He suffered several minor injuries including a head injury without complications. On admission into the hospital for this illness, his physical examination revealed hypertension. He had illusions of movement, sensations as if the external world were revolving around him (vertigo) and nausea, in which he felt "a whirl" in his head, he vomited, became giddy, and had blurred vision. The patient on neurological examination showed no subtle impairment of coordination and speech or involuntary movement of the eyeball (nystagmus), and no paralysis (paresis); all tendon reflexes were normal. He had reduced vision, and appeared senile and absent-minded. With antihypertensive drugs, his blood pressures were controlled, and the patient was discharged from the hospital.

Although his working capacity was reduced, for three years the patient had no complaints. After that, he had an attack in which he became giddy, complained of headaches, and vomited. He gradually became absent-minded and gloomy, and was depressed. Because of his giddiness, he found it difficult to walk. He neglected his drugs and was reported to have blood pressure of 215/100 mm. A diagnosis of essential hypertension and cerebral arteriosclerosis was made. Ten days later, the patient had a fall and started to have an episode of transient confusion which occurred at night. He felt very giddy and had jerks in his left arm. On readmission, he was found to have aged suddenly. Except for the mental status,

283

the neurological examination revealed no abnormalities in the motor power, coordination, and eye movements. But there were no muscular atrophies and no fibrillation or local contraction of muscle visible through the skin (fasciculations). Over the next few weeks, the patient became increasingly confused and restless. His conversation was incoherent and he reacted when spoken to, while he still knew his date of birth correctly. He became incontinent of urine. The tendon reflexes were present and equal. There was muscular rigidity, generalised shock-like contractions of a portion of a muscle tremor (myoclonia) and then jerky spasms in the extremities. Babinski's sign was occasionally reported. The patient had convulsive seizures and died four months after the onset of his second bout of symptoms.

Male 59: duration of illness 16 months. The patient had previously been fit and well in the past. In his family history, his sister was diagnosed as alcoholic and psychotic, while other two sisters and three brothers were well. His mother had died of old age while in a state of dementia (diagnosed as arteriosclerotic in nature). The patient had always been considered to have erratic behaviour, unreliable in his carpentry trade and prone to alcoholic excesses. At the age of 58, it was noted that he could not concentrate and became forgetful and appeared to be preoccupied. Soon thereafter, he found difficulty in swallowing food and talking. Over the next few months, he became disorientated, confused, depressed and unable to talk. Speech was limited to an incomprehensible muttering. Nine months from the start of his symptoms, he was admitted to hospital where he was found to have weakness of his arms, atrophy and fibrillation of the interosseus muscles and increased deep reflexes. He had inconsistent Babinski sign on the left and was unable to talk or swallow. Mentally, the patient appeared confused, disorientated for time and place and depressed. He had frequent explosive attacks of laughter and crying. Routine laboratory studies were essentially negative. He lost a lot of weight and was clinically diagnosed as Psychosis with another disease of the nervous system viz., amyotrophic lateral sclerosis.

Male 46: duration of illness 14 months. The patient was a quiet, reserved, highly intelligent telephone executive. There was no family history of mental disorder; mother and two siblings were still alive while the father had died of a heart disease. Six months before admission to the hospital, the first manifestations of the disease in the patient were impairment of recent memory, lack of feeling (apathy), tiredness and occasional disorientation. Over the next three months, the mental state became increasingly more confused. It has been recorded that he had vague delusions. The patient believed he was back in the army service. Soon after, he became impotent and developed delusions of infidelity. On admission, he showed marked loss of memory, poor insight and impairment of judgment. However, physically, he appeared normal and there were no special preoccupations, obsessions or hallucinations. All laboratory tests were negative. Cortical biopsy performed revealed marked degeneration of the neurons. The patient underwent a marked deterioration in the processes of memory and learning.

284

He became restless, depressed and in the last two months of his life, he had difficulty in swallowing, and developed a fine tremor of hand and unsteady gait. His speech became almost incomprehensible and he died 14 months from the onset of his illness.

Male 50: duration of illness six months. The patient had been in good health and was considered as a pleasant, conscientious and intelligent person by his employer and family. He was a well developed, well-nourished and powerfully built man of medium height with no past medical history. However, five years before the present illness, the vision in his right eye became impaired for about three weeks which was attributed to retinal haemorrhage. There was no family history of any neurological disorder. About three months before his admission to hospital, he began to complain of feeling "run down" and tired, and became unusually irritable. He continued to go to work, but the efficiency and quality of his work deteriorated. He accomplished little or nothing and it seemed to his employer as though he no longer knew what to do or what was required of him. He lost interest in newspapers, radio, and never initiated conversation. He displayed fits of violent temper without any provocation. Over the following few weeks, he felt a "tight feeling" in his face on the right side and "numbness" of his right arm and leg. He developed unsteady gait. At the time of admission to the hospital, his physical condition was found to be good. His gait was found to be ataxic, more marked on the right side with no ataxia on the heel-to-knee test bilaterally. There were no reflex changes and sensation was recorded as intact everywhere. Unsteadiness in his walking gradually became worse and in the next four weeks, numbness also appeared in the left arm and leg. At this time, incoordination was noted equally on the right and left side. The patient appeared well orientated and gave a good account of his own illness to the physician and was not grossly demented. However, his attention span was limited. He could not, or would not do simple arithmetic calculations, his memory of a recent meal was imperfect. He could not describe the nature of his occupation. Although there was no imperfect articulation of speech, due to disturbances of the muscular control which results from the damage to central or peripheral nervous system (dysarthria) or well-defined aphasic disorder, his speech was impaired in such a way that he would frequently block in the middle of the sentence and be unable to continue. He showed no anxiety or concern about his illness; on the contrary, he was facetious, and he often smiled or laughed without reason. He could sit up in his bed, but was unable to stand or walk without help. There was no weakness or disturbances in his muscle tone in any part of the body. His poor performance of the finger-to-nose test was attributed to lateral ataxia. On some occasions, his hand would come to rest in a position some 12 to 14 inches in front of his face and be held there for a period of one minute. Frequently, the extraneous movements that were observed during the performance of this test had the character of conscious perversions, an example of which included was that the manoeuvres of this type included thrusting his finger into the examiner's eye,

285

followed by mischievous laughter. From the time of admission, the patient's behaviour became increasingly bizarre. The awareness and activities fluctuated with episodes of crying, incoherent shouting, violent laughter and wild thrashing about in bed. His speech disturbance became more and more pronounced until finally he was virtually mute. He became incontinent of urine and faeces. Eventually, he became comatose before his death.

Female 58: duration of illness eight months. The patient was in good health prior to the present illness. About 10 years earlier, a hysterectomy for uterine myoma was performed and then, one year before clinical onset of the CJD, she underwent a vaginal plastic operation. Both operations were uneventful. Four weeks before her admission to the hospital, she was seen in the Out Patients Clinic because of her onset of blurred vision and forgetfulness. Although the patient appeared depressed, her neurological examination was normal. Her physician suggested that she might be beginning of an involutional depression. In the next four weeks, the patient's difficulties increased. Objects seemed small and distant and not where they really were. Walking became difficult and the patient would frequently fall. There were intermittent paresthesias of her right arm and hand. There was a feeling of constriction around her head, but no headache. The patient became more forgetful and often did not complete a sentence. Her gait became unsteady and steered to her right. She would not cooperate sufficiently to perform a formal examination of her vision. Subsequently, confusion and loss of intellectual function appeared to increase. Her speech began to diminish spontaneously, and became unintelligible consisting of jargon. The patient became agitated and psychotic and developed paranoid delusions and visual hallucinations. She became incontinent of urine and faeces and essentially helpless. She became bedridden and had to be nourished by nasogastric tube till her death.

Male 38: duration of illness six months. The patient was a stable married man with two children and had worked for 20 years in the General Post Office as a sorter. He had sustained severe burns of the legs following an explosion of an incendiary bomb during the war. There was no family history of nervous mental disorder. About two to three months before the patient was admitted to the hospital, he became forgetful, experienced difficulty in concentration and could not cope with his work. He became irritable, suffered from headaches, his vision began to fail. On admission, the patient was reported to be confused, disorientated and suffering from memory defect. All tendon reflexes were found to be exaggerated but the plantar responses were flexor. There was no gross ataxia. According to the physician, the patient was difficult to examine owing to rapidly developing dementia. His condition deteriorated rapidly and he died six months after the onset of the symptoms. Histopathological examination of the brain did not reveal senile plaques or Alzheimer's neurofibril changes.

Female 47: duration of illness 10 months. She was healthy for many years before her present illness. She noticed intermittent blanching of her fingers and toes, which was diagnosed as Raynaud's disease (circulatory vascular disorder). The present illness started with the patient experiencing episodes of mental confusion to the extent that she often lost her way on returning from work. Two months later, she was forced to give up her job as a saleslady. She was admitted to hospital seven months after the first episode of confusion. Her general physical examination suggested no abnormalities. Mental status revealed disorientation, memory loss, visual and auditory hallucinations. She persevered with reading, but did not understand what she read. She had right left disorientation, impairment of the ability to do mathematical problems (dyscalculia), her fingers lost the power to react to sensory stimuli (agnosia), and omitted the left side while drawing a clock. There were no other neurological signs. All laboratory examinations were within the normal range. A diagnosis of presenile dementia with biparietal syndrome was made. She has been described as alternately restless and pathetic, giggling inappropriately. She lost weight and during her last two months her condition deteriorated rapidly and she became bedridden. Two days before her death she lapsed into stupor, accompanied by nuchal (back of the neck) rigidity, bilateral horizontal nystagmus and bronchopneumonia. Histopathologically diffused status spongiosus involving all layers of cortex were the striking find. No senile plaques or neurofibrillary changes were observed.

Female 56: duration of illness five months. The symptoms appeared after a series of dental extractions two months before hospital admission. One month prior to hospitalisation she lost her sight completely. Examination revealed the patient to be confused, irrational and intermittently combative. She could say only "mama" and "papa", and had to be spoon fed, although physical examination showed no abnormalities. There were purposeless movements of the upper extremities, and facial grimacing. Both arms were rigidly maintained in flexion and her lower extremities were extended, so that the patient assumed a "decorticate" posture. Examination of blood and cerebrospinal fluid revealed no abnormality. The patient became progressively less responsive, exhibiting almost continuous sudden jerking movements of the head, trunk and upper extremities. The clinical diagnosis of undifferentiated psychosis was made. The duration of her illness due to bronchopneumonia lasted five months. Neuropathologically, widespread degeneration with status spongiosus accompanied by a sparse astrocytic response was reported, barely visible in the second and third cortical laminae.

Male 53: duration of illness 36 months. The patient was well developed and nourished. Several weeks before hospital admission he was noticed limping and she became aware of a definite weakness of his left leg and inability to move his toes. His general physical examination at the time of hospital admission was negative. The neurological examination revealed hyperactive deep tendon reflexes in the left lower extremity, associated with positive Babinski sign, with diminished abdominal reflexes on the effected side. The clinical diagnosis of amyotrophic lateral sclerosis was made.

A year later the patient began to experience episodes of mental confusion. The weakness had progressed to involve all limbs, and he required crutches to walk. Local contraction of muscles visible through the skin (fasciculations), were present. In addition, blurry signs of imperfect articulation of speech due to disturbances of the muscular control which results from the damage to the central or peripheral nervous system (dysarthria), difficulty in swallowing (dysphagia), and drooling developed. He was intermittently incontinent. The patient died three years from the start of his illness. Microscopic diffused degenerative changes were seen throughout the cerebral cortex.

Male 53: duration of illness five months. About a year before his illness, an engineer was admitted to hospital with the complaint that he had been experiencing numerous brief attacks of fright associated with sweating for three years. Also, he had occasional convulsive seizures and noticed some difficulty in naming objects. He had been a heavy drinker. He had suffered from gout since the age of 38. There was no significant family history. His medical examination revealed that the only abnormal sensory signs, which were slightly increased, were the tendon-jerks in the right limbs. His mental status was reported to be normal while a minimal degree of impairment of speech (dysphasia) was present. Ventriculography showed displacement of the left temporal horn. When operated, a meningioma weighing 28 grams was removed. Post-operative, the degree of impairment of speech (dysphasia) was temporarily increased, but on discharge, it had improved. His spontaneous speech was good but he could only read the simplest words. Some eight months later, for no obvious reasons, he fell and fractured his big toe. Two weeks later, he complained that he could not see well and the objects looked distorted or appeared to "come at him". In the next four to six weeks, he gave up the light work he was doing and became unable to read newspapers. His gait became unsteady and his hands clumsy, first the left, then the right. He began to sleep during the day, and was restless at night. He was no longer able to walk, and had slurred and jerky speech. He eventually became blind. Jerky involuntary movements of the upper limbs and especially fingers, were frequently observed. He became confused and disorientated. His speech was unintelligible and he lay quietly, with sudden jerky movements of his left hand and fingers. His head or eyes also turned to the left. The tendon-jerks were not observed. Tapping of his forehead caused contractions. The patient went into a coma and the limbs became flaccid and tendon reflexes could not be elicited. The patient died five months from the onset of the illness.

Female 55: duration of illness 22 months. The patient had had a cerebral thrombosis two years previously and, after a fall, developed an illness which exhibited a rapid deterioration in memory. She became clumsy when using her hands and the left hand especially had myoclonic jerks. Two weeks before her admission to the hospital, she complained of "feeling queer" and her speech was noticed to be slurred. She had a fall during the night, which she could, next morning not remember. She also complained of double vision for several days after the fall. As a child she had had rheumatic carditis. During examination for her present illness, she was found to have an upper motor neuron weakness of the left side of the face and arms. Sensation was found to be normal and the visual field was reported to be full. She showed some improvement in the strength of her arms and was discharged from the hospital. At home, she had two falls. Her gait was noticed to be unsteady but seemed to improve. Soon the problem reccurred, and while walking she swayed in one or other direction. She became unable to walk. She was orientated and alert but restless. A marked deterioration in her memory, particularly of recent events, was noticed. She lost weight, and gross ataxia was observed when attempting to walk. Almost purposeless "plucking" movements were also reported in the upper limbs, especially on the left and occasional myoclonic twitches of the left shoulder. She became drowsy and incontinent, deeply unconscious, and her breathing became stertorous and later periodic. She died about 11 weeks after the onset of her final illness.

Female 57: duration of illness three months. The patient had a past history of migraine with left-sided headaches and vomiting attacks. For the past ten years, she had had none of these attacks. While on holiday, she noticed an impairment in the control of her left hand, and appeared irritable. Ten days after her return home, she became subject to unaccountable fluctuations of mood, referred to as "tantrums". She was noticed to be negligent. Her left arm became progressively weaker so that she could not raise it or tie the ends of her pyjama cord. She complained of "muzziness behind her eyes". She denied any loss of vision, but was noticed to grope for the door, and at the table to feel for her food on the plate with her left hand. Two weeks later, she had to be fed, dressed and assisted wherever she went. Emotional and mental deterioration was noticed. There were occasional rapid jerk-like movements of short duration. Her speech seems to have stayed remarkably clear but she took a long time to answer simple questions. Like many other patients recorded here, she was not incontinent. Her posture was noticed to become more fixed. The arms were held in a position of abduction with the elbows fixed or extended while the hands were clenched. Her head was noticed to be slightly extended at the neck. Her legs were in a position of moderate flexion at the hip, knees and ankles. Any disturbance or handling of the patient resulted in an immediate further accession of muscular tone. Involuntary movements were reported from time to time consisting of isolated myoclonic twitching involving proximal limb segments, mainly the arms. This stage was followed by a period of delirium associated with hallucinations and fear, and she went into coma. She died 12 weeks after the onset of her illness.

Male 61: duration of illness two months. The patient, a civil servant, enjoyed good health, apart from a history of pulmonary tuberculosis. Some six years later, he was "all mixed up" and could not think clearly to accomplish his work. On his return home, his wife did not notice anything abnormal in her husband. He appeared in good physical health. A week later, he complained to a doctor that he was feeling muddled-up and had a slight sense of instability.

Three weeks later, members of his family noticed that he was experiencing lapses of memory, and at the same time, he complained, his eyes were "not clear". In the hospital examination, he was noticed to have myoclonic jerking of the left arm and to a lesser extent, of the left foot. He could not maintain the position of his left arm in an outstretched position. The patient became disorientated and confused . Coarse action tremor was now experienced in the left upper limb, and myoclonic jerking previously noticed became more evident. There was no impairment of coordination of the eyeball (nystagmus), and no imperfect articulation of speech (dysarthria). Over the next few days, his awareness was found to vary and it was noticed, at times he could recognise relatives and nurses. At times, he was able to conduct simple conversations, and at other times, he was reported to be very restless and deluded. The myoclonic jerking was now noticed to extend to the limbs of the right side. Two weeks later, these myoclonic movements were recorded in the muscles of the mandibles and the neck. The patient died two months from the start of his illness.

Male 58: duration of illness four months. The patient was taken ill five days after two teeth were removed under gas. He was well except for a discharge of pus from dental wound (pyorrhoea alveolaris). He made a normal and rapid recovery from the anaesthesia, and walked home. Five days later, he complained of a feeling of muzziness in the head, especially on turning the head quickly. He also experienced aching in the back of the head, the neck, and across the shoulders. He was unable to sleep. Two days later, he was bothered with involuntary movements of the limbs, more especially when he lay in bed. He complained of the feeling that his legs or arms would "shoot out quickly" and when he dozed off, his limbs would jump and waken him up. Two weeks after the first extraction, a further six teeth were removed (under gas) with no change in his general condition. When he returned to work, he noticed his movements were very slow and he had difficulty in walking as he kept "losing balance". Jerking of his limbs was so bad at night that he slept in a separate bed from his wife.

Six weeks from the start of his illness, his memory began to fail. He could not remember events which had occurred a few minutes earlier. He complained of being muddled, could not remember the day of the week, and could not sign his name. He could not remember the names of his friends or recognise them. He would forget to shave. He was unable to dress. Mental deterioration progressed, walking became more uncertain, and he had to use a stick. He received electroconvulsive therapy. His condition seemed to have deteriorated, he failed to touch his nose, his answers to all questions were "No". His legs were held in an extended position, but he would flex them on command. The tendon jerks were noted to be brisk and equal, and the plantar responses flexor. Frequently, diverse non-rhythmic small myoclonic twitches were seen in the fingers, hands and arms, varying in distribution and in the muscles. Spontaneous, purposeful voluntary movements were well coordinated. A week later, he did not appear to recognise his wife, and became inarticulate. Both arms were outstretched on command while his right arm showed "flapping" movements. Gradually, the patient passed into a "pseudo-wakeful state," his posture became more fixed with arms and legs extended. He remained in this condition for 12 days till his death.

Male 53: duration of illness two months. The patient was a family man in good health six weeks before admission to the hospital. He developed double-vision and appeared to be depressed. He had an illusion of movement, a sensation as if the external world were revolving around him (vertigo). Two weeks later, some ataxia was noticed. He became forgetful, drowsy and also started dropping things. He slept most of the time. Over the next two weeks he became confused. The symptoms of dementia were progressing so rapidly that he was admitted to a local hospital. He had lost a stone in weight. Mild weakness was noted in all four limbs. At times he appeared agitated, anxious and hallucinated. At nights, he attempted to get out of bed, and twice fell to the floor but there were no injuries. The patient became incontinent of urine at times. At this stage he started to get more aggressive. He refused to take fluids. He became very confused, had violent outbursts, and became very difficult to control, requiring sedation in the first few days of his admission. Diagnosis of CJD was considered. EEG records showed a severe diffused slow wave abnormality with loss of the normal background rhythm. There were virtually persistent periodic sharply contoured discharges which were widely spread, but mostly constant in the left frontal region. The repeats of EEG a week later showed more prominent recordings than the previous one and confirmed a diagnosis of CJD. No other laboratory tests showed any abnormality. His condition gradually deteriorated over the next few days and the patient died about nine weeks from the onset of his illness.

Kuru

Kuru, a rare exotic disease only found in a small region south and east of Mount Michael, New Guinea, has been classified as one of the slow virus infections - as spongiform encephalopathy (SEs). Histopathological changes induced are similar to those seen in CJD, scrapie and BSE. These disorders are grouped together because of the striking similarly microscopical histopathological vacuolation in the neurons. Kuru was the first fatal degenerative CNS disease of man with an incubation period measured in years. Understanding of kuru has brought us a considerable insight into many human and animal diseases including Alzheimer's disease (AD).

These transmission studies suggest that the viruses of all of the SEs, human or animal, are not only closely related, but are in fact different strains of a single virus which has been modified in different hosts. The passage of sheep scrapie into other sheep and goats has been shown by inoculation and by feeding with contaminated material such as placenta and embryonic membrane (Pattison, et al, 1972). It is believed that cannibalistic ritual was the sole mode of transmission of kuru from man to man by somewhat similar methods as scrapie. The original source of contamination may have been a spontaneous case of CJD (Gajdusek, 1976).

Discovery of Kuru

Gajdusek as a medical researcher based in Melbourne, Australia visited New Guinea and New Britain in 1956. While there he learned of kuru from Dr. Zigas, and saw a few cases. Interested in the disease, he decided to investigate it further. He realised that it was a unique and unprecedented disease and a suitable explanation was required. He was so determined to find the cause and cure, or a way to control the incidence of the disease, that he even considered flying several patients with interpreters to the National Institute of Health (NIH) in the USA. At that time, he thought kuru was a new epidemic syndrome of some sort of Parkinsonism, spinal ataxia or a hereditary cerebellar ataxia, and wrote "It is the work that I must go on with, but since I left, Sir Mac has converted most of the institute work to this type of auto-immune study,.."

Dr. Gajdusek noticed one of the guides demonstrating a first stage of Kuru.

Accompanied by a number of local youths on an expedition in March, 1960, Gajdusek noticed that one of the boys, Azibara, was shivering and shaking, demonstrating a late first stage of kuru. It was noted by Gajdusek that Azibara, although suffering from kuru and with his fate sealed, still insisted on making this last expedition "It was his last wish." Later he found Kageinaro - another of his carrier boys - dying of kuru.

Kuru is a rapidly developing chronic neurological disease with a degenerative pathology, found exclusively among the Fore people in the Highland rain forests of New Guinea. The presence of kuru in the Eastern Highlands of New Guinea was already known from earlier Government anthropological surveys carried out by anthropologist Charles Julius in the early 1950s. The disease has great similarities with "classical advancing Parkinsonism" to be seen in whole groups of well nourished healthy people, and was considered a very peculiar syndrome. Kuru with unusually high incidence resembled paralysis and was predominantly seen in young children of both sexes and young adult females but was present in all age groups. Gajdusek and Zigas first described the disease in 1957.

The disease was to be found in the highlands and a number of adjacent valleys, 160 villages with a total population of just over 35,000 in the interior of Papua New Guinea. In the Fore cultural and linguistic group, among whom over 80% of the kuru cases occurred, the incidence rate and prevalence ratio was about 1% of the population. A small group of 700 Lagaria people who had migrated to this region east of Mt. Michael several generations ago and extensively intermarried with the native Fore were also affected with kuru.

Kuru, a major cause of death among the Fore people

Kuru was undoubtedly considered a major disease and the most likely cause of death after warfare wounds amongst the Fore people. Natives during the 1950s were very familiar with kuru. Their diagnosis of the disease was considered as reliable as medical appraisal, especially in their capacity of spot early cases reliably. According to the natives, kuru had been known for at least two decades in some villages, and had spread to several adjacent ones in the previous decade. In family histories, the father would describe multiple cases of kuru and deaths from other causes including spear wounds, arrow wounds and old age. He was able to account for one to two family generations but no more within his immediate families. By this technique, Gajdusek collected data and thought it would be possible to find kuru in parents, siblings, children, aunts, uncles and cousins. In adolescence the female-male ratio was lower, of the order of nearly 1:1. In adults the female-male ratio was about 4:1. This marked excess of deaths of adult females over males had led to a male-to-female ratio of over 3:1 in some villages, and 2:1 for the whole South Fore group. The authors in their first report described 114 cases of kuru, based on epidemiological and clinical observation, suggesting a possible genetic cause. In the early years of kuru investigation, the disease was increasingly distorting the sex ratio.

A few families were recorded where two or more siblings died of kuru, as were families, where both parents were affected and two or more children died at the same age. This caused Gajdusek to think that kuru was probably a hereditary ataxia.

Local names and Beliefs about cause of Kuru

The two medical officers tracked miles of mountain learning about the mysterious fatal neurological disease which local people called "kuru", meaning "to be afraid" and "to shiver". It was also known as "tavaravain avie" another term for shivering, and "kogaisa en avie" meaning possessed by "kogaisa". Kogaisa is a tall, broad leafed plant whose leaves tremble in a breeze, suggestive of the tremors of the Kuru-affected patient. The Fore believed that if a pregnant woman breaks this plant, she will be visited by a "dream man", and subsequently deliver a child suffering from kuru.

The Fore tribe believed the disease was caused by evil sorcery cast by their enemies because of inter-tribal animosity. From time to time, they held meetings to find ways to stop the sorcery, but when kuru continued, they suspected the other side of cheating, and their bitterness grew intense. Thus the animosity between these tribes continued to grow. Kuru magic was traditionally regarded as the province of the Fore people. The neighbouring people who suffered from kuru, blamed Fore sorcery.

Origin and spread of Kuru

Kuru is a naturally occurring infectious disease, related to a biologically active replicating agent. The disease it initiated, was not an artificial disease of the mind. Since kuru was common in children and young adults of both sexes and adult females but rare in adult males, Gajdusek considered kuru to be a sex-linked genetic or endocrine disorder.

Unique epidemiological findings and changes in kuru over the past four decades have given an insight into the spread of the disease. The mourning family group would open the skull of the dead victim in a rite of cannibalism, during which all the girls, women, babes-in-arms, and toddlers of the kuru victim's family were unwittingly contaminated with the virus (Gajdusek, 1972; 1973; 1959-1977). With the cessation of cannibalism, the disease is gradually disappearing and has already disappeared in children with progressively increasing age.

The crucial question relating to the origin and mode of transmission of the agent of SEs in the Fore people still remains unanswered. It is believed that kuru first appeared among the Fore in the early years of this century, gradually increased and reached epidemic proportions by the middle of the 1950's. Was there a spontaneous sporadic case of CJD in New Guinea which produced a unique epidemic? There is a report of a spontaneous case of CJD in a 26 year old native of Chimbu, New Guinea from the central Highlands (Gajdusek, 1977). Another anecdote tells of an immigrant from Europe who died of sporadic CJD, and as a mark of respect, was consumed, infecting the tribe.

The mode of dissemination or maintenance of the virus in the tribe might have been cannibalism. This would explain the long term survival of the viral agent which produced a unique epidemic. Multiple inoculations of the brain occurred in successive victims by cannibalistic rituals. The serial passages through humans might have resulted in mutation and selection from the original strain of the agent.

Europeans in small numbers had been in contact with Fore people since the early 1930s, while hunting for gold. The Australian Government established their first patrol post in the region in 1952. A few early reports of the disease were made in 1953 in patrol officers reports. Kuru has been referred to as skin guria in Pidgin English. The disease became known to the government officers as "shaking disease", and recognised as a major disease in the area.

Between 1951 and 1953, Dr. and Mrs. R. M. Berndt, doing anthropological work in the linguistic blocs of Kamano, Usurufa, Jate and Fore, reported the illness among the Fore, Usurufa, and Jate people. Further data on anthropological studies, had revealed that the disease had been present for nearly 30 years, by a conservative estimate, long before any European contacts. It is believed that kuru first appeared among the Fore and speard to their immediate neighbours. Gajdusek recorded that 10,000 out of a total 15,000 population were Fore natives, and the disease was found in every village inhabited by them. It has been suggested that during the early years of this century, the incidence of the disease gradually increased, eventually reaching epidemic proportions by the middle of the 1950's. Gajdusek and Zigas, after conducting exhaustive epidemiological investigations in 1957, and carefully crosschecking the pooled information, documented that at least 300 deaths had occurred in the preceding five years in the region. According to their calculations, 1% of the population died yearly from the disease, while in some Fore tribes, it reached 5 to 10 per cent. This single disorder was probably the highest natural cause of death ever recorded in any population, and in some of these tribal communities, over 50% of deaths were due to kuru. There is no record of any other disease in the history of mankind anywhere in the world having such a devastating effect on a small population.

Self diagnosis

In most cases, the patient would himself diagnose his illness before his friends became aware of his illness. A remarkable aspect in the communities was the extraordinary good spirited fatalism with which the patient and his relatives came to terms with the disease. Patients knew, they were dying, since they so frequently saw the terminal stages of the disease in others and, yet they could face their advancing illness without apparent anxiety. They would laugh at their own stumbling gait and falls, their clumsiness, their inability to get food into their mouth, and their exaggerated involuntary movements.

Their kinsmen would join them. Family members would live with the dying patient, siblings slept closely huddled together, and husbands would lie patiently beside their terminally uncommunicative, incontinent, foul-smelling spouses. It might be that they abandoned such supportive measures as feeding, washing and bringing the patient out into the sunlight, but they never ceased to give strong emotional support and security. The patients themselves had accepted the inevitable fact of impending death from the onset of the illness with equanimity.

Clinical picture

At first sight kuru appeared a strange disorder, somewhat similar to paralysis, which was possibly not previously recognised by the medical profession; a new subacute, familial, degenerative disease of the CNS, affecting children, adult males and predominantly adult females. Kuru, the disease found originally only in the Fore linguistic tribe, had also spread to their immediate neighbours, with whom they intermarried, and caused half of all their total deaths.

The diagnosis of the disorder, which at first sight looked more hysterical, appeared unique and the progress predictable. So it was hard to believe that it could be anything other than a progressive neurological disease. The shaking of the body resembled the classical advancing Parkinsonism syndrome seen in old age in developed countries. However, the true sporadic cases of Parkinsonism and typical paralysis were also known in some parts of New Guinea. The occurrence of familial cases suggested that kuru could be Wilson's disease, or akin to it, that is a known familial disease, usually starting in young adults, and showing signs and symptoms of degeneration of the cerebral cortex, basal ganglia, and cerebellum. Although clinically the disease was closely akin to Wilson's hepatolenticular degeneration, liver involvement was not observed in any of the kuru patients. Similar neurological manifestations were, to some extent, also seen in manganese (Hunter et al, 1954), and chronic mercury poisoning.

Symptoms of Kuru

The medical officers interviewed many patients and relatives of patients suffering from kuru, following self-diagnosis of the disease. The clinical course and the uniqueness of the disease were well established after the investigation of several hundred patients. Kuru appeared remarkably uniform, with cerebellar symptoms progressing to total incapacitation and death within three to nine months. In obtaining the clinical history of the onset of kuru, Gajdusek often recorded that many patients made no complaint of malaise, neck stiffness, or vomiting, but many did have a very definite story of severe irregular headaches for a few days prior to the kuru symptomatology being clinically recognised. The clinical course has been conveniently divided into three stages: first stage - ambulant; secondary, and terminal.

The first stage of the disease as reported by Gajdusek

The illness usually started on an afebrile course, followed by development of a striking uncoordinated gait (ataxia). About one-third of the patients also reported headache and knee pains. However, where knee pain was associated with the onset, it rarely persisted for longer than a few weeks. This was followed by subsidence of headache, but the patients developed ataxia, and later tremors were reported in these cases. In many, however, there were no complaints of malaise or symptoms suggestive of an acute event; no lack of physical or intellectual power or any other illness such as stiff neck, convulsions, coma or even moderate interference with normal activities. None of the patients observed recent weight loss, nor was there any suggestion of acute onset of infectious encephalitic disease.

On examination of the abdomen, there was no hepatomegaly or spleenomegaly. No evidence of systemic disease involving any of the organs was ever found. As the disease progressed, the ataxia became more marked with awkward placement of the feet, and a swaying and weaving gait, causing the patient to trip and stumble. This phase was known as "loose knees." As ataxia became gradually more severe, a distinctive tremor became apparent. The tremor was first usually of fine quality and irregular, at a rate of approximately two or three per second. Later, the tremors became characteristic in that they were closely associated with the muscle groups used to maintain posture. Therefore, in attempt to maintain balance when standing, these patients would grip their toes and claw the ground more than usual and often stamp their feet. This incoordination affected the lower extremities first, then progressed to the upper extremities. A useful diagnostic test for this was the Rhomberg test, where the muscles of feet and legs show exaggeration when the patient tries to stand on one foot for many seconds. It was noted that the patient first lost the ability to stand on one foot with eyes closed, and subsequently, could not stand on one foot even with his eyes open. Kuru patients were asked to execute a finger-to-nose test, which revealed very marked excessive tremors of the outstretched arms, which persisted until the finger came to rest on the nose where it stabilised and was supported. Gajdusek recorded that he could succeed in almost totally abolishing their tremors by cuddling young violently trembling patients tightly in his arms and restraining their heads and extremities against his body.

Hearing in these kuru patients remained normal. Examination of the eyes revealed no abnormalities other than the uncontrollable deviation. This first appeared late in the illness, although vision remained normal. When severe tremors were present, the patient had difficulty in maintaining a fixed gaze, and his glance tended to shift about rapidly and irregularly. The tongue protruded but positioned normally, and showed no fibrillation or tremors. However, if carefully observed in the late stage of illness, quick shock-like jerking movements of the protruded tongue were noted. The optic nerve fundi remained normal. The involuntary tremor and incoordination continued to increase.

The second stage of the disease

The second stage was reached when the patient could no longer walk without complete support. The ataxia progressed and became characterised by severe involvement of the trunk and head as well as the arms and legs. As is typical of a gradual oncoming paralysis, the patients required the support of a stick for walking. The patient from time to time walked about with the help of a stick, unaided by others. However, it was noticed that some of the severe cases who were unable to walk and showed extreme tremors one day, would walk nervously the next day without a sign of the disease. Possibly, some of the advanced symptoms of patients temporarily reversed overnight. This did not mean that the patient had recovered. Gajdusek described a group of kuru patients together as a 'real sight', they looked more hysterical than afflicted by an organic disease. Any attempt to control the tremors in a patient produced a fixed pained face, showing slow, clumsy, voluntary movements. Symptoms were less evident while the patient was resting, and completely disappeared during sleep. Any slight provocation or sudden shift of one part of the body often produced a violent tremor of the entire body, combined with a marked emotional hilarity and foolish laughter. This is not a feature recorded in true Parkinsonism.

As the tremors became more severe and rather coarse in quality, they interfered with eating and fine motor performance involving hands or feet. A continual wide variety of rapid, highly complex, partly coordinated, jerky movements might enter into the involuntary movements and tremors (choreiform jerks). This was particularly noticeable when patients tried to get up from a recumbent or sitting posture. The patient might remain sedentary, but still moderately well integrated in the native society, sitting outside the house, and half-carried to attend pig feasts or other social functions. The condition invariably deteriorated rapidly until the patient could no longer balance, even in the sitting posture, without support, and thereafter he would be carried out of the low, dark , kunai grass house only for urination and defecation, or to lie indoors with faecal or urinary incontinence and rapidly developing decubitus ulcerations. Patients at this stage usually became unresponsive.

The third and final stage of the disease

In the third and final stage, the patient could no longer even sit without support. Accidents often happened, such as burns from the house fire. Further, most commonly, the patients were afflicted with a secondary static bronchopneumonia. When the patient was no longer mobile, he was usually left to die and seldom, if ever, carried out into sunlight. Urinary and faecal incontinence developed and speech was almost lost, although eye movements and occasional voluntary motor responses and grunts remained. As the illness progressed, the speech became blurred and slurred and finally, was no longer intelligible.

Usually, reflex patterns were normal, and for a long time throughout the course of the disease, the patient remained mentally alert showing emotional feelings with expressive facial appearance, but often with slow relaxation of facial expression. According to Gajdusek and Zigas, these symptoms are often passing aspects of behaviour. In general, the patient remained well integrated in his family society until he increasingly deteriorated, although a few patients became belligerent and aggressive. Some of the patients showed mood swings, and others showed depression. The clinical course was often fatal within three to six months, and rarely lasted more than a year. There was no seasonal variation in the time of onset of the disease.

Finally muscular contractures, muscular spasm and rigidity developed. Swallowing and chewing were no longer possible and the patient rapidly starved. The patients lost the ability to bring food to their mouths and had to be spoon-fed, or else were left to starve to death.

To see a disorder regularly progressing to neurological degeneration and death within three to six months was not known in any other condition. Many of the severe cases were among the children of five to ten years who, from the onset of the symptoms, only survived for about three months. It appeared that once the neurological symptoms were evident, there was very little anyone could do for the patients.

Remission and Recovery

It was stated in one of the earlier studies that out of 114 cases of kuru, two patients had completely recovered. In another patient, kuru remitted twice in eighteen months, and after the second remission, began again for a third time. No advanced case of the disease ever recovered. Since there was no histopathological examination of the brains of patients who remitted, it is possible that many early clinically suspected cases which recovered might have been misdiagnosed cases of kuru. Dickinson et al (1965), who examined histopathologically the brains of several scrapie sheep suspected of recovery, found that none showed the specific brain lesions, thus demonstrating clinical misdiagnosis of the disease in some sheep.

Gajdusek (1976), recorded that 14 of his 200 cases had apparently recovered. "Of these, we only have studied and examined six actually during attacks of kuru, and for the others we have accepted what appear to be reliable anamnestic data to the effect that they have recently had typical early kuru which has subsided. Of these, six fully examined cases, now apparently recovered, only three were considered unquestionable kuru cases while we first examined them. The remaining three have been so mild or early in the ataxia or tremor that we have always been in doubt about accepting the native diagnosis in those cases. The three moderate advanced cases, however, had marked ataxia, incoordination and tremors and emotionalism characteristic of moderately severe kuru, and in their case, at least, we must concede that they are observed kuru recoveries. All three were adults of somewhat hysterical temperament, two women and a young man. It is our current hypothesis that the illness is uniformly fatal, and that recoveries which we have documented and the six cases we have observed, are cases of hysterical mimicry of the ataxia and the dramatic involuntary tremors and incoordination of kuru." Since the pattern of kuru occupies a very significant place in Fore culture in that it is believed to be a purely sorcery-induced malady, where all recoveries are attributed to counter-sorcery, or removal of the kuru-induced spell, it would not be surprising to find an occasional case of hysterical mimicry.

Course of the disease and effect of pregnancy

The course of the disease is usually unrelentingly degenerative with continuous and uninterrupted deterioration. However, a rare case with remission and exacerbation has been recorded. In addition to these rare recoveries and remission, Gajdusek found two atypical cases of kuru which were already of several years duration, which regularly appeared and remitted with the onset and termination of the patient's menstrual periods. Kuru does not interfere with normal pregnancy. Many of the kuru patients were pregnant, and four had delivered normal children while suffering from moderately advanced disease. He also recorded many cases of normal pregnancies and deliveries of normal infants, even during very advanced and incapacitating stages of the disease. Other pregnant cases had died before term, without miscarrying before death. However, when a mother died of kuru leaving a small suckling infant, the child frequently starved to death since no other women cared for the infant. This was a double loss in a small family.

Although kuru had no effect on pregnancy, pregnancy did appear to have a significant affect on the progression of kuru. Long term observations have suggested that the progression of the disease in patients who were pregnant and while nursing young infants, may have stabilised for a period, but these patients deteriorated rapidly during the months after parturition, a feature also frequently observed in scrapie sheep.

Treatment of Kuru patients

Patients in all stages of illness, particularly those in the early phases, were placed on a variety of therapeutic regimens, in an attempt to determine whether any of the drugs employed could influence the course of the disease. High doses of sulphadimidine, penicillin, streptomycin, chloramphenicol and aureomycin were given, without effect. High doses of fish liver oil, crude liver extract given parenterally, thiamine, other components of vitamin B complex, folic acid and also a few different multivitamin preparations and therapeutic doses of ferrous sulphate and ferrous gluconate were also given, again, without any noticeable change in the patient's condition or in the course of disease. None of the treatments including antibiotics, steroids, or anti-histamines affected the course of the disease. The Fore people came to believe that kuru was beyond the European treatment (as it really was)., and under these circumstances, it was considered that a thorough epidemiological data compilation which might throw some light on the nature of the disease was the most important contribution that Western researchers could make.

Early Laboratory findings

Repeated blood tests were carried out including haemoglobin determinations and erythrocyte sedimentation rates. Urine analyses, specific gravity, sugar, albumin and microscopic examination all proved negative. No abnormalities were found in copper, manganese or other trace metals in either the urine or blood.

Serological studies of known brain viral infections gave no further clue to the origin of kuru. None of the results of these tests were consistent or indicated it as an infectious disease or provided any other known cause. However, many new cases of kuru continued to develop in the region during the period of intense surveillance.

Laboratory investigation of Kuru

Gajdusek collected thousands of blood and urine specimens from both kuru patients and their relatives, and sent them to USA for further investigation. He found some resistance to venepunture, since he was bleeding the patients and some of their relatives. The victims died just as quickly or quicker. Since it was not a treatment, and nothing was helping them, the simple answer was that a further study of several years was needed. He told the natives that "nothing in the venepuntures is curative or palliative, and nothing in the autopsy promises "counter magic" or any thing of the sort, and that the only thing he was seeking was further knowledge and understanding of kuru, and that was the only hope and route ever in preventing the disease or finding a means of therapy in our world of civilised medicine. To have enthusiastic co-operation and assistance, and willing participation in research with every bit as good an understanding of what this means... study and not cure or therapy ... from most of the group, is a wonderful experience." These people had learned to live with their tragedy, to accept it, and to complain so little that it is possible they failed to sense its magnitude.

They understood this frank approach and, in desperation, the older people could only have replied, "Look, our village was much larger, our hamlets more numerous, and now the bush is engulfing them. Houses stand vacant, our women are all dying, our men are disappearing, and so are our children. Please understand us if we are a bit "touchy" and exasperated ... we are in the hands of a wicked fate which is the work of ourselves alone!" "Ourselves alone" probably meant by their own wicked sorcerers who would not hear the pleas. The community begged and demanded relief from of all this sorcery. Fore men believed that this sorcery could cause kuru to their enemy. They were also sure that their enemy's sorcerers in return would cause kuru in their group.

Post-mortem and histopathological findings

The post-mortem showed no gross lesions of any of the internal organs and histological examination of these organs also revealed no microscopic pathological lesions. In contrast, neuropathological examination of the first brain did reveal degenerative changes in the basal ganglia, which were more striking in the cerebellum. Examination of additional kuru brains showed hypertrophy of astrocytes throughout the brain, with vacuolation of nerve cells, a diffused mild spongiosis, degenerative involvement which went beyond the cerebellum. It was realised from these earlier findings, that the damage seen did not fit into any other known hereditary degenerative disease patterns. With no indications of any

301

inflammatory response, a hallmark of common infections, scientists were misled into believing that it was not an infectious disease. The very early pathological evidence obtained from the examination of brains showed that kuru was not Wilson's Disease (hepatolenticular degeneration due to copper deficiency). It was previously suggested that the extensive widespread neuronal degeneration might be due to a toxic effect of cyanide poisoning from the tapioca plant commonly eaten by the natives.

Dr. Igor Klatzo, at the NIH USA in 1957, had the opportunity to examine microscopically a further six brains from kuru cases. He also observed pathological changes similar to those seen in the first brain. The astrocytic hypertrophy with diffused spongy degenerative involvement of the nerve cells was observed throughout the brain and went beyond the cerebellum. It was realised that the damage in the brain and spinal cord was extensive and although, at the time, Dr. Klatzo recorded that these pathological changes closely resembled those described by Jacob and Creutzfeldt (later known as Creutzfeldt-Jakob disease), he was misled by the fact that kuru involved children of all ages as well as adults, while CJD was a disease exclusively of adults. A similar age difference was to provide problems during clinical and histological diagnoses of CJD in human growth hormone cases.

Transmission of experimental Kuru

It was in 1966 that Gajdusek and Gibbs inoculated brain tissues into chimpanzees which became ill and developed similar histopathological degenerative lesions in the brain to those in the human condition. Subsequently, the disease was passaged from chimpanzee to chimpanzee. The time sequence of disease progression also mimicked that in man, ranging from several months to over a year until death. Since 1966, the disease has been regularly transmitted from kuru patients to New and Old World monkeys, gibbon and nonprimates such as ferret and mink (Gajdusek, 1972; 1978). The same strain of kuru or CJD viruses, after incubation periods of two years or more, produced chronic clinical disease in the spider monkey, closely mimicking the human disease (Gajdusek, 1976). The brain pathology in the experimental animals is indistinguishable, at the microscopical level, from that in the natural disease or in kuru, CJD and scrapie (Beck et al, 1969; Lampert et al, 1972). Gibbs et al (1980) have reported the successful oral transmission of CJD, kuru and scrapie to squirrel monkeys that were allowed to eat brain, kidney and spleen tissues from deceased victims of the disease.

In a serial passage, the incubation period for the transmissible agents of kuru, like the scrapie agent, typically becomes shorter and stabilises at the shorter times. Brown et al (1993) gave a typical example; 10% brain homogenate from a kuru patient transmitted disease to a chimpanzee after an incubation period of 20 months; on passage, the incubation period was 10 to 12 months, and remained within this limit during further passage.

Ritual cannibalism

The distances separating a hamlet or villages in New Guinea ranged from a few hundred yards to about a mile, and the customs and behaviours varied between one Fore area and another. In the past, it was the custom of all Fore groups to practice ritual cannibalism, involving the eating of their own dead kindred. The actual practice differed slightly in different tribe groups. An anthropological study revealed that, in the Atigina and Kimi areas, only females and the uninitiated young males had the right and duty to eat their dead, while, in other areas, both males and females were duty bound to eat various portions of the body of their dead relative.

Considerable numbers of people were murdered in revenge for having worked or being suspected of having worked kuru magic. In addition, kuru victims were often women with nursing infants, and after the death, their children would usually die of malnutrition. This was because the Fore people had not generally accepted the practice of transferring the infant to another nursing woman.

Cannibalism, a common way of life

Ritual killing and cannibalism were prominent features of Fore culture. The peoples of Papua New Guinea speak several different languages, with several dialects, and form different recognisable cultural complexes. It has been stated that the Eastern Highlands groups, Barua and Simbari, were not cannibals at the time of the first European contact, though stories have been told of rare episodes of cannibalism in the past. The cultures of these people in different groups are characterised by their very distinctive pattern of house construction and way of life. Some of these groups, particularly the Kapau speaking in the Golf District, earned a reputation for their cannibalistic consumption of their enemies. Headhunting in some of these tribal groups was considered important for many different reasons.

Head hunting was always considered to be a group affair, carried out by "jeus" as a unit, and indulged in by the organising and hunt-leading "jeu" and all the allied "jeus" they could muster from their own or adjacent communities. The "jeu" chiefs arranged the hunts, assembled allies and picked the victim group to be attacked. Accounts differ on the rituals and ceremonies. According to some of the information gathered, butchering human bodies and consuming meat from the victims was often done with little or no ceremony. After the massacre, the tribal group would stop to cook and eat the flesh of the murdered men and boys, simply as they would any other meat from hunted animals, the pig or the crocodile. The more successful the hunt, the happier they were. The human corpses called 'dua' or 'dow', were divided unskinned, and cooked by roasting, as any other meat. This roasted meat was considered fresh and good, and was eaten by everyone, including children and women. It has been stated that many of the local boys working with the Missionary groups had eaten their share of human flesh, but were embarrassed to talk about it.

Hypothesis

At a conference of the Medical Officers of the Eastern Highlands on the 8th October, 1963, everyone seemed to have his own theory. Dr. Sorenson, in the Journal, gave an account of the expedition to the kuru region and stated that Blu Russell considered that kuru was caused by eating spiders and frogs. Why men-folk didn't get the disease, was because they left their delicacies for women and children. Shirley Glass, however, strongly implied that kuru was transmitted by cannibalism, particularly the eating of the brain of the deceased person. Gajdusek with his great deal of first hand experience with kuru cases, originally had considered it to be viral meningoencephalitis, but failed to find any febrile response in the clinical picture, or any of perivascular cuffing (cells coming out of blood vessels) or other neuropathological reactions in the laboratory findings. Since it had not been possible to demonstrate contact infections in people living in close association to kuru victims throughout the course of their disease, the epidemiological data did not fit the pattern or support speculations about an infectious cause.

Genetic Hypothesis

Gajdusek recorded many cases where old women and their daughters, living in the same hamlet, had fallen ill with kuru. Since the coincidence of mother-child cases appeared more and more common, he concluded that the short course of kuru from onset to death followed the expected concurrent rate. He also experienced the incidence of the disease among the genetically related people but living in areas outside the centre of the epidemic region, and this epidemiological pattern suggested some genetic determinant of the disease. Even at this stage, investigators saw many problems in the simple genetic constructions for kuru. Dr. Leonard Kurland, of the Epidemiology Branch of the NIH, found the genetic hypothesis difficult to accept and gave a number of reasons. If the assumption was correct that this disorder was a new genetic disease which had only been around for 20 to 30 years, it would be impossible to explain the extremely high gene frequency, for this could not be explained as a spontaneous mutation rate. Similarly, the age distribution and the ratio in male to female, 1:1 in children to 1:13 in adults is not sustainable if the genetic hypothesis is correct.

Dr. Kurland thought that kuru might perhaps appear only after marriage when chromosomes were exchanged. Findings from this study would show if kuru was transmissible or genetically transmitted, or whether a milk-factor-like agent was involved. He also found a case of a married woman who developed kuru while visiting the kuru region. She lived outside the kuru region with her husband who took her back to non-kuru region during her early illness (maybe in the hope that she would recover in kuru free area) but unfortunately, she died within three months of her return.

304

Gajdusek also considered the link between kuru and the extensive cannibalism which was common practice in the region, but dismissed that as the sole cause, since he thought and believed that some individual cases of kuru had not engaged in the ritual cannibalistic consumption of diseased relatives. It was also considered that the disease could be an auto-immune disorder induced through cannibalism of human brain consumed in infancy or early childhood. This hypothesis was not supported by antibodies to brain antigen or to any other known infections in the serum samples.

A new lead into investigation of Kuru

Hadlow (1959) made comparative pathological investigations of both scrapie and kuru. The similarities described between the neuropathology in these two disease conditions gave the study of kuru a new lead. Both diseases tended to run an afebrile course with no change in the cerebrospinal fluid, and, hence, the pathology of these two conditions differed from other known viral infections of the CNS. The clinical symptoms and epidemiology in scrapie of sheep as well as a CNS degeneration known to be caused by slow virus infection, appeared very similar to kuru, the human disease. At that time, infection had seemed very unlikely as an aetiological possibility for kuru. In many respects, scrapie was similar to kuru. The two disorders differed from other known viral human diseases in that they did not evoke any virus-associated antibody immune or inflammatory responses. Based on common factors, further experimental investigations were begun in various centres.

Relationship of Kuru, CJD and Scrapie

Work by Hadlow (1959), and transmission studies by Chandler (1961) of scrapie of sheep into mice with a long incubation period, brought a transformation in the approach to studying kuru and other neurological diseases of unknown aetiology, in particular CJD. These findings prompted an intensive comparative study of the two diseases with renewed attempts to transmit kuru to laboratory animals. A new line of thought was that this was a group of disorders caused by a slow virus infection, with the possibility that kuru might be a slow virus with prolonged incubation period. Consequently, observations of the inoculated animals were extended to years rather than months. Although these experiments were laborious and time-consuming, and even after long periods of waiting might turn out to be negative, they were considered necessary.

A new programme was therefore planned for long term observations of inoculated animals, which included many species of primates including chimpanzee, chick embryos, eggs and tissue culture. In many of the earlier transmission attempts, inoculated animals had been kept for only a few months. By keeping and observing chimpanzees, which had been inoculated intracerebrally with suspensions of human brain from kuru patients, for longer periods, it was possible to see that after one and half years they eventually developed the disease. What appeared to be an inherited disease was established as a virus infection which produced the disease only after long delay. After years of unsuccessful experiments using laboratory rodents, Gajdusek and his co-workers succeeded in 1966 in transmitting kuru after 1.5 years of incubation to chimpanzees intracerebrally inoculated with suspension of human brain from a kuru patient. The disease was serially transmitted from chimpanzee to chimpanzee using either brain tissue or visceral tissues containing no brain. The tissues were inoculated intracerebrally or peripherally by intramuscular, subcutaneous or intravenous routes. Incubation periods varied from 14 to 39 months on the first pass and dropped to 10 to 12 months after serial passage.

It was well known that ritual cannibalism was practised among the Fore and might be linked to the spread of the disease. At the time, this fact was not appreciated probably because of natural reticence to reveal the details of a ritual that had been declared illegal. The fact was that adult men generally ate meat, leaving the remaining parts of the body, including the brain to the women and children. The transmission of kuru into animals supported the belief that the disease had been transmitted through ceremonial cannibalistic rituals in New Guinea with a possible route of spread involving handling fresh brain tissue and inoculation through mucous membranes and wounds including skin abrasions (Gajdusek, 1977).

During the early years of investigation, kuru was found to affect all ages other than infants and toddlers. However, kuru has been disappearing gradually during the last 30 years, and by 1985, the disease was no longer to be seen in persons under 35 years of age. This change in the incidence of kuru appears to result from the cessation of ritual cannibalism. The conjunction of these experimental observations with the details of ritual consumption fully explained the age and sex distribution of the disease, and represents the closest human analogy to the epidemiology of scrapie in sheep for which placental ingestion appears to be the major, and perhaps sole, cause of the disease spreading. Recently, the occurrence of BSE in British cattle was traced to the contaminated feed prepared from the remains of sheep, the agent of scrapie having entered though the oral route.

Transmissible Mink Encephalopathy

Transmissible mink encephalopathy (TME) is a rare chronic wasting disease of the CNS of ranch-reared mink (Hartsough et al, 1965; Burger et al, 1965). The disease is not considered to be naturally infectious. The epidemiological studies have pointed strongly to an outside source of infection, probably the feeding of scrapie infected tissues obtained from sheep or goats at slaughter (Hartsough et al, 1965; Burger et al, 1965). Marsh et al (1979) suggested that infection is also likely to occur in kits fighting with each other and their bites and wounds, teeth acting as needles for inoculation. TME in its clinical and histopathological lesions is a disease very similar to scrapie. The disease was first observed on a few Wisconsin ranches in 1947 and since then on other occasions. It soon became apparent that this disease was distinct from other known neurological disorders of mink. Since the original incident,the disease has been recognised on many mink ranches in Canada and Finland where carcasses of infected sheep had been added to the mink feed. Later, it was established that the clinical syndrome is indistinguishable from the disease experimentally induced in mink by inoculation with scrapie-infected tissue of sheep or mouse (Marsh et al, 1975). In mink, the pathological features in all respects were reminiscent of scrapie of sheep.

Clinical observations

The affected animals exhibit CNS disturbances. The first apparent change observed is in the normal habits of the animals, starting with their cleanliness. Mink have a normal habit of keeping the pen clean by depositing droppings in a single area; this habit disappears, and the nest box becomes soiled with droppings scattered throughout. The animals frequently walk and trample through their food tray. Soon, the animals become more excitable and rush around aimlessly in the cage. Some difficulty has been noticed in their eating and swallowing food. At a very early stage, it appears that females with litters,often neglect their kits. The tail arches over the back, as seen in squirrels. Locomotor incoordination soon develops, and the clinical disease rapidly progresses showing typical jerky stepping action of the hind legs. At this stage, the animals will often bite their own tails, while moving their feet in a circular motion. Animals with bitten tails appear to die sooner. During advanced stage of the clinical disease, the animals sit in a corner of the box, their bodies pushed against the wire mesh, and stay in this position for long periods as if they were tired and need sleep. Sick animals disturbed or briefly aroused,show no interest in anything around them. After the appearance of symptoms females die between two to six weeks with males tending to die sooner. The dead mink are usually found with their teeth firmly fastened to the mesh of the wire cage. The carcass is usually dehydrated with greatly reduced adipose tissue deposits.

Pathological findings

As observed in all other spongiform encephalopathies, no gross or microscopical changes are seen in liver, spleen, heart, lung, kidney, small or large intestine and muscles. Microscopic examination of sections from the brain and spinal cord consistently revealed typical astrocytic "spider" cell proliferation and widespread vacuolation of the neuroglial cells. Neuronal degeneration is a prominent feature and widespread in the cerebral cortex and brain stem where neuron cells appear shrunken.

Outbreaks of mink encephalopathy

Burger et al (1965) in the first outbreak of TME in 1947, gave a detailed account of the development of the disease on two farms which they termed A and B. They described movement of animals from one farm to the other. On farm A, in a breeding herd of 5,250 mink, 4,000 were young, born in May, 1947, and the remaining 1,250 animals were over one year old from the previous whelping season. Each breeding female has four to seven kits a year, during the month of May. Young ones are kept and housed together with the dams until September, for about four months, after which all mink are housed in individual wire mesh pens. The kits are in a prime state usually by November or December. After selection of mink for the new breeding herd, the rest are pelted. Although all mink, young and old, were fed on the same feed, the disease only appeared in those over one year old with a mortality rate of 99 to 100%. The first clinical signs of locomotor incoordination were experienced during the last week of November, 1947. The affected animals became progressively somnolent and debilitated and died over a four month period.

These animals had received two injections of a formalinised distemper vaccine in June of 1946 followed by a booster of the vaccine in February 1947. There were no preserved samples of food or vaccine left, therefore no further investigations were carried out. On these farms, the mink were fed on beef by-products, fish, liver and cereal. In the feed preparation, meat from dead and sick cattle was used as part of the diet. It appears that on farm A, dead or paralysed cattle "downer" cows were also used as part of the raw meat ration.

It has been recorded by the same researchers that in April, 1947, 125 pregnant mink as bred from females at farm A, were transported to farm B. They had kits on the farm B in May and young ones were raised without difficulty. Once the female mink were moved from the farm A in April, there was no further contact between the animals of the two farms. However, in November, at the same time as on farm A, disease also broke out on farm B, but only among the 125 female mink brought from the Farm A. There were no cases in animals raised at the farm B. Eventually all these 125 female mink died of the disease over a four month period. On further investigation, it was found that there was no common feed used on these two farms. None of the kits born of these 125 dams, who at the time were under one year old, developed the disease during that year. No record is available as to what happened to these young mink born later.

The same nervous disease with identical clinical course as had been seen in the 1947 incident, was observed on several different mink farms on different dates starting from July 1961. All animals on these mink farms were being fed with a ready mix ration prepared in a common feed plant. The feed was prepared and delivered daily to these farms. Deaths were recorded on all farms in dams over one year old while none of the kits born there became affected. Although the incidence rate was of the order of 10 to 30%, it was much lower than that experienced in 1947. There is also another incident where animals brought in from one farm developed disease on the new farm.

There is another report of an outbreak on a farm in Sawyer County, USA in 1963, where there were 1,178 adult and 4,500 kits. The disease was noticed in the month of June, and from then on, a steady number of deaths were recorded each day. By September, all 1178 adult mink had died of the disease except one. The survivor was an unknown, caught in the wild in April, 1963, about two months before the onset of the outbreak. This gave a significant clue that the herd on the farm may have been exposed to the agent before this wild animal was introduced. There is no record as to what happened to this animal, and it is not known whether it was killed or died.

There was 100% mortality among the adults in contrast to none in 4500 kits who were also fed on the same diet and water. The kits were housed under similar conditions and brought up with the affected dams, and still remained fit and well.

It is also reported that ten male mink were transported from the above farm to another farm in Eau Claire County, Wisconsin on December 9, 1962. All these males also developed an identical clinical neurological disorder, and died at approximately the same time as the animals on the original farm. At the same time, about 70% of the other adults over one year born on this second farm, also developed neurological degenerative disease which invariably ended in death. The rest of the adults were killed in late November of the same year.

None of these animals had received vaccination, which ruled out the possibility of contamination from vaccine or the needles. The clinical signs of the disease were indistinguishable from the previous outbreak on the other farms. Burger et al speculated that the disease did not appear to spread readily from affected to non-affected mink and, therefore, it was a self-limiting disease. The analysis of the record of all these outbreaks suggested that the disease was unknown previously in the mink. The source was considered to be some unknown contaminated substance present in the feed. In order to discover the contaminated component of the feed, records of food rations were compared with those farms where disease had not occurred. It was found that in May, 1963, the feed ration contained horse meat, fish, cereals, and packing house and poultry by-products. During March and April, 1963, carcasses of locally captured beavers were also added into the feed. Since one mink caught in the wild, who was also fed on the

309

captured beavers flesh, survived, this would suggest that beavers did not contribute to the outbreak of the disease on the farm in the mink.

Previous to this, from July through October, 1962, feed rations often contained beef carcasses ("downer" cows) considered unfit for human consumption. It has also been suggested that feed might have contained sheep carcasses, and probably other meat unfit for humans. The feed was supplied to both the farms from a common source. Thus, it was considered that this was the most likely source of contamination.

From these findings, it was further concluded that the incubation period of the disease was about seven months between ingestion of the contaminated food and development of the clinical disease. Similarly on another farm in 1961, where feed supply was changed about six months before the clinical disease developed, it did not alter the course or severity of the disease.

Wild mink are solitary killers with a distinct taste for fresh fish and frogs, small mammals, birds and insects. The breeding mink are mainly fed on fish and raw meat which may be supplemented by cereal products containing vitamins. Since heat was not used in the preparation of this feed, it was often a source of parasites in mink including Botulism and anthrax. It could also act as a source of infection to humans handling the food and mink.

It is believed that carcasses from dead or diseased livestock contained the scrapie agent fed to the mink, and then the disease spread from mink to mink on the farms through fighting and cannibalism (Hartsough et al, 1965). It has been said that most of the feed consisted of beef and horse, but it has not been denied that sheep was used. In monkeys, the illness caused by TME is indistinguishable from experimental CJD in the same species. TME seems to be generally similar to scrapie, and the agent has been found to be widely disseminated throughout many tissues, and it has also been occasionally found in faeces, but not in urine.

Experimental investigation by Burger et al.

Like scrapie and other SEs, no abnormalities are seen in any tissue except brain and spinal cord. Microscopic lesions in the brain are widespread. Astrocytic proliferation is the prominent feature, with very impressive vacuolation of the nerve cells, a spongy degeneration which is hard to miss.

Brain from affected mink was homogenised as 10% suspension and the coarse particles were removed by sedimentation, and then by standing the tubes on the bench for 15 minutes . The homogenised inocula was further filtered, or treated with ether, formalin or boiled before use. Seventeen mink in all, were either inoculated with one ml of 10% suspension (one gram) intramuscularly, or it was mixed into their feed. The animals were inoculated on either 25 September or 7 October,1963. Two additional mink were exposed for one week in a pen occupied by affected animals and were designated as contact mink and were kept as control. These 19 animals were housed on the same farm, where 829 normal young adults were kept for farming and acted as additional control for the study.

From early March, 1964, some of the animals injected started to show abnormal behaviour, and by the end of March, all injected animals showed increased evidence of the disease. The survival time of the injected mink ranged from 183 to 197 days. Clinical observations were confirmed by histological changes which were typical of encephalopathy, and only seen in the nervous system and similar to those seen in the natural outbreaks.

Mink infected by feeding started to show evidence of abnormal behaviour from May, 1964, a delay of about of about two months. Thus, the incubation period from the injected animal to feed animals had increased from 183 to over 240 days. Inocula given in the same amount had about a five month incubation period by injection; as compared with around seven months by feeding, thus shortening the incubation period by two to three months. These studies demonstrate that the agent responsible for TME was a transmissible agent and indistinguishable from the natural disease. These incubation periods show that the previous outbreaks of TME during 1947, 1961 and 1963 were most likely the result of contaminated feed from scrapie infected tissue. The animals which were left in the contaminated pens did not develop the disease over the two year period.

Sporadic cases of mink encephalopathy were discovered among 829 normal mink kept for breading on the farm. The neurological symptoms were seen in 11 of the mink. Further investigation for a possible other source of infection revealed that five of these 11 mink were from litters whose mothers, in June, 1963, were cannibalised; parts of their entrails and flesh were missing, apparently ingested by the young. It was not long afterwards that researchers, while searching for the source of infection, discovered that five mink which developed the disease were from litters of the dam who had died with SE. Thus it was concluded that these five (of these litter mates) must have consumed the contaminated flesh while the one litter mate which did not develop the disease, might not have ingested the mother's tissue. These observations, and knowing that natural cannibalism of dead animals and fighting occurs, would explain the appearance of sporadic cases of encephalopathy in the control herd. Secondary cases seen were, therefore, attributed to cannibalistic ingestion of diseased flesh. The incubation period was about five months by inoculation compared to seven to eight months by feeding. Experience with the experimentally induced disease, with the incubation period extending to seven to eight months by the alimentary route of infection, strongly suggested that natural disease was not seen in the pelter herd, since the incubation period was longer than the age of the animals.

The study, where kits consumed the flesh of affected mothers and also developed the disease after nine to ten months, would suggest that the causative agent of TME was also present in tissues other than brain. The two months longer incubation after ingestion of flesh, would indicate a slightly lower amount of the agent compared to brain. This study is very important and interesting and explains the relationship of kuru to cannibalism and the aetiology thereof.

311

The disease has been transmitted to squirrel, rhesus and stump-tailed monkey and many nonprimate hosts, including sheep, goat and ferret. The disease does not transmit to mice. Repeated attempts to isolate bacterial pathogens from affected mink failed, while the disease was established in the mink by inoculating with bacterial free filtrate and heat formalin inactivated tissues. Thus, these results of the experimental study confirmed that TME was most likely a viral transmissible spongiform encephalopathy and that the agent responsible was resistant to heat and formalin.

TME has been transmitted by intracerebral inoculation to hamsters, producing clinical disease after an incubation period of over 600 days. In the subsequent passage-line from hamster to hamster, the isolation led to the identification of two different strains of agent with average incubation period of 130 and 230 days, respectively (Kimberlin et al, 1986). Strain variation has been amply demonstrated for the agents of scrapie, and has been discussed in great detail in the scrapie section of this book. These strain variations provide strong evidence that these groups of infectious agents have their own specific genome that is responsible for infectivity. However, in animals, the disease is indistinguishable from scrapie and related SE diseases.

References

Abbott J. 1959. Electroencephalograph Clin Neurophy. **11**:184-185.

Adams DH et al, 1967. Br Med J. **3**:173.

Ajuriaguerra J de et al, 1953. Rev Neurol (Paris). **89**:81.

Aiken JM et al, 1989. J Virol. **63**:1686-1694.

Aiken JM. et al, 1990. J Virol **64**:3265-3268.

Akowitz A. et al, 1990. Microbial Pathogenesis. **9**:33-45.

Alema G et al, 1959. Rivista Sperisentale Freniatria Med Legale Atienazioni Mentali. **83**:1485.

Allen IV et al, 1971. Brain. **94**:725-724.

Allen et al, 1977. Ann NY Acad Sci. **284**:676-681.

Alper T. et al, 1966. Bioch Biophys Res Communi. **22**:278-284.

Alper T. et al, 1967. Nature. **214**:764-766.

Amyx HL. et al, 1981. Proc Exp Biol Med. **166**:469-471.

Anderson et al, 1996. Nature. **382**:779-788.

Anonymous 1956. Lancet editorial. **ii**:767-768.

Araya G et al, 1983. Rev Chil Neuropsiquitat. **21**:291-295.

Aronyk K et al, 1984. Ann Neurol **15**:210-211.

Asher DM. et al, 1983. In: Genetics of neurological and psych disorders. Kety SS. et al Eds. Asso Res Nervous and Mental Dis, Res Pub. Raven Press, N Y. 273-291.

Au WJ et al, 1980. Neurol. **30**:611-193.

Austin AR. et al, 1994. In: Bradley R. et al, Eds. EEC Meeting Brussels, Proc Cons BSE Sci Vet Commi Comm E C. 277-287.

Bahmanyar S. et al, 1985. J Comp Path. **95**:1-5.

Baker HF. et al, 1993. Vet Rec. **132**:403-406.

Baker HF. et al, 1991. Lancet. **337**:1286.

Baringer JR. et al, 1978. Ann Neurol. **4**:205-211.

Baringer JR. et al, 1981. J Neuropathol Exp Neurol. **40**:281-288.

Baron H et al, 1986. Europe J Epidem. **2**:252-264.

Barry RA. et al, 1986. J Infec Dis. **153**:848-854.

Basler K. et al, 1986. Cell. **46**:417-428.

Bateman D. et al, 1995. Lancet. **346**:1155-1156.

Beck et al, 1964. Brain. **87**:153-176.

Beck et al, 1969. Post Med Med J. **45**:361-370.

Beck E. et al, 1988. Brain. **104**:755-586.

Bellinger-Kawahara C. et al, 1987. J Virol. **6**:159-166.

Bellinger-Kawahara C. et al, 1987. Virol. **160**:271-274.

Benbow GM. 1990. Vet Rec. **126**:441.

Bendheim PE. et al, 1984. Nature. **310**:418-421.

Bernoulli C. et al, 1977. Lancet. **i**:478-479.

Bernoulli C. et al, 1979. In: Slow Transmissible Dis of the NS. Prusiner SB. et al Eds. AP NY. **1**: 229-251.

Bertoni JM. et al, 1983. Arch Neurol. **40**:618-622.

Bertrand I. et al, 1937. Annals d'Anatomie Pathologique. **14**:565-586.

Bertrand I. et al, 1937. Recueil de Med Vet. **113**:540-561 and 586-603.

Besnoit C. et al, 1898. C R Soc de Biol. (Paris) **5**:536-538.

Besnoit C. 1899. Rev Vét Toulouse. **24**:265-277. and 333-343.

Bibb MJ. et al, 1981. Cell. **26**:167-180.

Bigoteau ML. 1919. Rev Gén Med Vét Toulouse. **28**:433-434.

Blalock JE. et al, 1984. Biochem Biophys Res Commun. **121**:203-207.

313

Bode L. et al, 1985. J Gen Vir. 66:2471-2478.
Bolton DC. et al, 1982. Science. 218:1309-1311.
Bolton DC. et al, 1984. Biochem. 23:5898.
Bolton DC. et al, 1987. Arch Biochem Biophys 258:579-590.
Bolton DC. et al, 1988. In: Novel infectious agents and the NS, CIBA Symp 135.
Bock G et al Eds Wiley Chichester. 167-184.
Bornstein S. et al, 1955. Arch Neu Psych. 74:598-610.
Bosanquet FD. et al, 1956. Lancet. 271:737-746.
Order 1988. TheBovine Spongiform Encephalopathy No 1039 HMSO Lon.
Bradley R. 1990. Proc Agri comm. House of Commons. 72.
Bradley R. et al, 1991. Epidémiol Santé Anim. 19:27-48.
Braham J . 1971. BMJ. 4:21-213.
Brandner S. et al, 1996. Nature. 379:339-343.
Brillon JC. et al, 1995. Lancet. 346:1155.
Brotherston JG. et al, 1968. J Comp Pathol. 78:9-17.
Brown P. 1988. Alan R Liss, Inc. 535-548.
Brown P. 1988. Paediatrics. 81:85-92.
Brown P. 1988. Discussions in Neurosciences. 5:57-69.
Brown P. 1988. Neurol. 38:135-137.
Brown P. 1989. Neurol. 39:1103-1105.
Brown P. 1990. Anti Chem Chemother. 1:75-83.
Brown P. 1992. Rev Neurol 148:317-327.
Brown P. 1994. Mol Neurobiol. 8:79-87.
Brown P. 1994. In: Calne DB Ed. Neurodegenerative Dis. Saunders Philad. 839-876.
Brown P. et al, 1979. Ann Neurol. 6:438-446.
Brown P. et al, 1984. New Eng J Med. 310:727.
Brown P. et al, 1984. Ann Neurol. 16:295-304.
Brown P. et al, 1986. J Inf Dis. 153:1145-1148.
Brown P. et al, 1987. Neurol. 37:895-904.
Brown P. et al, 1990. Neurol. 40:226-228.
Brown P. et al, 1990. J Inf Dis. 161:467-472.
Brown P. et al, 1990. Proc Natl Acad Sci USA. 87:7240-7244.
Brown P. et al , 1991. Lancet. 337:269-270 and 1019-1022.
Brown P. et al , 1992. Neurology. 42:422-427.
Brown P. et al, 1992. Lancet. 340:24-27.
Brown P. et al, 1993. Ann Neurol. 35:513.
Brownlee A. 1936. J Comp Path. 49:328-335.
Brownlee A.1940. Vet J. 96:254-364.
Brownwell B. et al, 1965. J Neurol Neurosurg Psych. 28:350-361.
Bruce ME. 1976. Neuropath App Neurol. 2:471-478.
Bruce ME. et al, 1985. J Neur Exp Neurol. 44:285-294.
Bruce ME. et al, 1987. J Gen Virol. 68:79-89.
Bruce ME. et al, 1991. J Gen Virol. 72:595-603.
Bruce ME. et al, 1992. In: Prusiner SB. et al, Eds. Prion diseases of humans and animals. Ellis Horwood Lon . 497-508.
Bruce ME. et al, 1994. In: Bradley R. et al, Eds. EEC Meeting Brussels, Proc Cons BSE Sci Vet Commi Comm E C.189-204.
Büeler H. et al, 1992. Nature. 356:577-582.
Büeler H. et al, 1993. Cell. 73:1339-1347.
Buge A. et al, 1977. Rev Neurol (Paris). 113:401-415.
Bulpitt KJ. et al, 1984. Brain Res. 130:41-48.

Butzow JJ. et al, 1975. Nature. **254**:358-359.
Burger D. et al, 1965. J Inf Dis. **115**:393-399.
Buzzard EF. et al. 1921. In: Pathol nervous system. Constable press Lon. 8.
Carlson GA. et al, 1986. Cell. **46**:503-511.
Carlson GA. et al, 1989. Proc Natl Acad Sci USA. **86**:7475-7479.
Carolan DJ. et al, 1990. Vet Rec. **126**:92.
Carp RI. 1982. Lancet **1**:170-171
Carp RI. et al, 1985. Gen Virol. **53**:596-606.
Carp RI. et al, 1991. New York Acad Sci. **2**:203-213.
Carp RI. et al, 1994. Ann New York Acad of Sci. **724**:221-234.
Cartier L. et al, 1985. J Neurol Neurosurg Psych **48**:234-238.
Casaccia P. et al, 1989. Arch Virol **108**:145-149.
Casaccia-Bonnefil P. et al, 1993. J Inf Dis. **167**:7-12.
Cassirer R. 1898. Archiv Path Anat Physiol Klinische Med. **153**:89-110.
Ceroni M.et al, 1990. Neurology. **40**:508-513.
Chandler RL. 1959. Vet Rec. **71**:58-59.
Chandler RL. 1961. Lancet **1**:1378-1379.
Chandler R. et al, 1968. Res Vet Sci. **9**:228-230.
Chandler R. et al, 1963. Lancet. **2**:165.
Chatelain J. et al, 1981. J Nero Sci. **51**:329-337.
Chellé PL. 1942. Bull Academie Vét. France. **15**:294-295.
Chesebro B. 1992. Nature. **356**:560.
Chesebro B. et al, 1985. Nature. **315**:331-333.
Chiofalo N. et al, 1980. Arch Neurol. **37**:143-145.
Cho HJ. 1980. Intervirol. **14**:213-216.
Claridge 1795. Letters and Papers on Agri Society Bath. **7**:72.
Clarke MC. et al, 1966. Vet Rec. **78**:647-649.
Clarke MC. et al, 1970. Nature. **225**:100-101.
Clayton DA. et al, 1967. Nature. **216**:652-657.
Clayton DA. et al, 1975. Int Rev Exp Path. **14**:1-67.
Coates D. 1985. J Hosp Infec. **6**:31-40.
Cobb W. et al, 1952. Brain. **75**:343.
Cobb W. et al, 1973. Clin Neurophysiol. **34**:419-427.
Cochius JI. et al, 1991. Aust NZ J Med. **20**:592-593.
Collinge J. et al, 1989. Lancet. **2**:363-366.
Collinge J. et al, 1991. Lancet. **337**:1441-1442.
Comber T. 1772. Critical Rev Lon. **34**:72-73.
Come JH. et al, 1993. Proc Natl Acad Sci USA. **90**:5959-5963.
Complete Farmer, 1807. Vol 1.
Cooke B. 1990. Proc Agri commi House of Common. 132-134.
Corsellis JAN. 1986. Br Med Bull. **42**:111-114.
Costelloe JA. 1994. In: Bradley R. et al, Eds. EEC Meeting 1993. Brussels, Proc Cons BSE Sci Vet Commi Comm E C. 49-56.
Creutzfeldt HG. 1920. Z Ges Neurol Psych. **57**:1-18.
Creutzfeldt HG.1921. In: Histotosische und Distopatbological Arbeiten Gber die GrossnIrnrinde. Nisst F et al Eds. Verlag von Gustav Fiscsber, Jena, **6**:1-48.
Croxson M .et al, 1988. Neurol. **38**:1128-1130.
Cuillé J. et al, 1938. Revue Pathol Comp d'Hygiene Gen. **38**:1358-1372.
Cuillé J. et al, 1936. Comptes Rendus Seances de l'Aced des Sci, **203**:1552-1554.
Cuillé J. et al, 1938. Compt Rendus Seences l'Aced Sci. **206**:78-79 & 1687-1688.
Cuillé J. et al, 1939. Comptes Rendus Seances l'Aced Sci. **208**:1058-1060.

Curnow RN. et al, 1994. In: Bradley R. et al, Eds. EEC Meeting Brussels, Proc Cons BSE Sci Vet Commi Comm E C.109-124.

Cutler NR. et al, 1984. Ann Neurol. 15:1017-110.

Czub M . et al,-1986. Arch Virol. 91:383-386.

Davanipour Z. et al, 1985. Am J Epid. 122:443-451.

David-Ferriera J. et al, 1968. Proc Soc Exp Biol Med. 127:313-320.

Davis T. 1811. In General Views Wiltshire Board of Agri.

Davis T. 1813. In General Views Wiltshire Board of Agri.

Davison C. 1932. Brain. 55:247-264.

Dawson M. et al, 1994. In: Bradley R. et al Eds. EEC Meeting Brussels, Proc Cons BSE Sci Vet Commi Comm E C. 161-168.

Dawson M. et al, 1990. In: Bradley R. et al, Eds. Subacute Spongiform Encephalopathies, Dordrecht Kluwer Acad Comm E C. 25-32.

Dawson M . et al, 1990. Vet Rec. 127:338.

DeArmond SJ. et al, 1985. Cell. 41: 221-235.

Dees C. et al, 1985. J Gen Virol. 66:851-859.

Denny GO. et al, 1992. Vet Rec. 130:113-116.

Dept Health and Social Security. 1984. Circular DA (84) 16.

Dickinson AG. 1976. In: Ed Kimberlin RH. Slow Virus Diseases of animals and man. North Holland Pub Co. Amst. 209-241.

Dickinson AG. et al, 1964. J Comp Path 74:250-254.

Dickinson AG. et al, 1965. Heredity. 20: 485-503.

Dickinson AG. et al, 1966. ARS 91-53 US Dept of Agri 244-248.

Dickinson AG. et al, 1968. J of Comp Path. 78:293-299.

Dickinson AG. et al, 1969. J Comp Path. 79:15-22; 23-26 and 363-366.

Dickinson AG. et al, 1971. Mol Gen Gene. 121:73-79.

Dickinson AG. et al, 1972. Nature New Bio. 237:244-245.

Dickinson AG. et al, 1974. Nature. 248:510-511.

Dickinson AG. et al, 1974. J Comp Path. 84:19-25.

Dickinson AG. et al, 1975. Nature. 256:732-733.

Dickinson AG. et al, 1979. In: S low Transmissible Dis of the NS. Prusiner SB et al, Eds. AP NY. 1:367-385. and 2:13-31.

Dickinson AG. et al, 1988. In: Bock G. et al, Eds. CIBA Symp no.135. Wiley, Chichester. 63-83.

Diedrich J. et al, 1987. Microbial. Pathogenesis. 2:435-442.

Diener J. 1972. Nature New Biol. 235:218-278.

Diener TO. et al, 1982. Proc Natl Acad Sci USA. 79:5520-5224.

Diringer H. et al, 1983. Euro J Biochem. 134: 555-560.

Diringer H. et al, 1983. Nature. 306:476-478.

Diringer H. et al, 1984. Lancet. 2:345.

Diringer H. et al, 1985. Lancet 2:661-662.

Diringer H. et al, 1989. Lancet. i:439-440.

Duffy P. et al, 1974. New Eng J Med. 290:692-693.

Duffy P. et al. et al 1988. Arch Neurol. 45:1097-1100.

Duguid JR. et al, 1985. Proc Natl Acad Sci USA. 85:5738-5742.

Eddy RG. 1990. Vet Rec. 126:537.

Ehlers B. et al, 1984. J Gen Vir. 65:423-428 and 1325-1330.

Eklund CM. et al, 1963. Proc Soc Exp Biol Med. 112:974-979.

Eklund CM . et al, 1969. J Am Vet Med Asso. 155:2094-2099.

Epstein CJ. et al, 1991. Ann Neurol. 29:95-97.

Esmonde TFG. et al, 1993. Lancet. 341:205-207.

Fair GM . et al, 1948. J Ame Water Asso. **40**:1051-1061.

Farquhar CF. et al, 1986. J Gen Vir. **67**:463-473.

Feinberg AP. et al, 1983. Anal Biochem. **132**:6-13.

Ferber RA. et al, 1974. Proc to Int Cong Neurol Barcelona. 358-380.

Field EJ. 1967. Vet Rec. **81**:495-496.

Field EJ. 1969. In: Pathogenesis and Etiology of Demyelinating Diseases. Burdzy K et al Eds. Karger, Basel and NY. 568-573.

Field EJ. 1969. In: Richter GW. et al, Eds. Int Rev of Exp Path AP NY. 129-239.

Field EJ. et al, 1964. Acta Neuropathologica. **4**:200-211.

Field EJ. et al, 1968. Vet Rec. **83**:109-110.

Field EJ. et al, 1968. Lancet. **1**:868.

Field EJ. et al, 1969. Nature. **222**:90-91.

Field EJ. et al, 1972. J Neurolo Sci. **17**:347-364.

Fink. 1804. Communication Board Agri Sec Ed Lon. Vol I. 286.

Fischer C. 1911. Zeitschrift gesmate Neurologie Psych. **7**:1-33.

Fitzsimmons WM. et al, 1968. Res Vet Sci. **9**:281-283.

Foerstl J et al, 1989. J Neutol Neurosurg Psychit. **52**:920.

Foley JM. et al, 1955. Proc Cong Neuropathol Exp Lon. 782-784.

Foote WC. et al, 1993. Ame J Vet Res. **54**:1863-1868.

Foster JD. et al, 1988. Vet Rec. **123**:5-8.

Foster JD. et al, 1994. Ann N Y Acad Sci. **724**:300-303.

Fradkin JE. et al, 1991. JAMA. **265**:880-884.

Fraser H. 1976. In: Kimberlin RH. Ed. Slow Virus Dis of Animals and Man. Amst, North-Holland. 267-305.

Fraser H. 1979. In: Slow Transmissible Diseases of the NS . Prusiner SB. et al Eds. AP NY. **1**: 387-406.

Fraser H. et al, 1968. J Comp Pathol **78**:301-311.

Fraser H. et al, 1970. Nature. **226**:462-463.

Fraser H. et al, 1973. J Comp Pathol **83**:29-40

Fraser H. et al, 1973. J Comp Pathol **88**:563-573.

Fraser H. et al, 1988. Vet Rec. **123**:472.

Fraser H. et al, 1989. J Gen Virol. **73**:1892-2897.

Fraser H. et al, 1990. In: Bradley R, Savey M, Marchant B. Eds. Subacute Spongiform Encephalopathies, Dordrecht: Kluwer Acad Commision EC. 131-136.

Fraser H. et al 1994. In: Bradley R. et al, Eds. EEC Meeting Brussels. Proc Cons BSE Sci Vet Commi Comm E C.145-159.

Gabizon R. et al, 1987. Proc Natl Acad Sci. **84**:4017-4021.

Gabizon R. et al, 1988. Proc Natl Acad Sci. **85**:6617-6621.

Gaches J. et al 1977. Acta neurol Belg. **77**:202-212.

Gaiger HS. 1924. J Comp Path. **37**:259-277.

Gajdusek DC. 1968. New Guinea J. 1961-1962. part i and 2. NIH.

Gajdusek DC. 1972. J Cli Path. **25**:78-83.

Gajdusek DC. 1972. Bull Looniest Pasteur. **70**:117-144.

Gajdusek DC. 1973. Ann Clin Res. **5**:254-261.

Gajdusek DC. 1977. Science. **197**:943-960.

Gajdusek DC. 1978. In: the Harvey Lectures. **72**:283-353.

Gajdusek DC. 1985. In: Human viral infect. Field BN. et al Eds. Raven, NY. 1519-1557.

Gajdusek DC. 1990. In Field BN. et al Eds. Virol, Raven NY. 2289-2324.

Gajdusek DC. et al, 1957. New Eng J Med. **257**:974-978.

Gajdusek DC. et al, 1959. US Dept HEW, PHS. March 442-469.

Gajdusek DC. et al, 1975. Adva Neurol. **10**:291-317.
Gajdusek DC. et al, 1977. In: tr Meulen V. et al Eds. Slow infections of the CNS. Springer-Verlag, NY. 15-53.
Gálvez S. et al, 1979. Neurocirugia. **37**:58-65.
Gálvez S. et al, 1980. Arch Neurol (Chil). **37**:11-14.
Gálvez S. et al, 1982. Nervenarzt. **53**:132-140.
Gálvez S. et al, 1983. J Neurol Sci. **59**:139-147.
Garcia Del J. et al. 1991. Med Vet. **8**:241-244.
Garcin R. et al, 1963. Rev Neurologique. **109**:419-441.
Gardner E. 1968. Neurology Saunders WB. Ed 84-85.
Garzuly F. et al, 1971. Arch Psych Nervenkran. **214**:207-227.
General Views of Agri. Hamphshire London 1815. p. 416.
German E. et al, 1983. Prog Mol Subcell Biol. **8**:111.
German TL. et al, 1985. J Gen Virol. **66**:839-844.
Gerstmann J. et al, 1936. Zeitschr Neurol. **154**:736.
Gibbons RA. et al, 1967. Nature. **215**:1041-1043.
Gibbs CJ. et al, 1967. Sci. **161**:388-389.
Gibbs CJ. et al, 1979. In: Slow Transmissible diseases of the NS. Prusiner SB et al, AP NY. **2**: 87-110.
Gibbs CJ. et al, 1980. J Inf Dis. **142**:205-208.
Gibbs CJ. et al, 1985. New Eng J Med. **313**:734-738.
Gibbs CJ. et al, 1990. Lancet. **335**:1275.
Gibson PH. et al, 1989. Acta Neuropathologica. **77**:420-425.
Gibson RA. et al, 1967. Nature. **215**:1041-1043.
Gilmour JS. et al, 1986. Neuropathol Appl Neurobiol. **11**:173-183.
Girard J. 1829. Recueil Méd Vét. **6**:680-683.
Goldgaber D. et al, 1987. Science. **235**:877-880.
Goldgaber D. et al, 1989. Exp Neurol. **106**:204-206.
Goldfarb LG. et al, 1992. In: Prusiner SB. et al, Eds. Prion diseases of humans and animals. Ellis Horwood Lon. 139-153.
Goldmann W. et al, 1991. J Gen Virol. **72**: 2411-2417.
Gordon WS. 1946. Vet Rec. **58**:516-520.
Gordon WS. 1957. Vet Rec. **59**:1324-1328.
Gordon WS. 1959. Proc Ann Meet USA Live Stock Sem Dept Agri. 286-309.
Gordon WS. 1960. Proc Ann Meet USA Live Stock Sem Ass Dept Agri. 1-12.
Gordon WS. 1966. Proc Ann Meet USA Live Stock Sem Ass Dept Agri. 8-18
Gordon WS. et al, 1957. Vet Rec. **69**:1444.
Goujard J. et al, 1988. Int J Epidemiol. **17**:423-427.
Grant H. 1990. Proc Agri comm. House of Commons. pp42-59.
Greig HS. 1940. Trans Royal Highland Agri Soc Scot. **52**:71-90.
Greig JR. 1950. J Comp Path **60**:263-266.
Gresser I. et al, 1983. J Gen Vir. **64**:1387-1389.
Hadlow WJ. 1959. Lancet **2**:289-290.
Hadlow WJ. 1961. Vet Sci. **2**:289-314.
Hadlow WJ. 1990. In: Bradley R, Savey M, Marchant B. Eds. Subacute Spongiform Encephalopathies, Dordrecht: Kluwer Acad Commision EC. 117-130.
Hadlow WJ. et al, 1974. J Inf Dis. **129**:559-567.
Hadlow WJ. et al, 1979. In: Prusiner SB. et al Eds. Slow Transmissible Disease of the NS. NY: AP. **2**: 3-12
Hadlow WJ. et al, 1982. J Inf Dis **146**:657-664.
Hadlow WJ. et al, 1984. Vet Res. **45**:26737-2639.

318

Haig DA. 1970. In VIth Int Cong Neuropath Paris. 856-857

Haig DA. et al, 1968. J Gen Vir. 3:281-283.

Hallervorden J. 1930. In: Handbuch der Geisteskrankheiten. Bumke O. et al Eds. Springer-Verlag, Berlin. 1063-1107.

Hallervorden J. 1952. Nervenarzt. 23:1.

Haltia H. et al, 1991. Eur J Epidemiol. 7:494-500.

Hanahan D. et al, 1983. Meth Enzymol. 100:333-341.

Hanson CV. et al, 1978. J Gen Virol. 40:345-358.

Hanson RP. et al, 1971. Science. 172:859-861.

Hartsough GR. et al, 1965. J Inf Dis. 115:387-392.

Hay B. et al, 1987. Mol Cell Biol. 7: 914-920.

Hecker RA. et al, 1992. Genes Develop. 6:1213-1228.

Heidenhain A. 1928. Zeitschrift für die gesamte Neurologie und Psych. 118:49-114.

Hoffman D 1981. In Disinfectants. Collins CH. et al, Eds. 7-83. AP Lon.

Holman HH. et al, 1943. J Comp Path. 53:231-236.

Holmes DS. et al, 1981. Anal Biochem. 114:193-197.

Hope JG. et al, 1988. Euro J Biochem. 172:271-277.

Hornabrook RW. et al, 1975. Papua New Guin Med J. 18:226-228.

Hourrigan JL. 1965. NINDB Mono No 2, PHS Publi. No 1378 US Govt. 263-272.

Hourrigan JL. 1990. J. Am Vet Med Asso. 196:1678.

Hourrigan JL. et al, 1979. In: Slow Transmissible Disease of the NS. Prusiner SB. et al Eds. AP NY. 1: 331-356.

House of Commons J. 1755. 27:87 and 164-183.

Hsiao KK. et al, 1989. Nature. 338:342-345.

Hsiao KK. et al, 1990. Science. 250:1587-1590.

Hsiao K. et al, 1991. New Eng J Med. 324:1091-1097.

Hörnlimann B. et al, 1994. In: Bradley R. et al, Eds. EEC Meeting Brussels. Proc Cons BSE Sci Vet Commi Comm E C. 13-24.

Hudson B. et al, 1967. Nature. 216:647-652.

Hudson AJ. 1981. Brain. 104:217-247.

Hunter D. et al, 1954. J Neurol Neurosurg Psych. 17:235-241.

Hunter GD. et al, 1964. J Gen Micro. 37:251-258.

Hunter GD. et al, 1969. J Comp Path. 79:101-108.

Hunter GD. et al, 1972. Nature N Biol. 235:31-32.

Hunter N. et al, 1987. J Gen Virol. 68:2711-2716.

Hunter N. et al, 1989. Vet Rec. 124:364-366.

Hunter N.et al, 1994. In: Bradley R. et al, Eds. EEC Meeting Brussels. Proc Cons BSE Sci Vet Commi Comm E C. 125-139.

Hurtrel D'Arboval. 1828. In Diction Med chirurgie Vét. Nol 4: 343.

Jack EJ. 1988. Vet Rec. 122:142.

Jacob H. et al, 1950. Archiv fur Psych Nerven Vereinigt Zeitschrift fur die gesamte Neurologie und Psych. 184:653-674.

Jacob H. et al, 1958. Deutsche Zeitschrift fur Nervenheilkunde, 178:330-357.

Jacob H. et al,1967. In: Spongy Encephalo, Venice, June 4-9, Guazzi GL et al, Eds. Acta Neuropathologica, Supl III, 148-151.

Jakob H. 1960. Nervenkran Verein Zeitschrift Gesam Neurol Psych. 201:17-52.

Jakob A. 1921. Deutsche Zeitschrift für Wervenheilkunde. 70:132-146,

Jakob A. 1921. Medizinische Klinik. 13: 272.376.

Jakob A. 1921. Zentralnervnsystems Z Gesam Neurol Psych. 64: 147-228.

Jakob A. 1923. In: Die Extrapvramidslen Erkrankungen. Julius Springer. Berlin. 215-245.

Jansen J. et al, 1939.   Zentralnervnsystems Z Gesam Neurol Psych. **64**:147-228.

Jeffrey M. et al, 1988. Vet Pathol. **25**:389-399.

Jeffrey MA. 1992. Vet Rec. **131**:332-337.

Jeffrey M. et al, 1994. In: Bradley R. et al, Eds. EEC Meeting Brussels. Proc Cons BSE Sci Vet Commi Comm E C. 347-358.

Jellinger K. et al, 1972. Wiener Klinische Wochenschrift. **84**: 245-249.

Jellinger K. et al, 1974. J Neurol. **207**:289-305.

Jervis GA. et al, 1942. Am J Psych. **99**:101-109.

Johnson RT. et al, 1968. New Eng J Med. **278**:23-30 and 84-92.

Jones DP. et al, 1954 . In: Transactions of the Am Neurol Assoc. Ann Meeting, At- lantic City, Houston H.et al Eds. William Byrd Press Richmond. 144-147.

Jones DP. et al, 1954. J Neurol Neurosurg Psych. **17**:148-159.

Jones DP. et al, 1985. Neurol. **35**:254-257.

Jones RL. et al, 1979. J Endocrinol. **82**:77-86.

Kahana E. et al, 1974. Science. **183**:90-91.

Kamin M. et al, 1984. AM J Med. **76**:142-145.

Kellings K. et al, 1992. J Gen Virol. **73**:1025-1029.

Khachaturian Z. 1985. Arch Neurol. **42**:1097-1105.

Khochneviss AA. 1962. Thèse Med Paris pp 88.

Kim YS. et al, 1987. J Gen Virol. **68**:695-702.

Kimberlin RH. 1967. Biochem J. **102**:18.

Kimberlin RH. 1976. Sci Progress, Oxford. **63**: 461-481.

Kimberlin RH. 1982. Trend s Neurosci. **5**:413-415.

Kimberlin RH. 1982. Nature. **297**:107-108.

Kimberlin RH. 1994. In: Bradley R. et al, Eds. EEC Meeting Brussels. Proc Cons BSE Sci Vet Commi Comm E C. 455-477.

Kimberlin RH. et al, 1975. J Inf Dis. **131**:978-103.

Kimberlin RH. et al, 1977. J Gen Virol. **34**:295-304

Kimberlin RH. et al, 1979. J Comp path. **89**:551-562.

Kimberlin RH. et al, 1979. J Gen Vir. **42**:107-118.

Kimberlin RH. et al, 1983. Arch Vir. **78**:9-18.

Kimberlin RH. et al, 1985. Intervirol. **23**:74-81.

Kimberlin RH. et al, 1986. Neuropath Neurobiol. **12**:197-206.

Kimberlin RH. et al, 1987. J Gen Virol. **68**:1875-1881.

Kimberlin RH. et al, 1989. J Gen Virol. **70**:2017-2025.

Kingsbury DT. et al, 1981. Inf Immu. **32**:1167-1180.

Kingsbury DT. et al, 1983. J Immu. **131**:491-496.

Kirkwood JK. et al, 1992. Proc Am Asso Zoo Vet Oakland, California. 26-27.

Kirkwood JK. et al, 1994. In: Bradley R. et al Eds. EEC Meeting Brussels. Proc Cons BSE Sci Vet Commi Comm E C. 29-48.

Kirschbaum WR. 1968. Jakob-Creutzfeldt Dis. Am Elsevier NY. 251.

Kitamoto T. et al, 1988. Ann Neurol. **24**:537-542.

Kitamoto T. et al, 1992. Am J Pathol. **140**:1285-1294.

Klein R. et al, 1993. Lancet. **341**:768.

Koch et al, 1985. New Eng J Med. **313**:731-733

Koponen H. et al, 1990. J Neurol Neurosurg Psych. **23**: 164-168.

Kott E. et al, 1967. J Neurological Sci. **5**:107-113.

Kretzschmar HA. et al, 1986. DNA. **5**:315-324.

Kroeker WD. et al, 1978. Biochemistry. **17**: 3236-3243.

Kuroda Y. et al, 1983.Inf Immu. **41**:154-161.

Lampert P. et al, 1972. Am J Path. **68**: 626-652.

320

Lampert PW. et al, 1971. J Neuropath Exp Neurol. **30**:20-32.

Laplanche JL. et al, 1993. Genomics. **15**:30-37.

Laskowski M. Sr. 1980. Meth Enzymol. **65**:263-267.

Lasmezas CI. et al, 1997. Science. **275**:402-405.

Latarjet R. 1979. In: Slow virus Transmissible Diseases of the NS. Prusiner SB. et al, AP NY **2**: 387-407.

Lechi A. et al, 1983. Ital J Neurol Sci. **1**:47-59.

Levy SR. et al, 1986. J Clin Neurophysiol. **3**:1-21.

Lewin B. 1988. In: Genes. Third edition. John Wiley & Sons. NY.

Liao YC. et al, 1986. Science. **233**:364-367.

Liao YC. et al, 1987. Lab Inv. **57**:370-374.

Liberski PP. 1990. J Am Vet Med Asso. **196**:1682.

Liberski PP. et al, 1988. Intervirology . **29**:115-119.

Liberski PP. et al .1990. Acta Neuropatholo. **79**:349-354.

Liberski PP. et al.1992. Acta Neuropathol. **84**:238-243.

Lovett M. et al ,1987. Biochem. Biophy Res Commun. **144**:1069-1075.

Low MG. et al, 1988. Science. **239**:268-275.

Lugaresi E. et al, 1986. N Eng J Med. **315**:997-1003.

Maciulis A. et al, 1992 . Am J Vet Res. **53**:1957-1960.

MacKay JMK. et al, 1961. Vet Rec. **73**: 394-396.

Manuelidis EE. et al, 1977. N Eng J Med. **296**:1134-1336.

Manuelidis EE. et al, 1978. Nature. **271**:778-779.

Manuelidis EE. et al, 1985. Lancet. **ii**: 896-897.

Manuelidis L. et al, 1985. Proc Natl Acad Sci USA. **82**:4263-4267.

Manuelidis L. et al, 1987. EMBO J. **6**:341-347.

Manuelidis EE. et al, 1988. Proc Natl Acad Sci USA. **85**:4898-4901.

Manuelidis EE. 1994. Ann New York Acad of Sci. **724**:259-281.

Marsh RF. 1990. In: Bradley R, Savey M, Marchant B. Eds. Subacute Spongiform Encephalopathies, Dordrecht: Kluwer Acad Commision EC. 41-46.

Marsh R. et al, 1970. Inf Immu. **2**:727-730.

Marsh R. et al, 1975. J Infect Dis. **131**:104-110.

Marsh RF. et al, 1979. In: Slow Transmissible Disease of the NS. Prusiner SB. et al, Eds. NY: AP **1**:451-460.

Marsh R. et al, 1981. Advan Exp Biol Med. **134**:359-363.

Marsh RF. et al, 1988. In: IV Inter Cong Fur Anim Prod. Murphy BD. et al Eds. Mink Breeders Asso Toronto: Canada. 204-207.

Marsh RF. et al, 1991. J Gen Virol. **72**:589-594.

Masters CL. et al, 1978. Brain. **101**:333-344.

Masters CL. et al, 1979. Ann Neurol. **5**:177-188.

Masters CL. et al, 1981. Brain. **104**:535-588.

Matthews WB. 1975. J Neurol Neurosurg Psych. **38**: 210-213.

Matthews WB. 1980. Acta Neurol Scan Sup. **62**:27-28.

Matthews D. 1990. State Vet J. **44**:3-18.

May G. 1868. Bréslau Band. **2**:241-252.

Mayer V. et al, 1977. Lancet. **2**:256.

McDonell MW. et al, 1977. J Mol Biol. **110**:119-146.

McFarlin DE. et al, 1971. Nature. **233**:336.

McGill IS. et al, 1993. J Comp Path. **108**:241-260.

McKinley MP. et al, 1981. Science. **214**:1259-1260.

McKinley MP. et al, 1983. Cell. **35**:57-62.

McKinley MP. et al, 1990. J Cell Biol. **111**:316a.

McLean C. et al, 1981. In: Beardwell C. et al Eds. The pituitary. Lon Butterworth. 238-264.

McMenemey WH. et al, 1941. Arch Neurol Psych. **45**:683-697.

McPherson A. et al, 1988. Science. **239**:385-387.

Medori R. et al, 1992. Neurology. **42**:669-670.

Merz PA. et al, 1981. Acta Neuropathologica. **54**:63-74.

Merz PA. et al, 1983. Nature. **306**:474-476.

Merz PA. et al, 1984. Science. **225**:437-440.

Merz PA. et al, 1988. In: Symp virus non-conventionnels système nerveux central, 2 nd Ed court Paris.

Meyer A. et al, 1954. J Neurol Neurosurg Psych. **17**:129-133.

Meyer RK. et al, 1986. Proc Natl Acad Sci USA. **83**: 2310-2314.

Meyer N. et al, 1991. J Gen. Virol. **72**:37-49.

M'Fadyean J. 1918. J Comp Path. **31**:102-131.

M'Gowan JP. 1914.Investigation into scrapie. Blackwood Edinburgh 1-111.

M'Gowan JP. 1918 .J Comp Path. **31**:278-290.

Michel B. et al, 1987. Rev Neurol (Paris). **143**:526-531.

Millson GC. et al, 1979. In: Slow Transmissible Disease of the NS. Prusiner SB. et al, Eds.NY: AP **2**:409-424.

Millson GC. et al, 1976. In: Slow virus diseases of animals and man. Kimberlin RH. Ed. Noth Holland Pub Amst. 243-266.

Miyamoto T. et al, 1994. In: Slow virus of the CNS. Ann NY Acad Sci. **724**:310-313.

MMC. 1985. Animal wate. A report. HMSO. London

Morgan KL. 1988. Vet Rec. **122**:445-446.

Morgan KL. et al, 1990. Vet Rec. **127**:373-376.

Morris JA. et al, 1965. Proc Soc Exp Biol Med. **184**:375-388

Mould DL. et al, 1967. J Comp Path. **77**: 387-391.

Multhaup G. et al, 1985. EMBO J. **4**:1495-1501.

Muramatsu Y. et al, 1992. Arch Virol. **127**:1-9.

Murdoch GH. et al, 1990. J Virol. **64**:1477-1486.

Murray A. 1811. County of Warwick, pp. 163

Narang HK. 1973. Res Vet Sci. **14**:108-110.

Narang HK. 1974. Acta Neuropathologica **28**:317-329.

Narang HK. 1974. Acta Neuropathologica **29**:37-43.

Narang HK. 1974. Neurobiology. **4**:347-363.

Narang HK. 1975. Acta Neuropathologica. **32**:163-168.

Narang HK. 1980. J Neuropath Exp Neurol. **39**:621-631

Narang HK. 1987. PHLS Microbiol Digest. **4**:64-67.

Narang HK. 1987. Proc Soc Exp Biol Med. **184**:375-388.

Narang HK. 1988. Neuropathol Appl Neurobiol. **14**:247 and 518.

Narang HK. 1990. J Mol Biol. **216**:469-473.

Narang HK. 1990. Proc Agri comm. House of Commons. App 22, 237-240.

Narang HK. 1991. Intervirol. **32**:185-192.

Narang HK. 1992. Intervirol. **34**:105-111.

Narang HK. 1992. Res Virol. **143**:381-386.

Narang HK. 1992. Res Virol. **143**:387-395.

Narang HK. 1993. Intervirol. **36**:1-10.

Narang HK. 1993. Res Virol. **144**:375-387.

Narang HK. 1994. In: Bradley R. et al, Eds. EEC Meeting Brussels, Proc Cons BSE Sci Vet Commi Comm E C. 385-419.

322

Narang HK. 1994. In: Slow virus of the CNS. Ann NY Acad Sci. **724**:314-326.
Narang HK. 1995. In Collinge, P., Ed. The BSE Business. Birmingham, The Public Health Trust pp, 30-44.
Narang HK. 1995. Proc Soc Exp Biol Med. **211**:208-224.
Narang HK. 1996. Proc Soc Exp Biol Med. **211**:306-322.
Narang HK. 1996. Recent developments. Evidence to the Agricultural and Health Committees. House of Select Committee. H. M. S. O., House of Commons London.
Narang HK. 1997. Laboratory News January 1997, 8A.
Narang HK. 1997. Clin Micobiol Rew. 1997. (In press)
Narang HK. et al, 1972. Nature. **24**:106-107.
Narang HK. et al, 1980. Neuropathol Appl Neurobiol. **6**:23-28.
Narang HK. et al, 1987. Proc Natl Acad Sci USA. **84**:7730-7734.
Narang HK. et al, 1987. Proc Soc Exp Biol Med. **184**:504-509.
Narang HK. et al, 1988. Proc Natl Acad Sci USA. **85**:3575-3579.
Narang HK. et al, 1990. Lancet. **335**: 663-664.
Narang HK. et al, 1991. Intervirol. **32**:316-324.
Nass MMK. 1969. Nature. **223**:1124-1129.
Nass MMK. 1970. Proc Natl Acad Sci USA. **67**:1926-1933.
Nass MMK. 1978. Nucleic Acids Res. **5**:403-424.
Nelson JR. et al, 1963. Arch Neurol. **8**:94-106.
Neugut RH. et al, 1979. Neurology. **29**:225-231.
Nevin S. et al, 1960. Brain. **83**:519-564.
New MI. et al, 1988. Neurol. **38**:1133-1134.
Nisbet TJ. et al, 1989. JAMA. **261**:1118.
Oesch B. et al, 1985. Cell. **40**:735-746.
Oesch B. et al, 1988. In novel infectious agents and the CNS. Ciba Found Symp 135: Bock G. et al, Eds NY, John Wiley. 209-223.
O'Keefe M. et al, 1983. J Sci Food Agri. **34**:192-197.
Oppenheimer DR. 1975. In: Viral Diseases of the CNS. L.S Illis, Ed. Bailliere TT. London. 161-174.
Oppenheimer DR. 1969. Bri Med J. **2**:250.
Outram GW. et al, 1974. Nature. **249**:855-856.
Outram GW. 1976. In: Kimberlin RH. Ed. Frontiers Biol series. AP. NY 44: 324-357.
Owen F. et al, 1989. Lancet. i: 51-52.
Owen F. et al, 1990. Brain Res Mol Brain Res. **7**:273-276.
Palmer AC. 1957. Nature. **179**:480-481.
Palmer AC. 1958. Zentra Vetetina. **5**:953-967.
Palmer AC. 1959. Vet Rev Annotations. **5**:1-15.
Palsson PA. 1959. Proc VIII Nordic Vet Cong. 179-191.
Palsson PA. 1979. In: Prusiner SB. et al Eds. Slow Transmissible Diseases of the NS AP NY. **1**:357-366.
Parkinson R. 1813. General Views Of Agri Leicester. 248-249.
Parry HB. 1960 . Nature. **185**:441-443.
Parry HB. 1962. Heredity. **17**:75-105.
Pattison IH. 1964. NINDB Monograph No 2. US Govt. 249-257.
Pattison IH. 1965. Vet Rec. **76**:333-336.
Pattison IH. 1965. J Comp Path. **75**:159-164.
Pattison IH. 1957. Lancet. **272**:104-105.
Pattison IH. 1966. Res Vet Sci. **7**:207-212.
Pattison IH. et al, 1961. J Comp Path. **71**:101-108 and 171-176.
Pattison IH. et al, 1962. J Comp Path. **72**:233-244.

Trabattoni G. et al, 1990. Eur J Epide. 6:239-243.
Traub RD. et al, 1977. In: Aging and Dementia. M. Kinsbourne M. et al, Eds. Spectrum Publications, NY. 91-172.
Tsuji S. et al, 1983. Neurol. 33:1503-1506.
Tyrrell D. 1990.Proc Agri Comm. House of Commons. 191-193
and Minutes of the Evidence and Appendices.
Tyrrell D. et al, 1996. In: Baker HF et al Eds. Prion Dis. Humana Press New Jersey. 175-198.
USDA. National Agricultural Statistic Service. 1991-1993. Quantitative analysis of B,SE risk factors in the United States.
Verweij CL. et al, 1988. J. Biological .Chem. 263: 7921-7924
Von Bose MJ. et al, 1991. Br J Psychiatry. 158:278-280.
Wagner RA. et al, 1954.J Ame Vet Med Asso. 124:136-140.
Walker AS. et al. 1983. Ame J Pub Health. 73:661-665.
Watson WA. 1978. Bull Off Inter Epizooties. 89:429-436.
Weissmann C. 1991. Nature. 352:679-683.
Wells GAH. et al, 1987. Vet Rec. 121:419-420.
Wells GAH. et al, 1989. Vet Rec. 125:521-524.
Wells GAH. et al, 1990 In: Bradley R. et al Eds. Subacute Spongy Encephalo, Dordrecht: Kluwer Acad, Commision EC. 11-24.
Wells GAH. et al, 1992. In: Prusiner SB. et al, Eds. Prion diseases of humans and animals. Ellis Horwood Lon. 256-274.
Wells GAH. et al, 1992. Res Vet Sci. 53:1-10.
Wells GAH. et al, 1992. Vet Rec. 128:199-203.
Wells GAH. et al, 1994. In: Bradley R. et al, Eds. EEC Meeting Brussels, Proc Cons BSE Sci Vet Commi Comm E C. 327-345.
Westaway D. et al, 1986. Nucleic Acid Res. 14:2035-2044.
Westaway D. et al, 1987. Cell. 51:651-662.
Westaway D. et al, 1989. Trends Neurosci. 12:221-227.
White DG. et al, 1994. In: Bradley R. et al, Eds. EEC Meeting Brussels, Proc Cons BSE Sci Vet Commi Comm E C. 169-182.
White MT. et al, 1975. Cancer Res. 35:873-879.
Wietgrefe S. et al, 1985. Science. 230:1177-1181.
Wight PAL. 1960. J Comp Pathol. 70:70-83.
Wilesmith JW. et al, 1988. Vet Rec. 123:638-644.
Wilesmith JW. 1990. Report and Proc The Agri committee. London: HMSO. House of Commons. Appendix 35, 258-259.
Wilesmith JW. et al, 1991. In Chesebro WB. et al Eds. Berlin-Heidelberg, Current Topics in Microbiol Immuno 21-38.
Wilesmith JW. et al, 1991. Vet Rec. 128:199-203.
Wilesmith JW. 1991. Sem Virol. 2:239-245.
Wilesmith JW. et al, 1992. Vet Rec. 130:90-94 and 197-210.
Wilesmith JW. et al, 1993. Vet Rec. 132:300-301.
Wilesmith JW. 1994. In: Bradley R. et al, Eds. EEC Meeting Brussels, Proc Cons BSE Sci Vet Commi Comm E C. 1-12.
Wilhelmi AE. 1961. Can J Biochem Physiol. 39:1659-1668.
Will RG. et al, 1982. J Neurol Neurosurg Psych. 45:235-238.
Will RG. et al, 1984. J Neurol Neurosurg Psych. 47:134-140.
Will RG. et al, 1986. J Neurol Neurosurg Psych. 49:749-755.
Will RG. et al, 1996. Lancet. 347: 921-925.
Williams ES. et al, 1982. J Wildlife Dis. 16: 89-98.

Williams ES. et al, 1992. Rev Sci Tech Off Int Epiz. 11:551-567.

Willich. 1802. Domestic Encyclopaedia. 3:495.

Wills PR. 1989.Alzheimer's and Related Disorders. 669-677.

Wilson SA. et al, 1940. In: Bruce AN Ed. Neurol. vol 2 Arnold Lon 907-910.

Wilson DR. et al, 1950. J Comp Path. 60:267-282.

Wilson DR. et al, 1952. Vet Rec. 64:468.

Wood JNL. et al, 1992. Vet Rec. 131:66-68.

Worthington M . et al, 1971. J Gen Vir 13:349-351.

Wyatt JM. et al, 1990. Vet Rec. 126, 513.

Wyatt JM. et al, 1991. Vet Rec. 129:233-236.

Xi YG. et al, 1992. Nature. 356:598-601.

Yanisch-Perron C. et al, 1985. Gene. 33:103-119.

Youatt. 1837. Sheep. 536.

Yoshimoto J. et al, 1992. Virus Genes. 6:343-356.

Young A. 1793 and 1799. In: Annals of Agriculture.

Zhang H. et al, 1988. Nucleic Acids Res. 16:1220.

Zlotnik I. 1957. Nature. 179:737.

Zlotnik I. 1963. Lancet. 2:1072.

Zlotnik I. 1958. J Comp Path. 68:148-166 and 428-438.

Zlotnik I. et al.1961. Vet Rec. 73:543-544.

Zlotnik I. et al, 1965. J Comp Path. 75:147-157.

Zochodne DW. et al, 1988. Neurol. 38:1056-1060.